BLUE MOLD
of TOBACCO

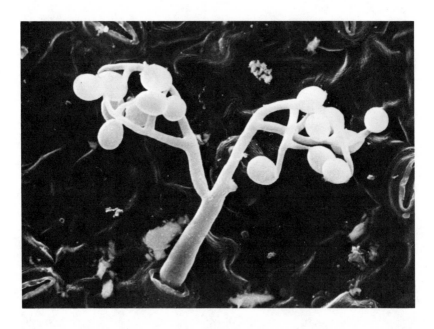

Mature sporangia of *Peronospora hyoscyami* on a sporangiophore (×600)

BLUE MOLD
of TOBACCO

Edited by
W. E. McKeen

APS PRESS

The American Phytopathological Society
St. Paul, Minnesota

Financial Contributors

Canadian Industries Limited
Ciba-Geigy Canada Ltd.
Department of Plant Sciences, The University of Western Ontario
Faculty of Science, The University of Western Ontario
Rhône-Poulenc Agrochimie
SEITA: Société nationale d'exploitation industrielle
   des tabacs et allumettes
The Australian Tobacco Research Council

Library of Congress Catalog Card Number: 88-083539
International Standard Book Number: 0-89054-097-7

Printed in the United States of America

The American Phytopathological Society
3340 Pilot Knob Road
St. Paul, Minnesota 55121, USA

Preface

This is an international book on a species of downy mildew fungus that is causing a 20th-century disease on one of the most economically valuable crops grown in the world today. Geographical barriers have prevented the blue mold pathogen from invading China, India, Japan, and Africa south of the Sahara, but humans accidentally carried it from Australia to Europe. In North America and Europe, this explosive fungus overwinters in the warmer regions and in the summer blows into the cooler regions where it develops best.

This unique book provides a complex and detailed picture of this colorful pathogen, its relationship with tobacco, its sensitivity to the environment, and the effect of human manipulation. Induced systemic resistance, epidemiology and meteorology, and social and legal implications are discussed in addition to environmental, molecular, biochemical, genetic, structural, and taxonomic aspects.

The problem of scientific names is always with us, and the blue mold pathogen, *Peronospora hyoscyami* or *P. tabacina,* is no exception. After the world collection of isolates being made by Drs. C. E. Main and H. W. Spurr, Jr. at the U.S. Department of Agriculture Foreign Weed and Disease Laboratory in Frederick, Maryland, has been studied, the taxonomy of this pathogen may be clarified. Similarly, in this book, the words *conidium* and *sporangium* are used synonymously.

The distinguished scientists who have provided excellent chapters and kind cooperation despite the pressure of their regular jobs are gratefully acknowledged. The slight duplication among some chapters strengthens and unifies this work.

In addition I wish to thank Mrs. Stephani Tichbourne and Miss Anne Crossley for typing and especially Mr. R. J. Smith and Anne Crossley for proofreading and for their many helpful suggestions during the preparation of this book.

W. E. McKeen

Contributors

I. A. M. Cruickshank—Division of Plant Industry, Commonwealth Scientific and Industrial Research Organization (CSIRO), Canberra, Australia

J. M. Davis—Department of Plant Pathology and Department of Marine, Earth and Atmospheric Sciences, North Carolina State University, Raleigh, North Carolina 27695-7616

René Delon—Département Scientifique, Seita (Société nationale d'exploitation industrielle des tabacs et allumettes), Paris, France

Aglika Edreva—Institute of Genetics, Sofia 1113, Bulgaria

G. I. Johnson—Queensland Department of Primary Industries, Indooroopilly, Queensland, Australia 4068

J. Kuć—Department of Plant Pathology, University of Kentucky, Lexington, Kentucky 40546

C. E. Main—Department of Plant Pathology, North Carolina State University, Raleigh, North Carolina 27695-7616

W. E. McKeen—Department of Plant Sciences, The University of Western Ontario, London, Ontario, Canada N6A 5B7

M. L. Menetrez—Plant Pathology Department, North Carolina State University, Raleigh, North Carolina 27695

R. C. Rufty—Department of Crop Science, North Carolina State University, Raleigh, North Carolina 27695-7620

Pierre Schiltz—Département Scientifique, Seita (Société nationale d'exploitation industrielle des tabacs et allumettes), Paris, France

R. J. Smith—Department of Plant Sciences, The University of Western Ontario, London, Ontario, Canada N6A 5B7

H. W. Spurr, Jr.—U.S. Department of Agriculture, Agricultural Research Service, Oxford, North Carolina 27565-1555, and Plant Pathology Department, North Carolina State University, Raleigh, North Carolina 27695

A. M. Svircev—Horticultural Research Institute of Ontario, Vineland Station, Ontario, Canada L0R 2E0

S. Tuzun—Department of Plant Pathology, University of Kentucky, Lexington, Kentucky 40546

Contents

Chapter 1

Peronospora hyoscyami de Bary: Taxonomic History, Strains, and Host Range

G. I. Johnson
Queensland Department of Primary Industries
Indooroopilly, Queensland, Australia 4068

The history of blue mold of tobacco (*Nicotiana tabacum* L.) began in Australia. Tobacco production commenced there before 1840 and was hampered by disease from the earliest times (Angell and Hill, 1932). In 1890, H. Tyron, who later became Queensland's first Government Plant Pathologist, noted: "The disease which threatened at Texas [Fig. 1] last year to render it impossible to raise the tobacco plant and which has been regarded by the planters of that district as nothing less than a scourge is immediately due to a presence of a fungus, a species of *Peronospora.*" Bailey (1890) listed *Peronospora hyoscyami* de Bary as affecting tobacco plants from various parts of Queensland, and Lamb and Sutherland (1893) reported its presence in a bale of cured tobacco from an 1889 Queensland crop. However, Angell and Hill (1932) noted that the disease may have been present in seedbeds in Australia as early as 1850–1860. These were the first records of blue mold, caused by *P. hyoscyami,* on cultivated tobacco. Blue mold is a downy mildew described in Europe by de Bary from the solanaceous weed *Hyoscyamus niger* L. (Skalický, 1964).

By the turn of the century, blue mold had been identified in New South Wales and Victoria as well as in Queensland and was regarded as the major disease problem of tobacco in Australia (Cobb, 1891; McAlpine, 1900). Blue mold is endemic to Australia, one of the countries of origin of the genus *Nicotiana,* and has been recorded on several *Nicotiana* spp. in their natural habitats, including central Australia (Hill, 1962; Hill and Angell, 1933).

Evidence that blue mold was also endemic to the Americas,

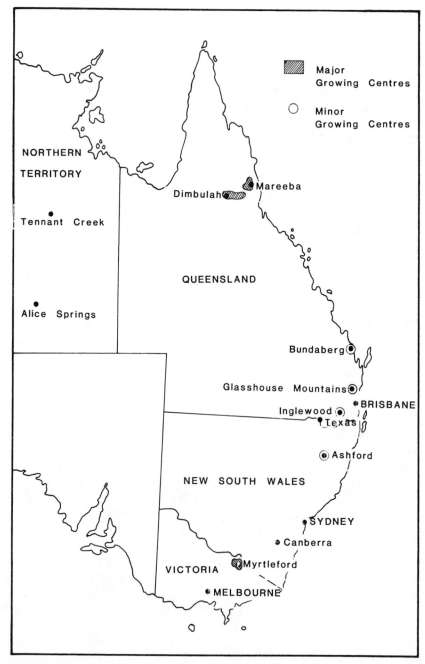

Figure 1. The tobacco-growing areas of Australia.

2

another center of origin of *Nicotiana* spp., is provided by the records of *Peronospora* spp. on *Nicotiana* by Farlow (1885), Harkness (1885), Spegazzini (1891), and Clayton and Stevenson (1943). In the United States, blue mold was not recorded from cultivated tobacco until 1921 (Smith and McKenny, 1921). *N. repanda* Willd., a wild species, contributed to its spread (Godfrey, 1941; Wolf, 1947).

In the following years, blue mold was reported on tobacco in Canada and Brazil (1939), Argentina (1939), Chile (1953), Cuba (1957), and Mexico (1964) (Schiltz, 1981). The parasite was unknown on tobacco in Europe until 1957, when it was observed on ornamental tobacco and *N. glutinosa* L. in a glasshouse in England after a chemical company imported it from Australia for use in fungicide trials (Klinkowski, 1961; Klinkowski and Schmiedeknecht, 1960). The pathogen was taken to Holland on virus host material and subsequently spread to cultivated tobacco in The Netherlands, Belgium, and Germany during 1959. Within four years, Europe, North Africa, and the Near East had been colonized (Corbaz, 1964). Accounts of the epidemic in Europe have been given by Berger and Müller (1961) (East Germany), Corbaz (1961), Klinkowski (1962), Peyrot (1962), Soydan (1971) (Turkey), and Zanardi (1960) (Italy).

The southern spread of blue mold may have been stopped by the Sahara Desert; Zimbabwe remains free of the disease. Eastward, it was reported to have reached Cambodia (now Kampuchea) by 1969 (Maximo, 1969), although the report may have been a misidentification of powdery mildew, since blue mold has not been reported from there since nor has it been reported from India, China, Japan, Southeast Asia, Papua New Guinea, or New Zealand (Holliday, 1980).

In North America, blue mold damage was confined to seedbeds until 1979, when a severe epidemic occurred in field tobacco in the United States and Canada as well as Central America, Mexico, and the Caribbean (Todd, 1980). The epidemic of blue mold in the Americas in 1979 has been reviewed by Todd (1980) and Davis et al (1981). Since 1980, a blue mold warning system has operated in North America (Nesmith, 1984b).

Taxonomy

P. hyoscyami (syn. *P. tabacina* Adam) belongs to the family Peronosporaceae in the order Peronosporales, class Oomycetes, subdivision Mastigomycotina of the division Eumycota of Fungi (Talbot, 1971). The Peronosporaceae, commonly known as the downy mildews, are obligate parasites. *Peronospora* species differ from many other oomycetes in producing aplanetic sporangiospores (which function as conidia) instead of either zoospores or conidiosporangia (which can function as facultative conidia) (Talbot, 1971).

The fungus causing blue mold of tobacco was first determined as *P. hyoscyami* de Bary by M. C. Cooke (Bailey, 1890; Cooke, 1891). Cooke (1892) published a description of *P. hyoscyami* that Adam (1933) considered was taken directly from de Bary's account. Cobb (1891) also reported that the disease "which threatened to extinguish the culture of tobacco" in certain parts of New South Wales was "caused by what appears to be *Peronospora hyoscyami* de Bary" and published a description that was original, in the view of Adam (1933). The first illustrations of sporangia and sporangiophores were published by Smith (1891) (Fig. 2), Cobb

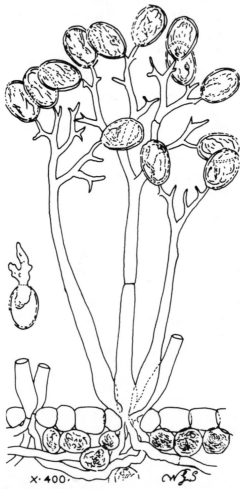

Figure 2. The first illustration of *Peronospora hyoscyami* from *Nicotiana tabacum* as published by Smith (1891).

4

(1891), and Cooke (1892). *P. hyoscyami* had also been applied by Farlow (1885) to a downy mildew on *N. glauca* Graham in California, while Harkness (1885) recorded *P. sordida* Berk. on *N. bigelovii* Wats. from Nevada, and Spegazzini (1891) recorded *P. nicotianae* Speg. on *N. longiflora* Cav. in Argentina (Clayton and Stevenson, 1935).

Most subsequent early records described the pathogen as *P. hyoscyami*, although Wilson (1908, 1914) preferred *P. nicotianae*. Wilson (1908) considered that European and American species were distinct, without giving any indication of having examined the material. Gäumann (1923) in his monograph of *Peronospora* Corda, without having access to all the type specimens, decided that the species of *Peronospora* recorded on *Nicotiana* spp., including *N. tabacum*, should be referred to as *P. nicotianae*.

Angell and Hill (1932) expressed doubts regarding the pathogen's name, and Adam (1933) reviewed the early descriptions and taxonomy, disputing the applicability of the names *P. hyoscyami, P. sordida,* and *P. nicotianae* to the pathogen of tobacco downy mildew. Adam (1933) could not infect *H. niger* (the original host of *P. hyoscyami*) with a tobacco isolate of *Peronospora*. Largely on the basis of host range and oospore characteristics, he erected the new name *P. tabacina* Adam, which became accepted in the literature for over 30 years (Clayton and Stevenson, 1935; McGrath and Miller, 1958; Wolf, 1947).

Skalický (1964) and others, including Clayton and Stevenson (1943) and Kröber and Weinmann (1964), reviewed the morphology and taxonomy of the organism and considered that *P. tabacina* and *P. hyoscyami* could not be distinguished on morphological grounds. Adam's (1933) failure to infect *H. niger* with a tobacco isolate of *Peronospora* was not sufficient justification for erection of a new species. Kröber and Massfeller (1961) found that tobacco isolates of the organism caused slight infection of *H. muticus* but not *H. niger*, and Schiltz (1967) reported that sporulation occurred on a few plants of *H. niger* and on 10% of plants of *H. albus*. Skalický (1964) suggested that the names should be combined as *P. hyoscyami* with two formae speciales, f. sp. *hyoscyami* (on *H. bohemicus* and *H. niger*) and f. sp. *tabacina* (on *Nicotiana* and other Solanaceae). His synonymy for *P. hyoscyami* was as follows: *P. effusa* Rabenh. var. *hyoscyami* Rabenh., *P. nicotianae* Speg. (nomen confusum), *P. dubia* Berlese, and *P. tabacina* Adam.

Shepherd (1970) reviewed the nomenclature of the blue mold organism. He considered that Spegazzini's (1891) observations regarding indirect germination of sporangia and dimensions of oospores cast doubt on whether his fungus was a *Peronospora*, echoing the views of Shaw (1949) and Skalický (1964), who regarded

P. nicotianae as a nomen confusum. Shepherd (1970) noted that Skalický's (1964) use of formae speciales to distinguish two morphologically similar but host-limited races was in accordance with the original use of the term by Eriksson (1894) and with the provisions of the International Code of Botanical Nomenclature. Shepherd (1970) supported the contention that this pathogen should be called *P. hyoscyami* de Bary.

What's in a Name?: *P. hyoscyami* versus *P. tabacina*

P. tabacina, proposed by Adam (1933), was the accepted name for the blue mold pathogen until its validity was questioned by Skalický (1964) and Shepherd (1970). *P. tabacina* continues to be popular in current literature. Lucas (1975) noted that "despite this increasing evidence as to the proper name of the blue-mold fungus the one most commonly used in 1974 was *P. tabacina*." Holliday (1980) stated that "the name given by Adam (*P. tabacina*), since it is the one that is commonly used, is adopted here." In 1978, the name *P. hyoscyami* was routinely changed to *P. tabacina* in papers published in *Plant Disease Reporter* (R. G. O'Brien, personal communication).

Since the blue mold epidemic in North America in 1979 and the subsequent resurgence of interest in the pathogen, some authors have reverted to *P. hyoscyami*. Just as tobacco workers meeting in Williamsburg, Virginia, in 1983 decided to change from the traditional "conidia" to the mycologically more correct "sporangia" in describing the asexual spores of the blue mold fungus (Spurr, 1983), a majority of authors may revert to the taxonomically more correct *P. hyoscyami* de Bary.

Strains

IN AUSTRALIA

Wark et al (1960) presented evidence for differentiation within the blue mold pathogen in Australia. Hill (1963) reported an isolate of *P. hyoscyami*, designated APT2, that attacked various *N. tabacum* × *N. debneyi* tobacco breeding lines that were resistant to the common strain, designated APT1. Strain APT2 was first reported from Canberra (Australian Capital Territory) and Myrtleford (Victoria) on wild *Nicotiana* spp. by Hill (1963) (Fig. 1). Hill (1966) also considered that APT1 and APT2 could be further distinguished by the fact that the latter frequently produced oospores, whereas the former did not. More recently, both strains have been shown to produce oospores in the laboratory (G. I. Johnson, unpublished). Shepherd (1970) noted that APT2 could be isolated from a sufficiently large population of APT1 sporangia produced from the inoculation of a single sporangium isolate by the use of selective *N. tabacum* × *N. debneyi* hybrids. Attempts to repeat this method to obtain APT2 at Mareeba in 1982 were unsuccessful (G. I. Johnson, unpublished).

Hill (1966) further defined the host range of these strains and described a third strain, APT3, distinguished from the other two by its inability to attack *N. trigonophylla* Dunal and a number of other *Nicotiana* spp. APT3 was collected from endemic *N. velutina* Wheeler in the Alice Springs district of the Northern Territory, an arid region over 1,200 km from a tobacco-growing area (Fig. 1) (Hill, 1962, 1966), and has not been recorded elsewhere.

Shepherd (1970) proposed formae speciales in addition to the two described by Skalický (1964): f. sp. *hybrida* for APT2 and f. sp. *velutina* for APT3, based on host range and oospore dimensions. He noted that the difference in oospore size between APT2 and APT3 could justify elevation of strain APT3 to specific rank, in view of Eriksson's (1894) criteria, but because he considered that APT2 and APT3 were clearly allopatric forms (Cowan, 1968), it was taxonomically more correct to regard APT3 as a third forma specialis rather than a separate species. He cited the classification of rusts, where differences in urediniospore size were found among formae speciales and among races within formae speciales (Dennis, 1952). Significant differences between APT1 and APT2 found in biometric studies on sporangia of *P. hyoscyami* by Smith (1970) similarly could not justify elevation to a new species. Although Smith (1970) found significant differences between the sporangial dimensions of APT1 and APT2 produced under the same conditions on *N. tabacum,* she also found significant variation in sporangial size using one isolate on random *N. tabacum* hosts and using isolates from several locations on a standard host. Probably, oospore dimensions are subject to the same influences.

Shepherd (1970) considered pathogenic behavior decisive in the determination of the formae speciales of *P. hyoscyami.* He examined the findings of Adam (1933) and concluded that the criteria Adam adopted to indicate infection were the production of macroscopically visible symptoms and the occurrence of sporulation. Shepherd (1970) recommended rigid adherence to these criteria, quoting his own observation that *H. niger,* highly resistant to f. sp. *tabacina,* supported an abundant growth of mycelium within its tissues but no sporulation, whereas *H. muticus,* rated by Kröber and Massfeller (1962) and Hill (1966) as slightly susceptible, produced only a sparse growth of mycelium and some sporulation under the same conditions.

As well as displaying host range differences, the strains of

P. hyoscyami vary in their environmental requirements for development. A narrower temperature range has been reported for f. sp. *hybrida* (20–28° C) than for f. sp. *tabacina,* and the former does not compete successfully with the latter on susceptible tobacco (Hill and Green, 1965; Shepherd and Mandryk, 1967).

The basis of differentiation of the four formae speciales is shown in Table 1. Skalický (1964), Hill (1966), and Shepherd (1970) list host ranges for these formae speciales. They provided a clear basis for comparison of the isolates of the blue mold pathogen that occurred at that time, and the system seems amenable to the classification of strains of the pathogen that occur at present.

In Australia, *P. hyoscyami* f. sp. *tabacina* predominated in tobacco-growing areas until 1972. Following the release of two cultivars, Sirone (1969) and CSIRO 40T (1972), with resistance to f. sp. *tabacina* derived from *N. goodspeedii* Wheeler and *N. debneyi* Domin, respectively, *P. hyoscyami* f. sp. *hybrida* appeared in tobacco-growing areas (O'Brien, 1973). The predominant tobacco cultivar grown in Australia since 1980, ZZ100, is unaffected by f. sp. *tabacina* (V. J. Hansen, personal communication), and the occasional blue mold outbreaks that have occurred since 1980 have been caused by f. sp. *hybrida* (G. I. Johnson, unpublished).

The strain system established by Skalický (1964) and Shepherd (1970) has been able to accommodate differences in host range among wild isolates of *P. hyoscyami* from the endemic *Nicotiana* spp. of Australia. As long as *Nicotiana* spp. remain a source of resistance genes, the wild pathogen may continue to prove a source of new strains.

IN EUROPE

In Europe, physiological specialization of *P. hyoscyami* probably occurred during 1965 (Hill, 1966; *Peronospora* Study Group, 1965). Tuboly (1966) reported that the new strain attacked *N. debneyi,* whereas the old strain did not. Jankowski (1972) also reported that a

Table 1. Differentiation of formae speciales of *Peronospora hyoscyami*[a]

Forma specialis	Sporulation[b] on		
	Hyoscyamus niger	*Nicotiana langsdorfii*	*N. tabacum* × *N. debneyi*
hyoscyami	+	0	0
tabacina	0	+	0
hybrida	0	+	+
velutina	0	0	+

[a] Data from Shepherd (1970).
[b] + = Sporulation, 0 = no sporulation.

8

new virulent strain of *P. hyoscyami* attacked *N. debneyi*. Ternovskii et al (1973) named the new race PT2. Unlike PT1, it caused a punctate necrosis on *N. debneyi*. *N. didebta* showed resistance to both races. Govi (1971) reported strains differing only in their pathogenicity toward *N. velutina* and suggested that hybridization of the two original strains had occurred.

Other authors (Egerer, 1972; Mihajlova and Ivancheva-Gabrovska, 1977; Ramson and Egerer, 1973) have reported further evidence of strain differentiation in Europe. In 1984, I observed tobacco cultivar Sirone (susceptible to f. sp. *hybrida*) infected with *P. hyoscyami* at Bergerac, France. It seems likely that strains similar to f. sp. *tabacina* and f. sp. *hybrida* occur in Europe.

IN NORTH AMERICA

Before 1979, *P. hyoscyami* was predominantly a pathogen of seedbeds in North America (Davis et al, 1981). The epidemic of 1979 may have resulted from the appearance of a new strain in the region. Its reported etiological behavior was similar to that of the European and Australian strains, causing extensive losses in the field and a high incidence of systemic infection (Spurr, 1983; Todd, 1980). Differences in oospore size and morphology from the strain recorded previously were also noted (Spurr, 1983; Spurr and Todd, 1980, 1982). Spurr (1983) compared the virulence of three American isolates of *P. hyoscyami*, two collected in 1979 and one from 1964, on a number of tobacco lines and concluded that a new strain had appeared. Unfortunately, he did not compare the isolates on the differentials of Shepherd (1970). According to Shepherd's (1970) system, a Canadian isolate of *P. hyoscyami* collected since 1979 conforms to f. sp. *hybrida* (W. E. McKeen, personal communication). There has been no systematic attempt to classify the isolates of North America and Europe using Shepherd's (1970) differentials.

RESISTANCE TO METALAXYL

In 1978, metalaxyl was introduced for control of *P. hyoscyami* in the seedbed and field (Johnson et al, 1979) and was rapidly accepted in blue mold-affected areas. Metalaxyl resistance was recorded in *P. hyoscyami* in Nicaragua in 1981 (T. Staub and D. Sozzi, unpublished). Subsequently, resistance to metalaxyl by *P. hyoscyami* has been recorded in Honduras, Mexico, and Cuba (Nesmith, 1982, 1984a, 1986). Bruck et al (1982) reported that in North Carolina, some field isolates of *P. hyoscyami* showed greater resistance (less than 100 μg/ml) to metalaxyl than others (less than 25 μg/ml). Johnson and Shepherd (1983) reported an LC_{50} of 0.51 μg/ml for an Australian isolate of *P. hyoscyami* f. sp. *tabacina*.

Metalaxyl usage has introduced another variable for the selection of new strains of *P. hyoscyami*. Incorporation of genetic resistance to Shepherd's (1970) strains of *P. hyoscyami* into commercial tobacco cultivars may reduce the selection pressure for metalaxyl-resistant strains.

Plant Resistance to Blue Mold

The early difficulties in controlling blue mold prompted attempts to locate sources of resistance. Australian tobacco breeding commenced in the 1930s in New South Wales, leading to the development of the cultivar Resistant-Hicks from a Canadian line of *N. debneyi* × *N. tabacum* (Lea, 1960). Leaf quality of Resistant-Hicks was unsatisfactory, and further selection led to the development of Beerwah H and Beerwah GG. Subsequently, attempts were made to introduce alternative forms of resistance from a range of *Nicotiana* spp., and two cultivars, Sirogo and Sirone, with seedling resistance derived from *N. goodspeedii,* were released (Wark, 1970). After the release of these cultivars, efforts continued in the development of a commercially acceptable cultivar with field resistance to f. sp. *hybrida* (seedlings susceptible) by backcrossing with lines carrying resistance from *N. debneyi, N. excelsior* Black, and *N. velutina* (Wark et al, 1976). Ovens 62, GA 955, KA 596, and Beerwah H and GG are immune to f. sp. *tabacina* and have field resistance to f. sp. *hybrida* (Marks, 1980).

In 1982, a program was commenced at Mareeba, Australia, to incorporate seedling resistance to f. sp. *hybrida* into commercially acceptable cultivars that already possessed seedling resistance to f. sp. *tabacina. Nicotiana* sp. (Ravenshoe) and *N. cavicola* Burb. were used as the sources of resistance to f. sp. *hybrida,* and ZZ100 was used as the source of resistance to f. sp. *tabacina* (V. J. Hansen, personal communication). Cultivars incorporating resistance to the two strains will provide selection pressure for the appearance of f. sp. *velutina* or other strains. The continued use of metalaxyl should reduce this likelihood, while the incorporation of resistance to f. sp. *hybrida* and f. sp. *tabacina* should reduce the chance of metalaxyl resistance.

Geographic isolation from the sources of diversity of *P. hyoscyami* (i.e., Australia and the Americas) could allow the successful introduction of resistance to f. sp. *hybrida* in Europe, especially if combined with rigid enforcement of crop hygiene and the use of metalaxyl in seedbeds to limit opportunities for oospore formation and sexual recombination.

The literature on the inheritance of resistance to *P. hyoscyami* has been complicated by the existence of strains of *P. hyoscyami* and by the failure of many authors to classify the strain of *P. hyoscyami*

10

using standard differentials from the same seed source. Rufty (1983) reviewed the literature of the genetics of resistance to *P. hyoscyami*. Clayton (1968) reported that resistance to *P. hyoscyami* involved three major genes derived from *N. debneyi* plus one factor from *N. tabacum*. Wark (1963) reported that resistance was controlled by several genes behaving additively. He considered that several genes were involved in the resistance reaction under environmental conditions favorable to disease development, whereas single genes were effective when the environment did not favor the pathogen. Others (Gillham et al, 1977; Marani et al, 1972; Schweppenhauser, 1974; Wuttke, 1969) reported a monogenic dominant factor modified by additional genetic factors. Most authors have noted that the expression of resistance depended on various factors, including plant growth stage at inoculation, temperature, light intensity, and relative humidity (Rufty, 1983).

Using parent-offspring regression, Marani et al (1972) obtained estimates of heritability for blue mold resistance ranging from 0.23 to 0.54. Rufty (1983) considered that the relatively low heritability values reflected the importance of environmental effects and explained some of the difficulties plant breeders encounter in developing resistance to *P. hyoscyami*. Breeding for field resistance has been further complicated by the apparent association between blue mold resistance and poor agronomic type, including low yield and poor quality (Clayton, 1968; Wark et al, 1976). To date, breeders have not been able to separate field resistance to blue mold from these undesirable traits (V. J. Hansen, personal communication).

Host Range

In studying strain variation, Shepherd (1970) emphasized the need for the criteria of production of macroscopically visible symptoms and the occurrence of sporulation. These criteria must also be applied in host range studies.

P. hyoscyami is a pathogen of solanaceous plants, particularly *Nicotiana* spp. and some other genera. The strain specificity of *P. hyoscyami* f. sp. *hyoscyami* to *Hyoscyamus* spp. in Europe and the low levels of sporulation induced by tobacco isolates on these species have meant that *Hyoscyamus* spp. do not have a role in survival of tobacco blue mold.

Hill (1966) provided comprehensive host ranges of the three known strains of the tobacco blue mold pathogen. He noted that slight sporulation could occur with highly resistant species if the seed line used, the plant age, and nutrition favored mycelial growth and that sporulation did not occur in all tests. Hill (1966) was unable to detect sporulation on *H. niger*. Hill (1966) also noted the hosts that

Table 2. Host range of *Peronospora hyoscyami*: Hosts with similar reaction to all three strains[a]

Highly resistant	Moderately resistant	Resistant	Susceptible to very susceptible
Nicotiana eastii Kostoff	*N. suaveolens* Lehm.	*N. goodspeedii* Wheeler	*N. benthamiana* Domin
N. exigua Wheeler	*N. megalosiphon* Heurck & Muell.	*N. umbratica* Burb.	*N. plumbaginifolia* Viv.
N. debneyi Domin	*N. rotundifolia* Lindl.	*N. maritima* Wheeler	*N. longiflora* Cav.
N. megalosiphon Heurck & Muell.	*Capsicum annuum* L.	*N. amplexicaulis* Burb.	*N. nudicaulis* Watson
N. occidentalis Wheeler		*N. excelsior* Black	*N. pauciflora* Remy.
N. ingulba Black			*N. otophora* Griseb
N. simulans Burb.			*N. arentsii* Goodspeed
N. cavicola Burb.			*N. corymbosa* Remy.
N. suaveolens Lehm.			*N. linearis* Phil.
Physalis peruviana L.			*N. miersii* Remy.
P. alkekengi L.			*N. repanda* Willd.
P. lanciflora Nees			*N. rustica* L.
Hyoscyamus muticus L.			*N. glauca* Graham
Petunia hybrida Vilm. 'Grandiflora'			*N. glutinosa* L.
			N. tabacum other than lines resistant to f. sp. *tabacina*

[a]Data from Hill (1966).

reacted similarly to all three strains of the pathogen (Table 2) and those that did not (Table 3).

Other hosts reported from Europe include *Schizanthus pinnatus* Ruiz & Pav., *Atropa belladonna* L., *Solanum boerhaavii* Thell. and *Nicandra physalodes* (L.) Gaertn., and *H. niger* (Kröber and Massfeller, 1962; Legenkaya, 1970; Schiltz, 1967). In North America, *Lycopersicon esculentum* Mill. and *Capsicum annuum* L. were reported as hosts by Wolf et al (1934). *C. annuum* has also been reported as a host in Australia (Simmonds, 1966). Other Solanaceae besides *Nicotiana* spp. may harbor blue mold (Marcelli and Pannone, 1965; O'Brien, 1974), but their role in survival of the pathogen is probably minor compared with tobacco volunteers and other *Nicotiana* spp. (Hill, 1962; Hughes, 1961; Wolf, 1947).

Table 3. Host range of *Peronospora hyoscyami:* Hosts with different reactions to the three strains of the pathogen[a]

| Host[b] | Reaction[c] to | | |
	f. sp. tabacina (APT1)	f. sp. hybrida (APT2)	f. sp. velutina (APT3)
Nicotiana rosulata Domin	1	1	3
N. knightiana Goodspeed	3	3	2
N. bigelovii Wats. (three subspecies)	5	5	1
N. acuminata (Grah.) Hooker (two subspecies)	5	5	1
N. attenuata Torr.	5	5	1
N. langsdorfii Weinm.	5	5	1
N. clevelandii Gray.	5	5	1
N. trigonophylla Dunal	5	5	1
N. velutina Wheeler	2	2	3
N. amplexicaulis Burb.	2	2	3
N. paniculata L.	4	4	2
N. trigonophylla	4	4	2
N. tabacum lines with resistance from *N. suaveolens, N. knightiana, N. goodspeedii,* or *N. amplexicaulis,* including Bel 3, 9, 10, 11, 12	2	2	3
Solanum melongena L.	0	1	1
Lycopersicon esculentum Miller	0	1	1
L. pimpinellifolium Miller	0	1	1

[a] Data from Hill (1966).
[b] Recent revision in the taxonomy of *Nicotiana* may have created synonymy for some of the species listed (see Purdie et al [1982]).
[c] No reaction = 0, highly resistant = 1, moderately resistant = 2, resistant = 3, susceptible = 4, very susceptible = 5.

Summary

Since the first records in Australia and the Americas late in the 19th century, blue mold has spread to the major tobacco-growing areas of Australia, Europe, and the Americas. The pathogen, initially described as *Peronospora hyoscyami* de Bary, has been known by other names favored by some authorities, notably *P. tabacina* Adam. *P. hyoscyami* is taxonomically more correct, and its use is recommended.

Strains of *P. hyoscyami* based on host range characteristics have been described from Australia. Evidence for their existence in Europe has also been reported. Until 1979, blue mold was a disease of seedbeds in North America; the epidemics of 1979 and 1980, which caused serious field losses in Central and North America of a type familiar to European and Australian growers, may have resulted from the appearance of a new strain.

The introduction of metalaxyl for control of *P. hyoscyami* has provided another force for strain selection. Resistance by *P. hyoscyami* to metalaxyl has occurred in Nicaragua, Honduras, Mexico, and Cuba.

P. hyoscyami has been shown to infect many *Nicotiana* spp. and other Solanaceae, notably *C. annuum. N. tabacum* and other *Nicotiana* spp. are the most significant hosts in blue mold epidemiology.

LITERATURE CITED

Adam, D. B. 1933. Blue mould of tobacco. J. Agric. Victoria Aust. 31:412–416.

Angell, H. R., and Hill, A. V. 1932. Downy mildew (blue mould) of tobacco in Australia. Counc. Sci. Ind. Res. Aust. Bull. 65. 30 pp.

Bailey, F. M. 1890. Contributions to the Queensland flora. Dep. Agric. Queensl. Bot. Bull. 1:3–7.

Berger, P., and Müller, B. 1961. Contributions on the occurrence of *Peronospora* of tobacco in Germany: Geographic distribution and weather. Ber. Inst. Tabakforsch. Dresden 8:31–66.

Bruck, R. I., Gooding, G. V., Jr., and Main, C. E. 1982. Evidence for resistance to metalaxyl in isolates of *Peronospora hyoscyami*. Plant Dis. 66:44–45.

Clayton, E. E. 1968. The transfer of blue mould resistance to tobacco from *Nicotiana debneyi*. Part IV—Breeding programs 1957–1967. Tob. Sci. 12:112–124.

Clayton, E. E., and Stevenson, J. A. 1935. Nomenclature of the tobacco downy mildew fungus. Phytopathology 25:516–521.

Clayton, E. E., and Stevenson, J. A. 1943. *Peronospora tabacina* Adam, the organism causing blue mold (downy mildew) disease of tobacco. Phytopathology 33:101–113.

Cobb, N. A. 1891. Notes on the disease of plants. Agric. Gaz. N.S.W. 2:616–624.

Cooke, M. C. 1891. Tobacco disease. Gard. Chron. 9:173.

Cooke, M. C. 1892. Handbook of Australian Fungi. Williams and Norgate, London. 457 pp.

Corbaz, R. 1961. Considerations concerning the blue mould (*Peronospora tabacina* Adam) epidemic in Europe. Phytopathol. Z. 42:39–44.

Corbaz, R. 1964. Development of the tobacco blue mould (*Peronospora tabacina* Adam) epidemic. Phytopathol. Z. 51:190–191.

Cowan, S. T. 1968. A Dictionary of Microbial Taxonomic Usage. Oliver and Boyd, Edinburgh. 118 pp.

Davis, J. M., Main, C. E., and Bruck, R. I. 1981. Analysis of weather and the 1980 blue mold epidemic in the United States and Canada. Plant Dis. 65:508–512.

Dennis, R. W. G. 1952. Biological races and their taxonomic treatment by mycologists. Proc. Linn. Soc. London 163:47–53.

Egerer, A. 1972. Resistance of some *Nicotiana* species to a virulent strain of *Peronospora tabacina* Adam. Ber. Inst. Tabakforsch. Dresden 19:5–13.

Eriksson, J. 1894. Ueber die specialisierung des parasitismus bei den getreiderostpilzen. Ber. Dtsch. Bot. Ges. 12:292–331.

Farlow, W. G. 1885. Notes on some injurious fungi of California. Bot. Gaz. Chicago 10:346–348.

Gäumann, E. 1923. Monograph of the genus *Peronospora* Corda. Beitr. Kryptogamenflora Schweiz 5:1–360.

Gillham, F. E. M., Wark, D. C., and Harrigan, E. K. S. 1977. Disease resistant flue-cured tobacco breeding lines for North Queensland. I. Resistance to blue mould, *Peronospora tabacina*. Aust. J. Exp. Agric. Anim. Husb. 17:652–658.

Godfrey, G. H. 1941. Noteworthy diseases of economic crops and native plants in lower Rio Grande Valley in the spring of 1941. Plant Dis. Rep. 25:347–353.

Govi, G. 1971. Spread and progression in Italy of lines of *Peronospora tabacina*. Tob. Roma 75:1–3.

Harkness, H. W. 1885. Fungi of the Pacific Coast. Bull. Calif. Acad. Sci. 1:256–271.

Hill, A. V. 1962. Sources of blue mould infections of tobacco seedbeds. Aust. Tob. Growers Bull. 4:2–4.

Hill, A. V. 1963. A strain of *Peronospora tabacina* pathogenic to tobacco lines with resistance derived from *Nicotiana debneyi* and *N. goodspeedii*. Nature (London) 199:396.

Hill, A. V. 1966. Physiologic specialization in *Peronospora tabacina* Adam in Australia. CORESTA Inf. Bull. 1966(1):7–15.

Hill, A. V., and Angell, H. R. 1933. Downy mildew (blue mould) of tobacco. J. Counc. Sci. Ind. Res. Aust. 6:260–268.

Hill, A. V., and Green, S. 1965. The role of temperature in the development of blue mould (*Peronospora tabacina*) disease in tobacco seedlings. I. In leaves. Aust. J. Agric. Res. 16:597–607.

Holliday, P. 1980. Fungus Diseases of Tropical Crops. Cambridge University Press, Cambridge. 607 pp.

Hughes, I. K. 1961. Blue mould in North Queensland. Queensl. Agric. J. 87:309–319.

Jankowski, F. 1972. Increase in parasitic ability of *Peronospora tabacina* Adam. Biul. Inst. Ochr. Rosl. 52:107–122.

Johnson, G. I., and Shepherd, R. K. 1983. Susceptibility of tobacco blue mould (*Peronospora hyoscyami*) to metalaxyl. Ann. Appl. Biol. 102:123–126.

Johnson, G. I., Davis, R. D., and O'Brien, R. G. 1979. Soil application of CGA 48988—A systemic fungicide controlling *Peronospora tabacina* on tobacco. Plant Dis. Rep. 63:212–215.

Klinkowski, M. 1961. Blue mould (*Peronospora tabacina* Adam). Dtsch. Landwirtsch. 12:229–239.

Klinkowski, M. 1962. The European pandemics of *Peronospora tabacina* Adam, the causal agent of blue mould of tobacco. Biol. Zentralbl. 81:75–89.

Klinkowski, M., and Schmiedeknecht, M. 1960. False mildew of tobacco, *P. tabacina*, a tobacco disease hitherto unknown in Germany. Nachrichtenbl. Pflanzenschutzdienst D. D. R. 14:61–74.

Kröber, H., and Massfeller, D. 1961. Studies on blue mould of tobacco in Germany. Nachrichtenbl. Pflanzenschutzdienst D. D. R. 14:81–85.

Kröber, H., and Massfeller, D. 1962. Investigations of resistance behavior in tobacco to *Peronospora tabacina* Adam. Nachrichtenbl. Pflanzenschutzdienst D. D. R. 14:82–85.

Kröber, H., and Weinmann, W. 1964. A contribution to the morphology and taxonomy of *Peronospora tabacina*. Phytopathol. Z. 51:241–251.

Lamb, S., and Sutherland, G. F. 1893. Report on the tobacco growing industry in the Tumut District. Agric. Gaz. N.S.W. 4:313–322.

Lea, H. W. 1960. The quest for a blue mould resistant tobacco. Agric. Gaz. N.S.W. 71:639–642.

Legenkaya, E. I. 1970. Specialization of *P. tabacina* in the central chernozem zone of the USSR. (Abstr.) Rev. Plant Pathol. 50:3160.

Lucas, G. B. 1975. Diseases of Tobacco. Biological Consulting Associates, Raleigh, NC. 621 pp.

Marani, A., Fishler, G., and Amirav, A. 1972. The inheritance of resistance to blue mold (*Peronospora tabacina* Adam) in two cultivars of tobacco (*Nicotiana tabacum* L.). Euphytica 21:97–105.

Marcelli, E., and Pannone, R. 1965. Susceptibility to *P. tabacina* of several hosts. Tobacco 69:33–47.

Marks, C. F. 1980. Blue mold in Australia. Lighter 50(2):5–7.

Maximo, Y. 1969. Tobacco trends—The Orient. Tobacco U.S. 169(10):7.

McAlpine, D. 1900. Report of the vegetable pathologist. Annu. Rep. Dep. Agric. Victoria 1899:256–258.

McGrath, H., and Miller, P. R. 1958. Blue mold of tobacco. Plant Dis. Rep. Suppl. 250:1–35.

Mihajlova, P., and Ivancheva-Gabrovska, T. 1977. Changes in the pathogenicity of *Peronospora tabacina* Adam under the conditions of Bulgaria. Rastenievud. Nauki 14:123–132.

Nesmith, W. C. 1982. Current blue mold status. Rep. 82-3, University of Kentucky, Lexington.

Nesmith, W. C. 1984a. Current blue mold status. Rep. 84-1, University of Kentucky, Lexington.

Nesmith, W. C. 1984b. The North American blue mold warning system. Plant Dis. 68:933–936.

Nesmith, W. C. 1986. Current blue mold status. Rep. 86-4, University of Kentucky, Lexington.

O'Brien, R. G. 1973. Changes in pathogenicity of *Peronospora hyoscyami* in North Queensland. Aust. Plant Pathol. Soc. Newsl. 2:2–3.

O'Brien, R. G. 1974. The control of blue mould of tobacco on the Atherton Tableland. M. Agric. Sci. thesis, University of Queensland, St. Lucia.

Peronospora Study Group. 1965. Report. CORESTA Bull. 1965(3):3–5.

Peyrot, J. 1962. Tobacco blue mould in Europe. FAO Plant Prot. Bull. 10:73–80.

Purdie, R. W., Symon, D. E., and Haegi, L. 1982. Solanaceae 9. *Nicotiana*. Flora Aust. 29:38–59.

Ramson, A., and Egerer, A. 1973. New race of the pathogen of blue mould of tobacco (*Peronospora tabacina* Adam) in G.D.R. Nachrichtenbl. Pflanzenschutzdienst D. D. R. 27:112–115.

Rufty, R. C. 1983. Sources and breeding approaches for the development of tobacco germplasm resistant to blue mold (*Peronospora tabacina* Adam). Pages 32–37 in: Blue Mold Symposium III. 30th Tobacco Workers Conference. J. J. Reilly, compiler. Virginia Polytechnic Institute and State University, Williamsburg. 61 pp.

Schiltz, P. 1967. Création de *Nicotiana tabacum* résistants à *Peronospora tabacina* Adam analyse histologique et biologique de la résistance. Ph.D. thesis no. 203, Bordeaux University, Bordeaux, France. 145 pp.

Schiltz, P. 1981. Downy mildew of tobacco. Pages 577–599 in: The Downy Mildews. D. M. Spencer, ed. Academic Press, New York. 636 pp.

Schweppenhauser, M. A. 1974. Anticipatory resistance breeding to *Peronospora tabacina*. S. Afr. J. Sci. 70:349–351.

Shaw, C. G. 1949. *Peronospora tabacina* Adam in Washington State. Phytopathology 39:675–676.

Shepherd, C. J. 1970. Nomenclature of the tobacco blue mould fungus. Trans. Br. Mycol. Soc. 55:253–256.

Shepherd, C. J., and Mandryk, M. 1967. A necrotrophic reaction in *Nicotiana* species induced by *Peronospora tabacina* Adam. II. Quantification of the resistance-susceptibility status of tobacco breeding lines. Aust. J. Biol. Sci. 20:1161–1168.

Simmonds, J. H. 1966. Host Index of Plant Diseases in Queensland. Queensland Department of Primary Industries, Brisbane. 111 pp.

Skalický, V. 1964. Contributions to the infraspecific taxonomy of the obligately parasitic fungi. Acta Univ. Carol. Biol. 164(2):25–90.

Smith, A. 1970. Biometric studies on conidia of *Peronospora tabacina*. Trans. Br. Mycol. Soc. 55:59–66.

Smith, E. F., and McKenny, R. E. B. 1921. A dangerous tobacco disease appears in the United States. U.S. Dep. Agric. Circ. 174. 6 pp.

Smith, W. G. 1891. Tobacco disease. Gard. Chron. 9:211.

Soydan, A. 1971. Investigations on factors affecting the increased incidence of *Peronospora tabacina* Adam in the Marmara Region. Tekel Enst.

Yaymlaria 13:134.

Spegazzini, C. 1891. Phycomyceteae Argentinae. Rev. Argent. Hist. Nat. 1:36–37; as cited by Wilson (1908).

Spurr, H. W., Jr. 1983. Delineation of races of the blue mold pathogen. Pages 28–31 in: Blue Mold Symposium III. 30th Tobacco Workers Conference. J. J. Reilly, compiler. Virginia Polytechnic Institute and State University, Williamsburg. 61 pp.

Spurr, H. W., Jr., and Todd, F. A. 1980. Observations of the extensive 1979 tobacco blue mold epidemic. (Abstr.) Phytopathology 70:693.

Spurr, H. W., Jr., and Todd, F. A. 1982. Oospores in blue mold diseased North Carolina burley and flue-cured tobacco. Tob. Sci. 26:44–46.

Talbot, P. H. B. 1971. Principles of Fungal Taxonomy. MacMillan, London. 274 pp.

Ternovskii, M. F., Vinogradov, V. A., and Ivanenko, B. G. 1973. Infection of resistant varieties of tobacco by an aggressive race of *Peronospora tabacina* Adam. Mikol. Fitopatol. 7:40–45.

Todd, F. A. 1980. The blue mold story. Tob. Int. 182:24–31.

Tuboly, L. 1966. The appearance of a new biotype of *Peronospora tabacina* Adam in Hungary. CORESTA Bull. 1966(4):27–38.

Tyron, H. 1890. Tobacco disease. *The Queenslander,* July 5, p. 29. Queensland Newspapers, Brisbane.

Wark, D. C. 1963. *Nicotiana* species as sources of resistance to blue mould (*Peronospora tabacina* Adam) for cultivated tobacco. Pages 252–259 in: Proc. World Tob. Sci. Congr., 3rd, Salisbury, Southern Rhodesia. Tobacco Research Board, Harare, Zimbabwe. 644 pp.

Wark, D. C. 1970. Development of flue cured tobacco cultivars resistant to a common strain of blue mould. Tob. Sci. 14:147–150.

Wark, D. C., Hill, A. V., Mandryk, M., and Cruickshank, I. A. M. 1960. Differentiation in *Peronospora tabacina* Adam. Nature (London) 187:710–711.

Wark, D. C., Wuttke, H. H., and Brouwer, H. M. 1976. Resistance of eight tobacco lines to blue mould in South Queensland, Australia. Tob. Sci. 20:110–113.

Wilson, G. W. 1908. Studies in North American Peronosporales. III. New records of noteworthy species. Bull. Torrey Bot. Club 35:361–365.

Wilson, G. W. 1914. Studies in North American Peronosporales. IV. Notes on miscellaneous species. Nature (London) 6:192–210.

Wolf, F. A. 1947. Tobacco downy mildew, endemic to Texas and Mexico. Phytopathology 37:721–729.

Wolf, F. A., Dixon, L. F., McLean, R., and Darkis, F. R. 1934. Downy mildew of tobacco. Phytopathology 24:337–363.

Wuttke, H. H. 1969. Different levels of resistance in blue mould resistant tobacco. Aust. J. Exp. Agric. Anim. Husb. 9:545–548.

Zanardi, D. 1960. Blue mould (*Peronospora tabacina*) of tobacco. Ital. Agric. 97:1075–1086.

Chapter 2

Spread and Control of Blue Mold in Europe, North Africa, and the Middle East

René Delon
Pierre Schiltz
Département Scientifique
Seita (Société nationale d'exploitation industrielle
    des tabacs et allumettes)
Paris, France

Introduction and Spread, 1959–1963

Although tobacco blue mold has been present in Australia since the 1800s (Cooke, 1891) and was reported in the United States in 1921, Canada and Brazil in 1938, Argentina in 1939, Chile in 1953, and Cuba in 1957, the pathogen, *Peronospora hyoscyami* de Bary (syn. *P. tabacina* Adam), did not appear in Europe until 1959. Blue mold was reported for the first time on tobacco crops on the continent of Europe, more precisely in the Netherlands, in July 1959. From there the disease spread to Schleswig-Holstein in the Federal Republic of Germany (Gerlach, 1966).

By September blue mold had appeared in southwestern German Democratic Republic, and it was in this region that the disease first reappeared in 1960, assuming catastrophic proportions before spreading to eastern and northern France (Vuittenez, 1961). In 1960, losses due to blue mold reached about 27,500 t in northern Europe, and the damage done in the French departments of Nord and Alsace alone amounted to 10,000 t, or a cash value of 40 million French francs (CORESTA, 1960).

Carried by the predominant west wind, the pathogen spread quickly and within four years had invaded all the tobacco-growing areas of Europe and the Mediterranean Basin (Fig. 1). By 1961, blue mold had reached the Mediterranean countries; the heaviest losses were recorded in Algeria (75%) and Italy (65%). In 1963, the disease could be considered endemic in most countries of Europe, North Africa, and the Middle East (Corbaz, 1964).

The progress of the disease toward southern Africa was probably halted by the Sahara Desert. However, blue mold continued to spread toward the East, and although the report was not subsequently confirmed, *P. hyoscyami* was reported in Cambodia (now Kampuchea) in 1968 (Maximo, 1969).

This veritable disaster on the economic level appears to have been the result of the unfortunate importation by a British firm in 1957 of a blue mold pathotype on tobacco from Australia (Corbaz, 1961; Viennot-Bourgin, 1985).

Epidemic Development, 1964–1985

The annual reports of the blue mold warning system of the Cooperative Center for Scientific Research Relative to Tobacco (CORESTA) have made it possible to monitor the annual spread of blue mold from south to north (Fig. 2). Starting in the spring of 1961, outbreaks of the disease occurred at successive dates from the edges

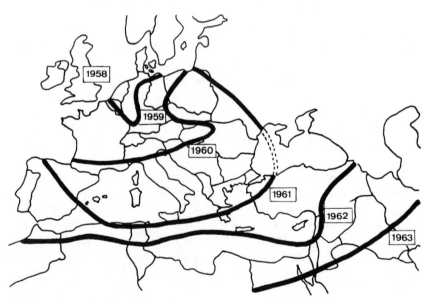

Figure 1. Spread of *Peronospora hyoscyami* in Europe and the Mediterranean countries.

20

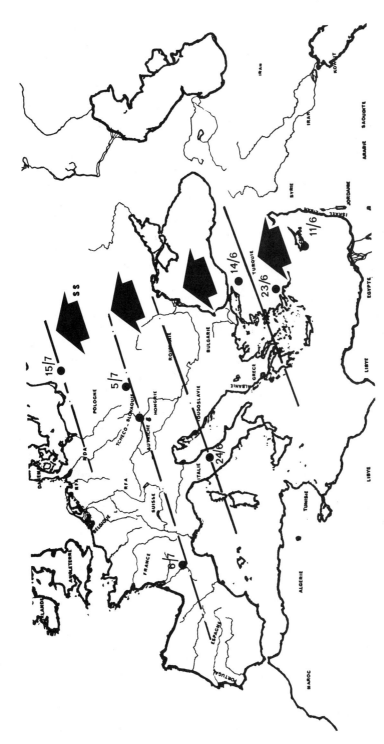

Figure 2. Spread of *Peronospora hyoscyami* each year in Europe and the Mediterranean countries. (Data from Cooperative Center for Scientific Research Relative to Tobacco [CORESTA], Paris)

21

of the Mediterranean toward northern Europe. Each year, the dates at locations where blue mold was reported followed the same pattern, and in 1961 and 1963 the boundaries of the area affected were pushed back (Populer, 1965). Schiltz (1981a) reached the same conclusions from his study of the situation from 1975 to 1980 in eight Mediterranean countries (France, Greece, Italy, Morocco, Spain, Tunisia, Turkey, and Yugoslavia).

The periods during which the parasite appeared during these six years are illustrated in Figure 3. Morocco was always the first to be affected and France the last. The Mediterranean Basin, therefore, appears to be the starting point year after year for blue mold epidemics in Europe. This hypothesis is generally accepted, in view of the overwintering of the pathogen on subspontaneous Nicotianae and the dissemination potential of the sporangia. The absence of severe frosts in the Mediterranean and the introduction of wild Nicotianae, such as *Nicotiana glauca* Graham, or the failure to destroy affected commercial tobacco crops may allow the parasite to survive in situ from one season to the next.

However, this progress from south to north may also correspond to the progression of reburgeoning vegetation (establishment of seedbeds) followed by their contamination from local sources. Mycelia of *P. hyoscyami* may well overwinter in host tissues, particularly in stalks left in the field after harvesting (Schiltz, 1967); also, sporangia may persist on leaves (Corbaz, 1964), thus constituting primary sources of infection.

In Europe, oospores (sexual bodies) are sometimes identified in the leaf tissue of infested tobacco. However, oospores do not appear likely to play any major role in the epidemiology of blue mold. In France it has not been possible to propagate the pathogen from oospores (Schiltz, 1967), whereas in the United States, before the 1979 epidemic, oospores were thought to constitute the main pool of primary infections in seedbeds (Lucas, 1980).

EXTENT OF DAMAGE

At the time of its introduction into Europe and the Mediterranean countries, *P. hyoscyami* was considered the main threat to tobacco crops, but the outbreaks that now occur annually no longer result in major losses. Concerted measures have been taken and have produced beneficial results. An integrated pest management program has been orchestrated in which the use of resistant cultivars has been accompanied by prophylactic measures (particularly in seedbeds) and the CORESTA warning system. Contamination of seedbeds in the spring is essential for the development of an epidemic.

Nonetheless, a cold, very damp spring in 1969 resulted in losses

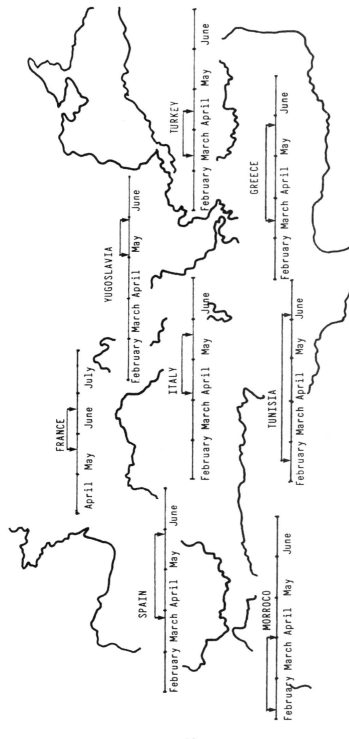

Figure 3.   Dates of appearance of blue mold in the Mediterranean Basin from 1975 to 1980.

23

estimated at 25% of the crop in Morocco. In Europe, primarily the seedbeds were destroyed, and a shortage of transplants resulted. The shortages were 5, 15, and 20% in France, Belgium, and Spain, respectively, but in southwestern France the shortage was 15% (Peyrot, 1969). In contrast there were virtually no losses in 1976 because of the drought that struck France, Germany, Switzerland, Austria, Belgium, and Czechoslovakia.

In 1973, the outbreak was mild in most European countries and the Mediterranean Basin; only southwestern France experienced a severe attack, with losses of 25%. In France, although the pathogen has been widespread, the losses sustained have been relatively light because of the use of resistant cultivars.

Since 1973, CORESTA has reported on the blue mold epidemics in the Mediterranean region (Flesselles, 1983; Ledez, 1984, 1985; Ray, 1973–1981, 1983). The outbreaks have usually been mild, sometimes moderate or severe, but always localized.

From 1977 to 1986, damage remained light, although heavier losses were registered in localities that had wet weather. Since 1981, the rather routine use of metalaxyl mixed with a dithiocarbamate has been another factor that must be taken into account in explaining the major regression of blue mold reported in all countries of Europe and the Mediterranean Basin.

In France, the Agronomic Services of Société nationale d'exploitation industrielle des tabacs et allumettes (SEITA) and the Tobacco Growers Insurance Fund (Caisse d'Assurance des Planteurs de Tabac) have monitored the progress of blue mold since 1961 on the basis of the area affected by the disease (Fig. 4). Although these figures do not give an accurate picture of losses in

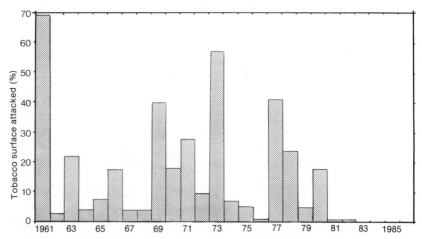

Figure 4.   Importance of blue mold outbreaks in France, 1961–1986.

terms of tobacco raw material, they do indicate the extent of contamination and, therefore, of the epiphytotic conditions.

APPEARANCE OF NEW BIOTYPES

Until 1964 no outbreak had been reported in Europe affecting the cultivars Bel 61-9 and Bel 61-10, selected at Beltsville, Maryland, which carry resistance derived from the Australian species *N. debneyi*. However, in 1965, unusual symptoms were detected at Bergerac (France) in first-generation hybrids (P. 48 × Resistant-Hicks) as well as in the resistant germ plasms Bel 61-9 and Bel 61-10. These symptoms revealed a sudden increase in the pathogenicity of *P. hyoscyami* (Schiltz, 1967). The same effects were reported in the same year from Switzerland (Corbaz, 1966, 1970) and Hungary (Tuboly, 1966).

Other countries were affected by a similar situation some time later. The increased virulence of *P. hyoscyami* was not reported until 1967 in the German Democratic Republic (Egerer, 1968), 1970 in Poland (Jankowski, 1971), and 1972 in the Federal Republic of Germany (Schmidt et al, 1972). This new biotype appears to have been propagated throughout Europe and even to have reached Iran (Zalpoor, 1970).

These observations indicate that the spread of resistant cultivars, particularly of first-generation hybrids, has favored the increased pathogenicity of *P. hyoscyami*. As early as 1963, Hill (1963) had shown that the virulence of the pathogen could be increased by passage onto a resistant host (SO_1). The hypothesis advanced by this Australian author is that resistant cultivars select virulent biotypes, which are the only ones able to sporulate on the resistant host. However, Schiltz (1967) attempted to reproduce this experiment under various conditions but was unable to obtain highly virulent strains. In contrast, he demonstrated that the increased pathogenic potential could be reversed following culture on a susceptible host. Thus, according to Schiltz (1967, 1981b), the new biotypes that have appeared in Europe since 1965 should not be considered a new race, genetically speaking, but rather are more virulent strains resulting from the physiological adaptation of the parasite.

The findings reported by Schiltz and Coussirat (1969) were more convincing than Schiltz's (1967) demonstration. Following a severe outbreak on genetically resistant but juvenile plants (seedbeds)— that is, plants that had not yet demonstrated their hereditary properties—Schiltz and Coussirat observed the emergence of a highly virulent strain of *P. hyoscyami*. This finding allowed the authors to propose the hypothesis that the induction of high virulence was related to inhibition by resistance factors and to a high sporulation rate.

PATHOGENICITY STUDIES
Cotyledon Test

As soon as more virulent biotypes of *P. hyoscyami* emerged, plant pathologists began to search for methods to investigate variations in virulence. The "cotyledon test" devised by Schiltz and Izard (1962) makes use of the properties of young plants at the cotyledonary stage (Fig. 5) under closely defined conditions of propagation. It appears to offer sufficient sensitivity and simplicity for this type of investigation. The results obtained by inoculating 10-day-old seedlings with a mixture of two strains with differing pathogenicity are presented in Table 1. Note that even a small proportion of the virulent biotype (30%) triggers abundant sporulation in the resistant cultivar Bel 61-10. This therefore confirms the sensitivity of the cotyledon test to variations in the aggressiveness or virulence of *P. hyoscyami.*

By altering the nourishment of the young plants, Schiltz (1967) and Schiltz and Coussirat (1969) demonstrated that genetic

Figure 5.   Tobacco seedlings at the cotyledonary stage, 10 days after germination. The cotyledon test uses about 500 seedlings per 6-cm petri dish.

resistance to virulent strains of the blue mold pathogen can be stimulated by providing the young plants with a magnesium salt as their only nutrient (Table 2). The genes for resistance that are expressed only in the vegetative stage of the plant (e.g., in *N. debneyi*) are expressed in the cotyledon within 10 days after the application of a magnesium salt. Only in *N. megalosiphon* and *N. exigua* was heredity expressed regardless of the nutrient received.

CORESTA Trap Collection

To improve monitoring of the pathogenicity of *P. hyoscyami* and to reveal any modification in the behavior of resistant cultivars, the CORESTA Phytopathology Group has been running a collective study since 1965. Every year, the reactions of a collection of cultivars (germ plasms) to *P. hyoscyami* infection are observed under natural conditions in most tobacco-growing countries in Europe, the Mediterranean, and the Middle East (Fig. 6).

This assortment of cultivars, or "trap collection," includes seven permanent cultivars, two susceptible and five resistant (Table 3). New genotypes are regularly added to this assortment to assess their resistance. For example, Pobeda 2, introduced into the collection in 1977, is a cultivar selected in Bulgaria, with resistance obtained from *N. debneyi*, and TU 8/4-7/2, studied since 1982, is a

Table 1. Results of the "cotyledon test" for the cultivars P. 48 (susceptible) and Bel 61-10 (resistant) inoculated with two strains of *Peronospora hyoscyami*

Inoculum composition		Sporulation (%)	
Normal strain (%)	Virulent strain (%)	P. 48	Bel 61-10
100	0	60	6.5
70	30	60	41
50	50	74	51
30	70	62	44
0	100	60	56

Table 2. Effect of magnesium on the efficacy of resistant genes in *Nicotiana debneyi* and *N. megalosiphon* against the virulent biotype of *Peronospora*

	Sporulation (%)	
Genotype or species	Water	$Mg(NO_3)_2$, $6H_2O$ (1.5 mg/ml)
P. 48 (sensitive)	98	98
Bel 61-10 (resistant)	95	53
N. debneyi (resistant)	78	6.4
N. megalosiphon (resistant)	0	0

dark, air-cured tobacco selected in Tunisia from a cross with Bel 61-10.

The damage caused to the tobacco by blue mold is assessed by reference to a score grid (Table 4), which takes into account three criteria, each of which is scored from 1 to 5 (Schiltz, 1974): the degree of attack (i.e., the proportion of the leaf surface affected); the host's reaction or degree of sporulation on the spots; and the extent and nature of the systemic form. The final score, which ranges from 2 (disease absent) to 30 (plants destroyed), is calculated by multiplying the first two scores and then adding the third score.

The data collected from this study of the moderate damage in the Euro-Mediterranean region reveal little change in the degree of

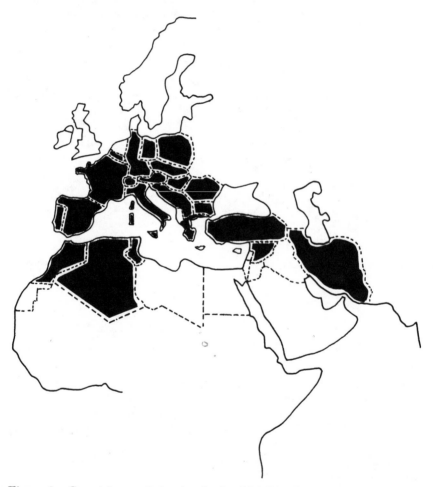

Figure 6.   Countries participating in the CORESTA "trap collection" blue mold study.

attack of resistant types. This seems to indicate that the pathogenic potential has not changed noticeably since 1965 (Delon, 1985).

At Bergerac (France) the changing pathogenicity of *P. hyoscyami* has been monitored since 1965 by recording the damage to the

Table 3. Permanent germ plasms in the CORESTA blue mold "trap collection"

Cultivar	Source
Bergerac C	Mutant of *Nicotiana tabacum* 'Paraguay' obtained at Bergerac, France; very susceptible
Samsoun	Oriental tobacco with medium susceptibility
Bel 61-10	Highly resistant tobacco, created in the United States, with resistance derived from *N. debneyi*
Chemical Mutant	Very resistant line, obtained by mutation in Australia
GA 955	Tobacco from Australia, very resistant in the field; resistance comes from *N. excelsior*
R × T	Type with medium resistance, selected in Poland and obtained from a cross of *N. tabacum* × *N. rustica*
Trumpf	Resistant strain created in the Federal Republic of Germany; resistance comes from *N. goodspeedii*

Table 4. Scores of blue mold symptoms (CORESTA grid)[a]

Score	Leaf area damaged	Amount of sporulation	Degree of systemic infection
1	No visible spot	No tissue response	No symptoms
2	1–10 spots on the group of 20 plants	Characteristic resistance response without sporulation	Benign deformations affecting secondary veins; a few scattered lesions
3	2–25 spots per plant (1–5% of the leaf surface)	Tissue necrosis with some conidiophores	Benign deformations affecting secondary veins; number of lesions exceeds number of leaves
4	5–6% of the leaf surface area affected	Moderate sporulation	Infection of the midribs (or the petiole) resulting in substantial leaf deformation; a few leaves affected
5	More than 25% of the leaf surface area affected	Very substantial sporulation	Infection of the midribs (or the petiole) resulting in substantial leaf deformation; most leaves affected

[a] Assessed on groups of 20 plants.

resistant cultivar Bel 61-10 (Fig. 7). Over the 20-year period 1965–1984, there was no indication of a change in pathogenicity of the parasite. Variations in pathogenicity appear in fact to be related to environmental effects or the expression of the resistance genes of the tobacco, which may be considerably affected by the stage of development of the plant and by its physiological state.

However, the results obtained in the CORESTA study do reveal different pathogenicity levels of the parasite in the various countries taking part in the study. During 1978–1985, the pathogenic potential of *P. hyoscyami* estimated from the CORESTA trap collection appeared to be higher in France than in Bulgaria (Palakarcheva and Delon, 1986).

Means of Control

In the fight against plant disease, the aim is to provide improved protection for the plant at lower cost while keeping pesticide levels at acceptable limits, avoiding the promotion of the emergence of "variants" of the pathogen, and maintaining the biological equilibrium of the plant. In the case of blue mold of tobacco, these goals necessitate a combination of strategies, including prophylactic measures, cultivation of resistant cultivars, and use of fungicides.

PROPHYLACTIC MEASURES

Three main prophylactic measures have been advocated. First, in areas where the winter is not severe enough to destroy the sources of inocula, subspontaneous *Nicotiana* spp. (*N. glauca,* ornamental

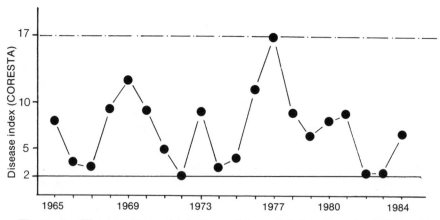

Figure 7. The reaction of tobacco cultivar Bel 61-10 to the blue mold pathogen in Bergerac, France, 1965–1984.

tobaccos) or crop residues that may harbor conidia or oospores should be destroyed. Second, the transport of pathogenic organisms from one region to another on contaminated plants should be avoided. And third, use of cultural conditions hostile to the blue mold fungus is recommended.

Although cultural practices in themselves are not sufficient to control blue mold, they can at least help to slow the spread of the disease and reduce the severity of attacks. In seedbeds, sterilization or disinfestation of the peat is recommended, with light sowing, limited humidity, and nitrogen fertilization. Any unused seedlings should be destroyed as soon as possible. For field plantings, a sunny location is recommended. Only healthy plants should be transplanted, and excess nitrogen should be avoided. Bottom leaves should be removed to ensure good aeration, and stalks and stumps should be destroyed immediately after harvesting to prevent the parasite from overwintering.

CULTIVATION OF RESISTANT CULTIVARS

The use of resistant cultivars is undoubtedly the simplest and cheapest way to fight disease. In the case of tobacco, resistance to *P. hyoscyami* is present initially only in certain *Nicotiana* spp., such as *N. exigua, N. debneyi, N. megalosiphon, N. goodspeedii,* and *N. suaveolens.* Resistance is never total and is generally manifested only after a few weeks' growth, the delay depending on the number of functional genes. In *N. megalosiphon,* however, Schiltz and Coussirat (1969) demonstrated resistance at all stages of development.

In Europe, resistance genes have been successfully transferred to commercial cultivars by hybridization between *N. tabacum* and *N. debneyi* (Bailov et al, 1964; Izard and Schiltz, 1963). In most cases, however, European breeders have preferred to use intervarietal hybrids obtained from mildew-resistant strains of *N. tabacum* produced in the United States (Bel 61-10) or in Australia (Resistant-Hicks). These hybrids have resistance genes derived from *N. debneyi.* In 1964, cultivation of a mildew-resistant first-generation hybrid cultivar (Paraguay × Resistant-Hicks) was introduced into France and was accepted rapidly. In Switzerland and many other European countries (Marcelli and Fantechi, 1967) in 1963 and 1964, the susceptible cultivar Mont Calme was replaced by an F_1 cultivar (Bel 61-10 × Burley Alsace) (Corbaz, 1981).

Stable cultivars soon replaced the first-generation hybrids. In France, the dark, air-cured cultivar PBD6, derived from a cross between Paraguay and Bel 61-10 (Schiltz, 1967), soon became dominant because of its good blue mold resistance and the quality of raw material provided. This cultivar remains in cultivation. In

Switzerland, the resistant cultivar SOTA 7, derived from a cross of A2-426 × Burley 61-2, was first cultivated in 1965 but had inadequate resistance and was replaced by the cultivars Bu S51 and Bu S62, introduced in 1975 and 1978, respectively. They offer higher resistance derived from Bel 61-10 (Corbaz, 1981).

Similar efforts have been made in most countries in Europe, the Middle East, and North Africa and have involved all types of tobacco, including oriental cultivars (Bailov, 1964; Bailov and Palakarcheva, 1962). Apart from some loss of resistance observed in many European countries in nearly all resistant cultivars from 1964 because of the increased virulence of *P. hyoscyami,* the level of resistance of these cultivars has been maintained to the present with no further modification of the parasite or emergence of a new strain. The continued acceptable level of resistance is probably due to genes derived from *N. debneyi.*

According to Schiltz et al (1977a), heredity may be trigenic, involving genes Rn, R_{v1}, and R_{v2}, where R_{v1} and R_{v2} are complementary genes, and the expression of resistance will vary with the physiological state of the host. In any case, this resistance is only partial and increases as the tobacco plant develops. As flowering draws near, the differences between resistant and susceptible cultivars are most marked (Fig. 8). Although the introduction of the blue mold-resistant cultivars has not eliminated the risks of the disease, these cultivars have reduced considerably the losses blue mold causes.

Figure 8.   Resistant (left) and susceptible (right) tobacco.

CHEMICAL CONTROL

Beginning in 1960, the failure to find a totally satisfactory genetic solution led to a search for chemical methods of fighting the disease. It was very soon found that some fungicides were effective against the blue mold pathogen.

Protectant Fungicides

Some substances whose vapors are active, such as para-dichlorobenzene and benzol, never provided satisfactory results because of the difficulties in applying them and the incomplete protection provided. The dithiocarbamates were found to be the most effective fungicides (Corbaz, 1960; Hitier et al, 1961, 1963). Among the derivatives of dithiocarbamic acid, maneb, mancozeb, and propineb are still the substances widely used, either alone or in association, in combatting blue mold of tobacco throughout Europe (De Baets, 1976).

The dithiocarbamates present a fairly wide spectrum and low phytotoxicity toward the tobacco plant. They act at the thiol group (-SH) to interfere with various functions of the parasite, resulting in the blockage of germination.

The main drawback of these chemicals is their failure to penetrate the plant; they protect the plant only if they are present on the leaf before contamination. Treatment is preventive and must be repeated fairly frequently to protect new growth and plant parts where the fungicides have been washed away by rain or watering.

Plants are treated either by dusting with powder or by spraying with wettable powder. The use of dithiocarbamates may vary slightly from one country to another. In France, where the protection against blue mold is obligatory (as a result of an administrative decision of the French Ministry of Agriculture, a prefectural order has mandated protection against blue mold since 1971), tobacco growers were supplied with this type of fungicide free of charge until 1981. Other countries, including Switzerland, have a similar policy toward blue mold prevention (Corbaz, 1981). Note that the efficacy of the dithiocarbamates has continued unchanged for more than 25 years of intensive use, and no resistance has been reported.

Other protective fungicides have been tried, notably substances effective against other downy mildews (on grape, potato, etc.). Chlorothalonil (or TCPN), a benzene derivative, and folpet (a phthalimide) have been found to be ineffective against *P. hyoscyami*. Bordeaux mixture, which contains lime and copper sulfate, does have some effect against blue mold, but its use should not be permitted because of the high levels of copper residues that would remain on the tobacco after harvesting.

Systemic Fungicides

Around the 1970s systemic or endotherapeutic fungicides, which were effective against the Oomycetes, especially the Peronosporales, appeared. The phytosanitary industry produced active ingredients belonging to a variety of groups: acetamides (cymoxanil), metalaxyl phosphites (fosetyl Al), and acylalanines (furalaxyl, metalaxyl, ofurace, benalaxyl). The last group, particularly metalaxyl, has been very effective against blue mold (Table 5).

Metalaxyl. The effectiveness of metalaxyl in the control of *P. hyoscyami* has been demonstrated by several authors (Avigliano and Sorrentino, 1977; Schiltz et al, 1977b; Tsakiridis et al, 1979). For this reason, this active ingredient was soon in routine use on tobacco crops throughout Europe, the Mediterranean Basin, and other countries where blue mold is a major problem, such as Australia, the United States, and Cuba.

Metalaxyl [dl-methyl-*N*-(2,6-dimethylphenyl)-*N*-(2-methoxy-acetyl) alaninate], which is similar in structure to the alpha-chloranilide herbicides, was developed by Ciba-Geigy under the trade names Ridomil and Acylon. Like other active principles in the acylalanine group, metalaxyl at very low concentrations inhibits mycelial growth of many phycomycetes but has no effect on ascomycetes, basidiomycetes, or deuteromycetes. This extreme specificity, combined with the risk of the development of resistant strains of the parasite, led the member organizations of CORESTA to suggest in 1977 (as recommended by the CORESTA Phyto-pathology Group) that guidelines should be issued for the use of this type of fungicide and, in particular, that these fungicides should be used only prophylactically and in association with protective fungicides such as the dithiocarbamates.

Metalaxyl is not phytotoxic. Under normal conditions of use, it is

Table 5. Fungicides tested against blue mold, 1970–1982[a]

Active ingredient	Trade name	Manufacturer	Efficacy[b]	Systemic activity
Cymoxanil	Various names	E. I. du Pont	1	No
Fosetyl Al	Aliette	Rhône-Poulenc	1	Yes
Metalaxyl	Ridomil or Acylon	Ciba-Geigy	3	Yes
Furalaxyl	Fongarid	Ciba-Geigy	3	Yes
Ofurace	Various names	Chevron	2	Yes
Benalaxyl	Galben	Montedison	2	Yes

[a] Source: Société nationale d'exploitation industrielle des tabacs et allumettes (SEITA), Paris.
[b] 0 = None, 1 = low, 2 = good, 3 = excellent.

particularly active against downy mildews affecting plants such as grape, potato, and tomato and against damping-off agents (*Pythium* and *Phytophthora* spp.). This chemical is absorbed not only by the leaves, but also by the stalks of annual plants and by the roots and the leaves of perennials (Staub et al, 1978). However, external redistribution may occur as a result of the vapors (Schiltz et al, 1977b), and this constitutes an additional route of transfer to plants.

Metalaxyl penetrates leaves within 30 min of spraying. This high rate of penetration limits the chemical, for the most part, from being washed off. The action lasts from two to five weeks, depending on the method of application and the dose administered.

The preventive action of metalaxyl is much greater than its curative effect, although in the laboratory it can halt pathogen development (Schiltz and Delon, 1981b). Because it is very difficult to determine the exact date of blue mold contamination in commercial fields, it would be very risky to use metalaxyl purely on a curative basis.

In most countries in which metalaxyl has been approved, it is associated with a dithiocarbamate (maneb, mancozeb, or zineb) and spraying the foliage is recommended. The formulation and dose of active ingredient vary among countries (Table 6). Metalaxyl has been applied to the soil in undiluted form in Australia (Johnson et al, 1979) and the United States (Lucas, 1980) to control both black shank (caused by *Phytophthora parasitica* var. *nicotianae* (Breda de Haan) Tucker) and blue mold. In France this method has not given satisfactory results in either nurseries or open fields (Schiltz et al, 1977a). In France, the fungicides authorized for use against blue mold of tobacco are dithiocarbamates (maneb, mancozeb, and propineb, in powder for dusting [6%] or wettable powder [80%]) at 120 g/hl, and a mixture of metalaxyl (25%) and maneb (50%), at 40 and 80 g/hl. The commercial product Acylon-Tabac contains 25% metalaxyl and 50% maneb and is used at a final concentration of 0.160 kg/hl; the rate of application depends on the stage of development of the tobacco crop but ranges from 300 to 1,000 L/ha. Fields are treated every seven to 15 days, depending on the stage of development of the crop and the resistance of the cultivars (Schiltz and Delon, 1981a).

Attempts to incorporate metalaxyl into tobacco seed coatings have been made in Austria (Schattauer and Schipfer, 1978), Italy (Beuchat and de Kuijper, 1981), and France (P. Schiltz and R. Delon, unpublished). Although this does protect the young plants for about five weeks, the protection is not sufficient to cover the entire life of the tobacco seedling in the nursery.

Resistance to metalaxyl. Before metalaxyl was launched on

the commercial market, Ciba-Geigy studied resistance phenomena in this compound. In the laboratory, metalaxyl-resistant isolates of *Phytophthora infestans* (Mont.) de Bary were obtained by treatment with sublethal doses but were found to be avirulent. Staub et al (1978) observed no case of adaptation to the substance in vivo, despite a number of passages through treated plants.

Yet by 1979 Reuveni et al (1980) in Israel had observed the appearance of *Pseudoperonospora cubensis* (Burk. & Curt.) Rostow isolates on cucumber crops under glass that were resistant to metalaxyl after weekly applications of the fungicide for one year. In 1980, metalaxyl used alone was quickly losing its efficacy in potato late blight (caused by *Phytophthora infestans*) control, whereas no resistance was found when metalaxyl was used in a mixture with copper oxychloride (Urech et al, 1981). Instances of metalaxyl resistance were reported from many countries. Also, Clergeau and Simone (1982) reported resistance in the downy mildew pathogen of grape.

Metalaxyl resistance in *P. hyoscyami* on tobacco was first reported in Nicaragua in 1981 (Anonymous, 1981). More recently, the emergence of resistant strains of *P. hyoscyami* has been noticed in Mexico (Bickers, 1986). Resistance to metalaxyl among downy

Table 6. The use of metalaxyl in some European countries[a]

Country	Formulation	Dose (g a.i./ha)
Austria	Metalaxyl + mancozeb (8 + 64)	375
Belgium	Metalaxyl + maneb	400
Czechoslovakia	Metalaxyl + mancozeb (8 + 64)	120
France	Metalaxyl + maneb (25 + 50)	120–400
Germany (East)	Metalaxyl + zineb (8 + 64)	160
Germany (West)	Metalaxyl + mancozeb (15 + 45)	60–120
Hungary	Metalaxyl + zineb (8 + 64)	170
Italy	Metalaxyl	150
Poland	Metalaxyl + mancozeb	60–200
Spain	Metalaxyl + mancozeb (8 + 64)	60–200
Yugoslavia	Metalaxyl + zineb or Metalaxyl + mancozeb (8 + 64)	120–240

[a] Data from a survey conducted by the Phytopathology Group of CORESTA in April 1987 and from Ciba-Geigy.

mildews appeared in most cases in response to strong inoculum pressure and when metalaxyl was used alone.

Strategy for the use of metalaxyl. Because of the risk of the appearance of resistant strains of the blue mold pathogen in Europe, the Phytopathology Group of CORESTA as early as 1975 recommended a strategy for using this type of fungicide, which can be compared with a major gene conferring vertical resistance. Parasites rapidly circumvent these types of protection. The strategy, defined by Schiltz et al (1977b) and taken up again by Urech (1980) and Urech and Staub (1985), can be summarized under three points.

First, in treating both seedbeds and field plantings, metalaxyl must be used only in a mixture with a protectant fungicide such as maneb, mancozeb, propineb, or zineb. The mixture must contain a sufficient quantity of metalaxyl, that is, 20–40 g a.i./100 L of mixture, and 80 g a.i. of maneb or an equivalent fungicide. The volume of mixture applied per hectare varies with the stage of development of the plants from about 300 L after transplanting to 1,100 L at the end of the vegetative stage. This clearly rules out the use of the mixture on soil to prevent blue mold.

Second, the mixture of metalaxyl and maneb must be applied prophylactically by spraying at intervals of no more than 14 days, in order to maintain the effect of the protectant fungicide. Metalaxyl must under no circumstances be applied to the soil to control a parasite affecting the aboveground parts of the plants.

And third, the foregoing measures should preferably be applied to resistant cultivars, if they are available. The same principles should obviously be adhered to if other acylalanines such as benalaxyl or ofurace are used on tobacco.

Monitoring for the appearance of resistant strains. Several methods have been developed to monitor the appearance of metalaxyl-resistant strains on tobacco and to take the necessary steps to combat this eventuality. Urech et al (1981) suggested a method using isolated leaves or whole plants treated with various doses. Delon and Schiltz (1981) developed a "cotyledon test" (see earlier subsection), which consists of observing the behavior of isolates of *P. hyoscyami* on young plants at the cotyledonary stage (Fig. 6). This simple and very rapid method has made it possible to monitor the sensitivity of the isolates of *P. hyoscyami* collected from various regions of France since 1980 (Fig. 9).

After six years of virtually universal use of Ridomil (or Acylon-Tabac) on tobacco crops, there has been no noticeable modification of *P. hyoscyami* isolates from the reference isolate (Y1), which has never been in contact with metalaxyl. To be more effective, this monitoring scheme should be systematically extended to all countries of Europe and the Mediterranean in the same way as the CORESTA warning system has been.

Other fungicides. Many other active ingredients are under study for use against blue mold; however, to date none has been found as effective as metalaxyl. However, some mixtures, such as oxadixyl plus cymoxanil plus maneb (or mancozeb), appear to reveal a synergistic interaction among the molecules that could be valuable if strains resistant to metalaxyl emerge.

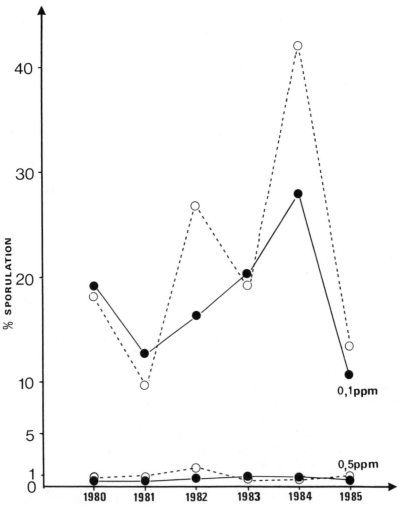

Figure 9. Sensitivity of *Peronospora hyoscyami* isolates (open circles, dashed lines) to 0.1 and 0.5 ppm metalaxyl, compared to a reference strain (Y1) (solid circles, solid lines), monitored by the cotyledon test.

In Europe it is generally agreed that the rapid propagation of tobacco blue mold epidemics can be explained only by conidial contamination. The conidia, which can be carried over long distances by the wind, make it possible for the disease to spread like wildfire, particularly if the climatic conditions are favorable.

Every year, the disease spreads from centers in North Africa northward toward northern Europe (Fig. 2). In the absence of a satisfactory model for forecasting epidemics, CORESTA organized a warning service in 1961. The system is a very valuable aid in determining strategies and adapting the fight against blue mold to circumstances.

Every outbreak of the disease, in seedbeds or in the field, is immediately reported to the secretary-general of CORESTA in Paris, who relays the information to the corresponding members by telex to allow them to take the necessary precautions to protect their crops and detect any outbreaks that may have occurred in their own countries. Periodic reports keep all members informed about the situation, and every year a general report is presented by the secretary-general, who coordinates the warning service.

Perspectives for the Future

Although the danger of a severe epidemic of tobacco blue mold in Europe or the Mediterranean countries has not been abolished, the present situation appears to provide tobacco growers with a wide range of effective weapons against this disease. However, possible modifications of the parasite could render the fungicides, and any resistant cultivars that may have been developed, quite useless. For these reasons, tobacco researchers must remain vigilant and be able to respond quickly to any future epidemic that might degenerate into a catastrophe and destroy the entire crop.

LITERATURE CITED

Anonymous. 1981. Blue mold active in Central America. Tob. Int. Dec. 25:92.

Avigliano, M., and Sorrentino, C. 1977. Un trienno di sperimentazione con prodotti sistemici nella lotta contro la *Peronospora* del tabaco. Ann. Ist. Sper. Tab. 1977:179–207.

Bailov, D. 1964. Travaux de sélection et génétique en vue de la création de tabacs résistants au mildiou en Bulgarie. *Peronospora* Working Group, Cooperative Center for Scientific Research Relative to Tobacco (CORESTA), Vienna.

Bailov, D., and Palakarcheva, M. 1962. Contribution pour surmonter incompatibilité entre *N. tabacum* et *N. debneyi*. C.R. Acad. Bulg. Sci.

15:571–574. (Also in Inf. Bull. CORESTA 1963(4):92)

Bailov, D., Palakarcheva, M., and Daslakov, S. 1964. Nouveaux amphidiploïdes de *N. tabacum* et *N. debneyi*. Rastenievud. Nauki 1(7):3–16. (Also in Inf. Bull. CORESTA 1964(3):66)

Beuchat, A., and de Kuijper, E. 1981. Control of blue mould through introduction of metalaxyl into coated tobacco seed. Pages 121–125 in: Commun. Reun. Groupe Agro-Phyto CORESTA, Torgiano, Italy, 28 Sept.–1 Oct.

Bickers, C. 1986. Mexican cigar leaf's resistant blue mold strain may head for U.S. Tob. Int. March 7:52–56.

Clergeau, M., and Simone, J. 1982. Apparition en France de souches de mildiou (*Plasmopara viticola*) résistants aux fongicides de la famille des anilides. Prog. Agric. Vitic. 3:59–61.

Cooke, M. C. 1891. Tobacco disease. Gard. Chron. 9:173.

Corbaz, R. 1960. Le mildiou du tabac en Suisse. Rev. Romande Agric. Vitic. Arboric. 16(5):45–47.

Corbaz, R. 1961. Considération sur l'épidemié de mildiou de tabac (*P. tabacina* A.) en Europe. Phytopathol. Z. 42:39–44.

Corbaz, R. 1964. Evolution de l'épidemié de mildiou du tabac (*P. tabacina*). Phytopathol. Z. 51:190–191.

Corbaz, R. 1966. Le mildiou du tabac paraît s'adapter aux variétés résistantes. Agric. Romande 4:41–42.

Corbaz, R. 1970. Apparition d'une souche virulente de *Peronospora tabacina* A. en Suisse. Phytopathol. Z. 67:21–26.

Corbaz, R. 1981. Vingt ans de lutte contre le mildiou du tabac (*P. tabacina* A.) en Suisse. Ann. Tab. 17:65–71.

CORESTA. 1960. Compte rendu groupe *Peronospora*. Inf. Bull. CORESTA 1960(4):2–11.

De Baets, A. 1976. Les substances phytosanitaires employées pour le tabac. Pages 8–85 in: Les Résidus de Pesticides dans le Tabac et les Produits de Tabac. Informations sur l'Agriculture: Commission des Communautés Européenes, Vol. 2, No. 23. Office des Publications Officielles des Communautés Européenes, Luxembourg.

Delon, R. 1985. Results of the CORESTA collaborative experiment on the pathogenicity of tobacco blue mold in 1985. Inf. Bull. CORESTA 1985(4):3–8.

Delon, R., and Schiltz, P. 1981. Etude du mode d'action exercée par le métalaxyl sur *P. tabacina*. III. Surveillance, en 1980, de l'activité du métalaxyl sur quelques isolats de mildiou du tabac: "Le test cotylédons-monitoring." Ann. Tab. 17:59–64.

Egerer, A. 1968. Die Aggressivitat von *Peronospora tabacina* A. in der D.D.R. im Jahre 1967. Ber. Inst. Tabakforsch. Dresden 15(1):38.

Flesselles, J. 1983. 1983 Blue mould report. Inf. Bull. CORESTA 1983(4):13–19.

Gerlach, W. 1966. II. Auftreten, Ausbreitung und Auswirkungen der Blauschimmelkrankheit in der Bundesrepublik. Mitt. Biol. Bundesanst. Land Forstwirtsch. Berlin-Dahlem 120:7–16.

Hill, A. V. 1963. A strain of *P. tabacina* pathogenic to tobacco lines with resistance derived from *N. debneyi* and *N. goodspeedii*. Inf. Bull.

CORESTA 1963(3):8–11.

Hitier, H., Michel, E., Mounat, A., and Bown, G. 1961. Essai de traitements fongicides contre le mildiou du tabac. Ann. Tab. 3:757–787.

Hitier, H., Michel, E., Mounat, A., and Bown, G. 1963. Nouvelles experiences sur les traitements fongicides contre *P. tabacina*. Essais 1962. Traitements appliqués en plein champ. Ann. Tab. 4:400–419.

Izard, C., and Schiltz, P. 1963. Le "test cotylédons": Technique et résultats. Inf. Bull. CORESTA 1963(2):7–10.

Jankowski, F. 1971. Studies into pathogenic changes of the fungus *Peronospora tabacina* A., a novel, highly virulent isolate of the pathogen. Biul. Cent. Lab. Przem. Tyton. 1-2:45–58.

Johnson, G. I., Davis, R. D., and O'Brien, R. G. 1979. Soil application of CGA 48988, a systemic fungicide controlling *Peronospora tabacina* on tobacco. Plant. Dis. Rep. 63:212–217.

Ledez, P. 1984. General report on the 1984 tobacco blue mould epidemic (Euro-Mediterranean zone). Inf. Bull. CORESTA 1984(2-3):12–17.

Ledez, P. 1985. General report on the 1985 tobacco blue mould epidemic (Euro-Mediterranean zone). Inf. Bull. CORESTA 1985(2):14–17.

Lucas, G. B. 1980. The war against blue mold. Science 210:147–153.

Marcelli, E., and Fantechi, F. 1967. Variazioni nella patogenicita della *P. tabacina* su ibridi Americani ed Australiani e su specie di *Nicotiana* immunoresistenti. Il Tabacco 71:3–8.

Maximo, Y. 1969. Tobacco trends—The Orient. Tob. U.S. 169(10):7.

Palakarcheva, M., and Delon, R. 1986. Studies on effectiveness of genes for resistance to blue mold of tobacco in Bulgaria and France. Pages 188–192 in: Compte Rendu First National Conference of Immunogenetics of Plants, Sofia, Bulgaria. Bulgarian Academy of Sciences, Institute of Genetics, Sofia.

Peyrot, J. 1969. Blue mould warning service. Inf. Bull. CORESTA 1969(3):3–4.

Populer, C. 1965. Le mildiou du tabac, *Peronospora tabacina* Adam. Chronologie de l'apparition annuelle des foyers en Europe. Parasitica 21(2):37–39.

Ray, P. 1973–1981. General reports on the annual tobacco blue mould epidemics. Inf. Bull. CORESTA 1973(3):11–17, 1974(3-4):19–25, 1975(3):3–11, 1976(3-4):43–52, 1977(3):4–16, 1978(3-4):26–39, 1979(3):3–14, 1980(3-4):40–50, 1981(4):3–13.

Ray, P. 1983. General report on the tobacco blue mold epidemic in 1982 (Euro-Mediterranean zone). Inf. Bull. CORESTA 1983(1):5–12.

Reuveni, M., Eyal, H., and Cohen, Y. 1980. Development of resistance to metalaxyl in *Pseudoperonospora cubensis*. Plant Dis. 64:1108–1109.

Schattauer, H., and Schipfer, L. 1978. Ridomil in Samenpille verhütet Befall durch Blauschimmel. Tabakpflanzer Osterreichs 77:1–3.

Schiltz, P. 1967. Contribution à l'étude de l'agressivité de *Peronospora tabacina* A. C.R. Acad. Sci. Paris 264:2785–2788.

Schiltz, P. 1974. Blue mould pathogenicity: An attempt to improve the collaborative experiment for determining the pathogenicity of *P. tabacina*. Inf. Bull. CORESTA 1974(1):16–22.

Schiltz, P. 1981a. Le mildiou du tabac (*Peronospora tabacina* A.) et ses particularités dans les pays Méditerranéens. C.R. VI Journ. Phytiatr. Phytopharm. Circum-Mediterraneennes 1:276–286.

Schiltz, P. 1981b. Downy mildew of tobacco. Pages 577–599 in: The Downy Mildews. D. M. Spencer, ed. Academic Press, New York. 636 pp.

Schiltz, P., and Coussirat, J. C. 1969. Mise en évidence de la résistance des Nicotianae aux lignées virulentes de *Peronospora tabacina* et détermination du pouvoir pathogène du parasite. Ann. Tab. 6:145–162.

Schiltz, P., and Delon, R. 1981a. Etude du mode d'action exercée par le métalaxyl sur *Peronospora tabacina*. I. Sensibilité du métalaxyl manifestée par le mildiou du tabac au cours de quelques étapes de son développement. Ann. Tab. 17:41–48.

Schiltz, P., and Delon, R. 1981b. Le mildiou du tabac: Historique et moyens actuels de lutte. Phytoma 327:37–41.

Schiltz, P., and Izard, C. 1962. Susceptibilité cotylédonaire et résistance à *P. tabacina* A. C.R. Seances Acad. Agric. Fr. 48:561–564.

Schiltz, P., Coussirat, J. C., and Delon, R. 1977a. La résistance au mildiou du tabac (*P. tabacina*) du type *N. debneyi*: Hérédité probable, apparition d'isolats virulents et stratégie de lutte. Ann. Tab. 14:111–126.

Schiltz, P., Delon, R., Cazamajour, F., Podeur, G., and Boulogne, R. 1977b. Comparaison de quelques fongistatiques et de produits endothérapiques pour la lutte contre le mildiou du tabac. Ann. Tab. 14:127–153.

Schmidt, J. A., Reisch, W., and Vogel, F. 1972. Neuer Biotyp von *Peronospora*. Dtsch. Tabakbau 24:208.

Staub, T., Dahmen, H., and Schwinn, F. J. 1978. Biological characterization of uptake and translocation of fungicidal acylalanines in grape and tomato plants. J. Plant Dis. Prot. 5(314):162–168.

Tsakiridis, J. P., Vasilakakis, C. B., and Chrisochou, A. P. 1979. Evaluation of new systemic and non-systemic fungicides for the control of *P. tabacina* in tobacco seedbeds and fields in Greece. Plant Dis. Rep. 63:63–66.

Tuboly, L. 1966. Apparition en Hongrie d'un nouveau biotype de *Peronospora tabacina* A. Bull. Inf. CORESTA 1966(4):27–34.

Urech, P. 1980. The use of metalaxyl against *P. tabacina*. Commun. CORESTA Congress, Manila, The Philippines, 1980.

Urech, P. A., and Staub, T. 1985. The resistance strategy for acylalanine fungicides. EPPO Bull. 15:539–543.

Urech, P. A., Margot, P., and Staub, T. 1981. Efficacy and use concept of metalaxyl for control of diseases in tobacco. Commun. Reun. Groupe Agro-Phyto CORESTA, Torgiano, Italy, 28 Sept.–1 Oct.

Viennot-Bourgin, G. 1985. Le diagnostic en pathologie végétale. C.R. Seances Acad. Agric. Fr. 71:957–968.

Vuittenez, A. 1961. Le mildiou du tabac. Bull. Tech. Inf. 158:343–349.

Zalpoor, N. 1970. Das vorkommen einer neuen Blauschimmel-rasse in Nord-Iran. Entomol. Phytopathol. Appl. 29:1–5.

Chapter 3

Host-Parasite Relations: Morphology and Ultrastructure

A. M. Svircev
Horticultural Research Institute of Ontario
Vineland Station, Ontario, Canada L0R 2E0

W. E. McKeen
R. J. Smith
Department of Plant Sciences
The University of Western Ontario
London, Ontario, Canada N6A 5B7

The tobacco blue mold pathogen, *Peronospora hyoscyami* de Bary f. sp. *hybrida* Shepherd (syn. *P. tabacina* Adam), escaped the careful early scrutiny the rusts and the powdery mildews received from the scientific community. However, as the economic importance of tobacco increased, interest was generated in this pathogen, which has the potential to destroy the entire tobacco crop in many countries around the world. The historical background of this pathogen, its impact on the tobacco crop, and the importance of the sporangia, weather conditions, the presence of susceptible tobacco, and agricultural practices are closely examined by other contributors to this book.

Because we found that developmental and morphological studies of the pathogen and the host-pathogen interaction were limited, we began to investigate the host-parasite interactions. Ingram (1981) stated that the "Oomycetes, which includes the downy mildews, are phylogenetically, physiologically and genetically unique and its members may, therefore, have evolved relationships with their hosts which differ significantly from those evolved by other fungi." It follows that the Oomycetes in addition evolved unique interactions with their respective hosts.

We examined the structure and histocytological aspects of the blue mold fungus using the traditional light microscope and transmission and scanning electron microscopes. In addition, the

43

new and exciting technique of immunocytochemistry was used in conjunction with electron microscopy. This approach to the study of host-parasite interactions contributed unique and interesting information to our study of *P. hyoscyami* f. sp. *hybrida* and its host.

In the work described in this chapter, we used the susceptible *Nicotiana tabacum* L. cultivar Virginia 115 (Plates 1–3) and the resistant species *N. exigua* Wheeler. The isolate of *P. hyoscyami* was obtained from an infected plant during the 1979 blue mold epiphytotic in southern Ontario.

Sporangia

GERMINATION

Airborne sporangia are the main source of inoculum of the obligate parasite *P. hyoscyami* f. sp. *hybrida*. The optimal conditions for sporangium germination are high relative humidity and temperatures from 15 to 20°C; however, the thin-walled sporangia can withstand extreme temperatures and low humidity. Svircev (1984) found that germination was not possible at temperatures continuously above 30°C; nonetheless, the sporangia were not killed when exposed to 25–35°C and regained the ability to germinate when returned to lower temperatures. Clayton and Gaines (1945) found that neither infection nor spore germination occurred above 29°C, but Cruickshank (1961b) found that germination could occur at temperatures as high as 35°C. Moss and Main (1988), however, found that sporangia produced under high-temperature conditions (30/25°C, day/night) are not able to germinate at temperatures above 25°C.

The sporangia of the tobacco blue mold pathogen germinate erratically in vitro and in vivo (Cruickshank, 1961a; Hill, 1966; Lucas et al, 1985). For example, the sporangia of *P. hyoscyami* germinate well on water agar. If the spores are placed on agarose or washed agar (Noble agar), germination is inhibited (Stewart, 1983). The spores need to be washed to remove an intrinsic germination inhibitor (Hill, 1966; Shepherd, 1962).

The ellipsoidal sporangia (Plate 4), 15–22 μm in diameter, are full of dark-staining, dense cytoplasm. Electron micrographs of quiescent sporangia show that the sporangia are thin-walled and contain 12–18 nuclei, numerous mitochondria, electron-dense particles, and small vacuoles (Fig. 1).

The sporangium wall is relatively thin and pliable. It tends to wrinkle longitudinally when the sporangium is not in water or 100% relative humidity. The plasma membrane always remains tightly bound to the cell wall even during extreme desiccation of the spore.

Once the sporangium contacts water, it instantly loses its corrugated appearance and becomes ellipsoidal.

The first indication of germination is an alteration in the morphological appearance of the spore cytoplasm. Numerous small vacuoles present in the cytoplasm coalesce (Fig. 2) and form a large central vacuole (Figs. 3 and 4). The enlargement of the vacuole displaces the sporangial cytoplasm to the periphery of the spore and vice versa. Uptake of water increases the pressure in the spore and coincides with the flow of spore protoplasm into the newly forming germ tube. The loss of free water, as a result of desiccation or a drop in the relative humidity, causes a volume reduction in sporangial cytoplasm; the spore loses its turgidity and ellipsoidal shape, and its wall becomes wrinkled (Fig. 5).

Hollomon (1973) examined the germination process in *P. hyoscyami* on the molecular level. He proposed that when germination begins, mRNA is released from stable templates in the dormant sporangium. The mRNA complexes with the free small ribosomal subunits forming the initiation complex. Once the initiation complex attaches to the large ribosomal subunits, protein synthesis commences. The process of germination in *P. hyoscyami* requires the synthesis of new proteins from stable mRNA templates already present in the dormant sporangium. The formation of germ tubes does not involve new RNA synthesis.

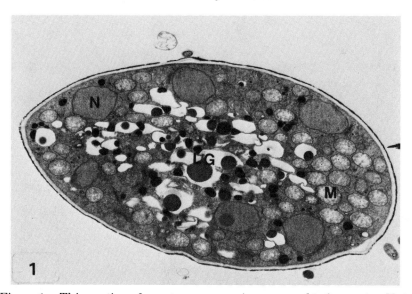

Figure 1.   Thin section of a mature sporangium exposed to free water. Note the numerous nuclei (N), lipid granules (LG), mitochondria (M), and small vacuoles. The outer surface of the spore cell wall has an electron-dense layer. (×4,800)

The germ tube first appears as a bulge (Fig. 6) on the sporangium wall in a zone midway between the equatorial plane and the point of attachment of the sporangium to the sporangiophore. It does not emerge anywhere on the surface, as claimed by Shaw (1981). The germ tube is often bulbous at its base. On susceptible tobacco the

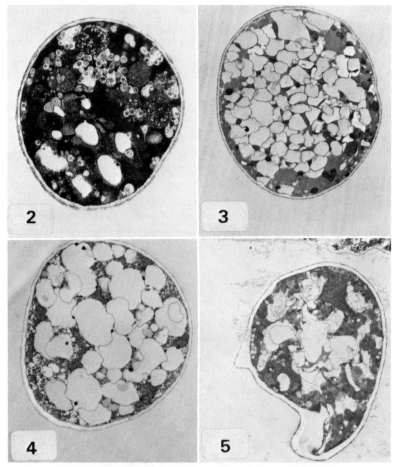

Figure 2. Cross section of an ungerminated sporangium 0.5 hr after inoculation. The spore is filled with a few vacuoles. (×3,500)

Figure 3. Cross section of an ungerminated sporangium 1.5 hr after inoculation. Large vacuoles are present. (×3,500)

Figure 4. Cross section of an ungerminated sporangium 2.5 hr after inoculation. (×3,500)

Figure 5. Cross section of a sporangium maintained in air before embedding. The convoluted wall and collapsed vacuoles indicate a loss of water content. (×3,500)

germ tube remains short, whereas sporangia germinating on glass slides or nonhost species produce germ tubes up to 400 μm long.

Once the germ tube initial appears, a new cell wall underlies the existing sporangium wall (Fig. 7); the new wall is centered around the germ tube bulge. The old sporangium wall also initially surrounds the germ tube bulge. When the germ tube reaches approximately 4 μm in length, the new wall pushes through the old sporangium wall, which extends along the germ tube for 1–3 μm. The germ tube wall extends under the sporangium wall for about 2–3 μm and while in close contact is separated from it by an electron-dense line. The germ tube wall (0.09 μm thick) is thinner than the sporangium wall (0.16 μm), but both appear to have the same electron density in thin sections. An electron-dense layer is present on the outside of the sporangium cell wall (Fig. 8).

Bartnicki-Garcia (1968) noted three mechanisms of vegetative wall formation during the course of spore germination; each mechanism is characteristic of a certain group of fungi. In type I fungi, the germ tube wall is an extension of the spore wall, or one of its innermost layers. This mode of genesis is thought to be the most

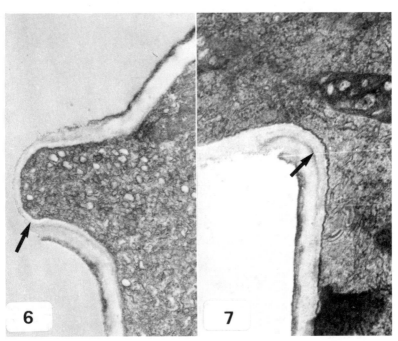

Figure 6. Section of a sporangial germ tube initial. Note the inner new wall (arrow). (×12,500)

Figure 7. Section of a germinated sporangium, showing the inner germ tube wall (arrow) and the outer sporangium wall. (×25,000)

common, appearing throughout the true fungi, for example, *Botrytis, Aspergillus, Melampsora,* and *Neurospora.* With type II fungi, the wall is formed de novo on the naked protoplast, such as the encysting zoospores of phycomycetes. With type III fungi, a

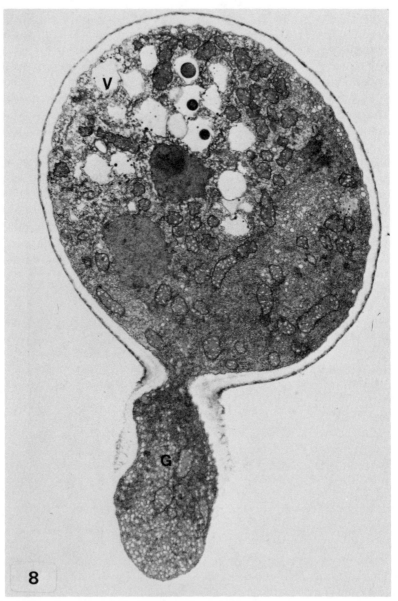

Figure 8.   Section of a sporangium and germ tube. Note the tiny vesicles in the germ tube cytoplasm and the vacuolation (V) in the sporangium distal from the germ tube (G). (×8,000)

vegetative wall forms de novo under all of the existing spore wall. This type of wall formation is evident in the Mucorales.

Wall formation in *P. hyoscyami* does not resemble any of the types described by Bartnicki-Garcia (1968). Moreover, its developmental mode is unique in its own order, the Peronosporales. In *P. parasitica*, another downy mildew in the same order, a new wall layer (type III) forms underneath the entire sporangium cell wall. The germ tube wall becomes continuous with the newly formed layer (Hemmes and Hohl, 1969). The latter appears to represent a more primitive cell wall type.

Germ tube formation in the blue mold pathogen is similar to that of the arthrospore of *Geotrichum candidum* Link ex Pers., an anamorphic species whose teleomorph belongs to the subphylum Ascomycotina (Steele and Fraser, 1973). Similarities between the Mastigomycota and Amastigomycota indicate no pronounced distinction in wall synthesis between these two major groups of fungi.

At 1.0–2.5 hr postinoculation, cytoplasm flows from the sporangium into the germ tube (Fig. 8). The electron-dense cytoplasm inside the germ tube contains electron-dense granules, free ribosomes, and many mitochondria. The plasma membrane of the sporangium is continuous and is not separable from the germ tube.

INHIBITION

The effects of temperature, relative humidity, β-ionone, riboflavin, age of host, leaf position, and cuticular waxes on the germination of *P. hyoscyami* sporangia have been well documented (Cruickshank, 1961a, 1977; Hill, 1966; Leppik et al, 1972; Salt et al, 1986; Shepherd, 1962; Shepherd and Mandryk, 1963).

In addition, the sporangia of this obligate parasite exhibit an extreme sensitivity to elevated concentrations of carbon dioxide in the atmosphere. The sporangia lose their ability to germinate in carbon dioxide-enriched atmospheres. Sporangia removed from carbon dioxide-enriched environments can germinate and function normally.

To monitor the effect of carbon dioxide on sporangium germination, equipment was designed to allow the admission of known concentrations of carbon dioxide into a sealed chamber (Svircev et al, 1984). Spores of *P. hyoscyami, Aspergillus niger* v. Tiegh., and *Botrytis cinerea* Pers. ex Fr. were exposed to atmospheres enriched with 0.5, 0.6, 0.8, 1.3, 5.0, 7.5, and 15% carbon dioxide. After 2.5, 5.5, 11.5, and 17.5 hr, the sporangia were removed from the enriched atmospheres and treated with acid fuchsin in lactophenol to prevent further development.

49

Spore germination was retarded at 0.8% carbon dioxide. This was the lowest carbon dioxide concentration that inhibited germination and subsequent germ tube development. At 1.3% carbon dioxide for 2.5 hr, germination was 51% of the control (Table 1).

Carbon dioxide induces morphological changes at levels of 0.8% and 1.3%. The sporangium germ tubes are shorter and thinner (Fig. 9) than those of the controls (Fig. 10). In contrast, *B. cinerea* and *A. niger* did not exhibit such sensitivity to carbon dioxide. Germination of *B. cinerea* is initially inhibited at 5% and 7.5% carbon dioxide, reaching 100% inhibition at 17.5 and 11.5 hr, respectively. *A. niger* germination is not significantly altered at 1.3, 5.0, or 7.5% carbon dioxide. Exposure to 15% carbon dioxide for 17.5 hr reduces germination of *A. niger* conidia to 92% of that of the control.

The normal germ tubes of *B. cinerea* and *A. niger* differ morphologically from the germ tubes that are exposed to elevated carbon dioxide atmospheres. These germ tubes are shorter and wider than those of the controls. Ultrastructurally, the germ tubes of *P. hyoscyami, B. cinerea,* and *A. niger* exposed to 0.8, 7.5, and 15% carbon dioxide, respectively, exhibited short and distorted mitochondria (Fig. 11), whereas the mitochondria in the controls (Fig. 12) remained turgid, with the cristae easily distinguished.

Spores of *P. hyoscyami, B. cinerea,* and *A. niger* removed from the carbon dioxide-enriched environment regain their ability to germinate and produce germ tubes structurally similar to those of the controls. The mitochondria regain their normal turgid appearance with well-defined cristae.

Inhibition of fungal development by carbon dioxide has been observed in other fungi (Durbin, 1959; Mitchell and Zentmyer, 1971; Wells and Uota, 1970). Increased carbon dioxide in the atmosphere prevents the formation of fruiting structures in *Agaricus bisporus*

Table 1. Effect of carbon dioxide and duration of exposure on germination of sporangia of *Peronospora hyoscyami* at $20°C$

Exposure (hr)	Germination at indicated CO_2 concentration (%)[a,b]						
	0.5	0.6	0.8	1.3	5	7.5	15
2.5	103 c	100 c	90	51	35	10	0
5.5			100 c	84	43	27	0
11.5			100 c	87	59	30	0
17.5				100 c	64	33	9

[a] Percent germination of treated spores relative to control spores (85% germination in control spores). Based on 1,000 sporangia per observation in each of three trials.
[b] Numbers followed by the letter *c* are not statistically different from the control; all others are significantly different according to a Z-test ($P = 0.05$).

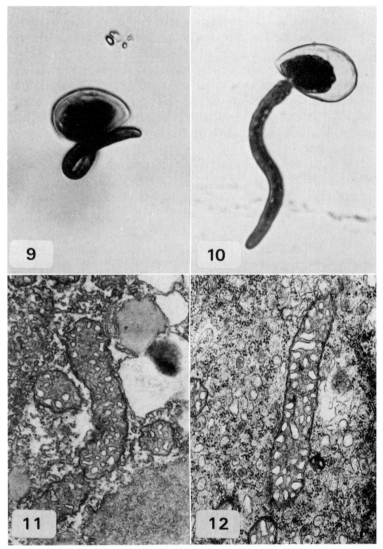

Figure 9.　Light micrograph of a germinated sporangium of *Peronospora hyoscyami* exposed to 0.8% carbon dioxide. The germ tube is shorter and thinner than that of the control maintained in air. (×1,425)

Figure 10.　Light micrograph of a germinated sporangium maintained in air (0.03% carbon dioxide). (×1,425)

Figure 11.　Cross section of a mitochondrion in a sporangium of *Peronospora hyoscyami* exposed to 0.8% carbon dioxide. Note its shrunken appearance. (×23,750)

Figure 12.　Cross section of a mitochondrion from the control treatment (air). The cristae are well defined, and the organelle is tubular in structure. (×23,750)

(Lange) Imbach (Rast et al, 1976); carbon dioxide inhibits the activity of succinate dehydrogenase, the enzyme needed for fruiting structure formation. The enzyme is located in mitochondria, and it functions as an enzyme of the Krebs cycle (Rast et al, 1976). The inhibition of fruiting structure formation and the inhibition of germ tube formation cannot be considered similar events. Nonetheless, the inhibition by carbon dioxide of germ tube formation in sporangia of *P. hyoscyami* affected the fungal mitochondria. This cellular organelle is responsible for the major enzymatic activities of the Krebs cycle.

Carbon dioxide is fungistatic, not fungicidal. The spores of *P. hyoscyami, B. cinerea,* and *A. niger* regain the ability to germinate once they are returned to air, and the mitochondria regain their turgid appearance and well-defined cristae.

Host and Parasite

INFECTION

The leaf of the host species *N. tabacum* produces an inhibitor that prevents the germination of *P. hyoscyami* sporangia. However, percentage germination on leaves of the resistant species *N. debneyi* is much higher than on susceptible tobacco (Cohen et al, 1987; Shepherd and Mandryk, 1963). Hill (1966) reported that the position of the leaf on the tobacco plant influences susceptibility to blue mold; the lower leaves were found to be the most susceptible to invasion by the blue mold pathogen. In addition, the susceptibility of tobacco to *P. hyoscyami* infection changes with ontogeny. Reuveni et al (1986) found that the age of the host plant is more important than leaf position in the resistance of *N. tabacum* to blue mold infection. Cuticular waxes on *N. tabacum* inhibit the germination of *P. hyoscyami* sporangia. The waxes were identified as two macrocyclic diterpines, α and β isomers of 4,8,13-duvatriene-1,3-diol (Cruickshank, 1977).

The upper leaf surface of susceptible tobacco, when observed in a scanning electron microscope, resembles a topographic map that displays hills and valleys. Leaf surface water frequently collects in the valleys or depressions, remains for a long time, and becomes the most suitable area for sporangium germination (Figs. 13 and 14).

A club-shaped appressorium, 7 μm wide and 13 μm long, forms immediately adjacent to the anticlinal wall on the upper leaf epidermis (Plate 4, Fig. 14). The topography of the upper epidermis enables the sporangia to roll into the depressions between the cells. The lowest point in the depression is directly above an anticlinal wall, the junction between two adjacent cell walls. As a result the

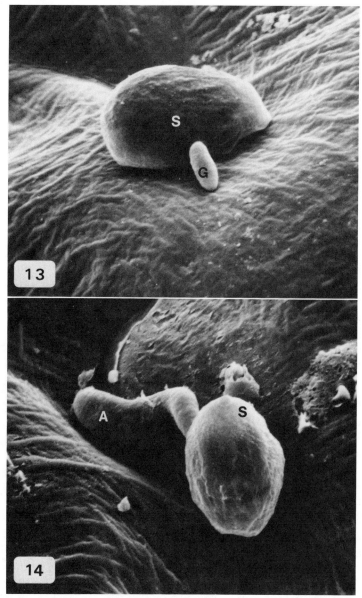

Figure 13. Scanning electron micrograph of a sporangium (S) with a lateral germ tube (G). The area where the sporangium and germ tube are connected is constricted. (×1,800)

Figure 14. Scanning electron micrograph of a sporangium (S) lodged in the depression between two epidermal cells. The short germ tube and the club-shaped appressorium (A) are situated in the depression directly above the anticlinal wall. Observe the sporangial attachment scar. (×1,800)

germ tubes, appressoria, and penetration pegs are all located above the anticlinal cell wall. The narrow penetration peg, 2 μm wide, passes through the host epidermal cell wall. A flange, consisting of host wall debris, surrounds the infection peg and lies on the upper surface of the epidermal cell wall (Fig. 15). The flange may be cuticular and/or waxy material degraded by *P. hyoscyami* enzymes and pushed out around the infection tube as it passes through the cuticle.

A large spherical vesicle, 10–15 μm in diameter, forms within 5 min following penetration of the host epidermal cell wall (Fig. 16) (McKeen and Svircev, 1981). The vesicle, infection tube, or both do not break through the plasmalemma and consequently are not in the host cytoplasm. Sporangial cytoplasm moves from the appressorium into the vesicle. The cytoplasmic contents of the vesicle have approximately the same volume as the contents of the ungerminated sporangium. A net increase in cytoplasmic content occurs once the fungus is inside the host.

When cytoplasmic movement from the appressorium into the newly formed vesicle is completed, a plug forms at the inner end of

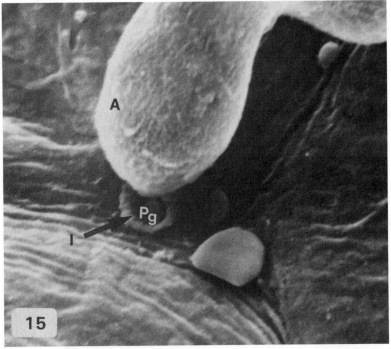

Figure 15. Micrograph of an appressorium (A) separated from the infection tube (I). Note the plug (Pg) in the infection tube. (×6,600)

the infection tube (Fig. 17). The plug consists of small pieces of electron-dense material. The cell wall of the vesicle continues around the plug (Fig. 18), and a small quantity of cytoplasm and a nucleus may remain in the recently isolated infection tube and

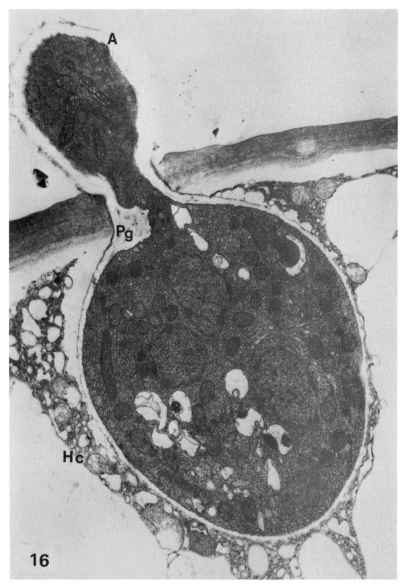

Figure 16. Thin section through a portion of the appressorium (A), incomplete plug (Pg), and spherical vesicle. The vesicle is full of densely packed cytoplasm. A thin layer of host cytoplasm (Hc) surrounds the vesicle. (×12,000)

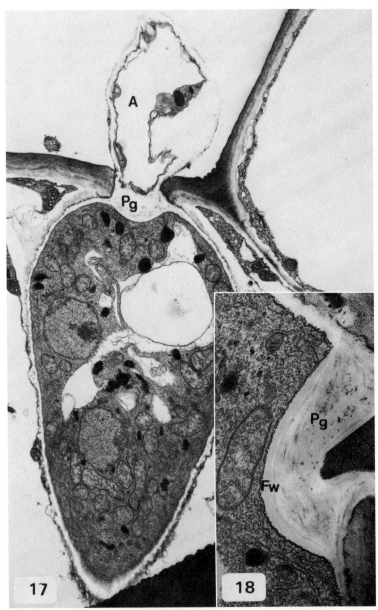

Figure 17.   Section through an empty appressorium (A), plug (Pg), and carrot-shaped vesicle. The plug is electron-transparent, and a fungal wall separates the plug from the fungal cytoplasm. The fungal cytoplasm contains numerous tubular vesicles, nuclei, mitochondria, and endoplasmic reticula. The fungal plasmalemma is highly convoluted. (×12,350)

Figure 18.   Section through a fully formed plug (Pg). Note the fungal wall (Fw) around the plug. (×28,500)

appressorium. The production of a plug protects the parasite from the external environment via the infection tube, and the fungus can continue to colonize the leaf.

The maturation of the vesicle commences when a nipplelike hypha projects toward the palisade layer (Fig. 19). The nipple and the vesicle are filled with numerous nuclei with closely associated

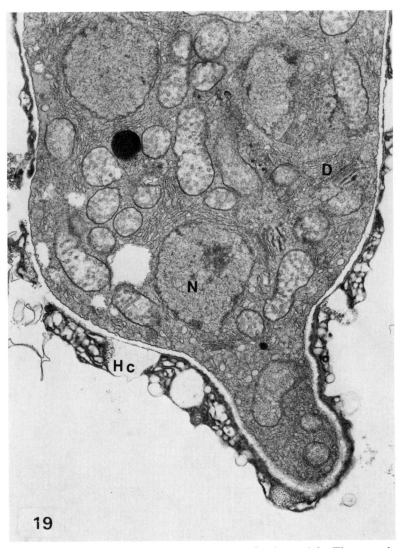

Figure 19. Transmission electron micrograph of a vesicle. The cytoplasm is dense, containing nuclei (N) and nucleoli. Two dictyosomes (D) beside the nucleus appear to be cutting off vesicles. A thin layer of epidermal cell cytoplasm (Hc) surrounds the fungus. (×16,000)

dictyosomes and large numbers of mitochondria. The nipple
develops into a carrot-shaped body (Fig. 17, Plate 5), which orients
toward the lower portion of the epidermal cell. A thin layer of host
cytoplasm is observed around the pathogen between the host
plasma membrane and the tonoplast (Fig. 19). Occasionally a
branch develops from the vesicle and invades an adjacent
epidermal cell (Fig. 20). At 20°C, the hypha exits from the epidermal
cell 2.6–4.1 hr after penetration and invades the adjacent
intercellular space or cell in the palisade layer (Figs. 21 and 22,
Table 2).

Trigiano et al (1984a) recently observed *P. hyoscyami* penetrating
and invading tissue cultures of *N. tabacum.* On calli of the
susceptible host *N. tabacum,* the germ tubes become exceedingly
long (50 μm), forming appressoriumlike structures that are 13–17 μm
in diameter. These structures facilitate penetration of the callus
cells and form intracellular hyphae or haustoria and/or produce
intercellular hyphae that radiate from these structures and cover
the callus surface.

Trigiano and co-workers (1984a) suggested that the appressorium-
like structures may be analogous to the primary vesicle observed

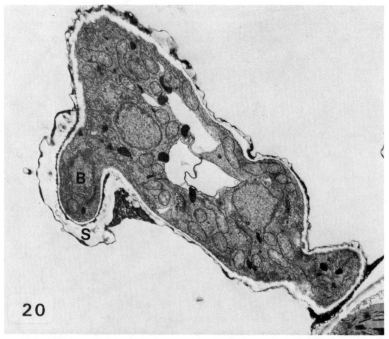

20

Figure 20.   Thin section through an intracellular hypha and a branch (B).
A well-defined sheath (S) surrounds the branch. Three nuclei and numerous
mitochondria are present in the dense cytoplasm. (×10,000)

during the invasion of the susceptible leaf. Size, similarity in ultrastructure, formation at 18 hr, and formation of various intercellular and intracellular hyphae strongly indicate homology. It is unfortunate that the structure was described as "appressorium-like," because the word *appressorium* means a swollen hypha that

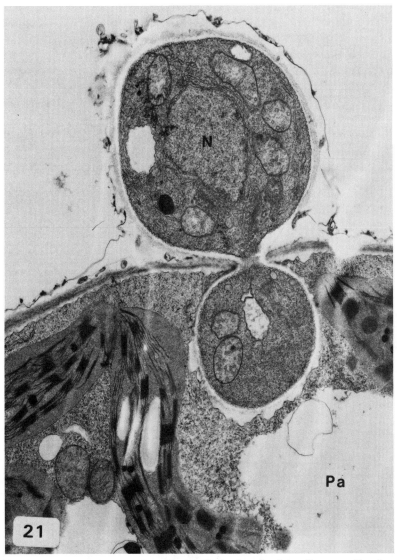

Figure 21. Thin section of an intracellular hypha invading a palisade cell (Pa). A prominent nucleus (N) and dictyosome are present in the fungal cytoplasm. The fungus invading the palisade cell is surrounded by host cytoplasm and chloroplasts. (×21,000)

presses against its host and from which a minute infection peg usually grows and enters the epidermal cell of the host. The formation of an appressorium is the result of the interaction between the fungus and its host.

In the infected epidermal cells of leaves, the host mitochondria and cytoplasm appear healthy, but we will show later in the chapter that physiological and antigenic changes are already present. Five to 10 hr following penetration, there is no ultrastructural evidence of disorientation or destruction of host tissue.

Actively growing and developing fungal cytoplasm is packed with cellular organelles. The ungerminated sporangia, germ tubes,

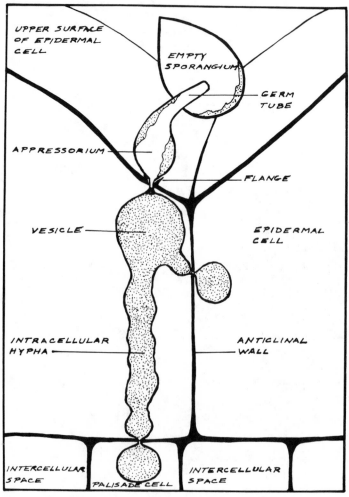

Figure 22.   Schematic diagram depicting the early infection stages when tobacco tissue is invaded by *Peronospora hyoscyami.*

60

appressoria, primary vesicles, and vegetative hyphae always contain nuclei that are approximately 3 μm in diameter and have prominent nucleoli. At least one dictyosome is found immediately adjacent to the nucleus. Blebs of the nuclear membrane were observed projecting into the cytoplasm toward the adjacent dictyosome. Few lipid and myelin bodies (Fig. 23) are observed in the hyphae, while no glycogen or protein crystals are detected in any part of the fungus. In other members of the Oomycetes, such as *Aphanomyces* and *Pythium* spp., lipid and fingerprint bodies are common inside the hyphae. In *P. hyoscyami,* large clusters of tubules, known as plasmalemmasomes, are found on the plasma membrane (Fig. 24). Centrioles, with a distinct 9+2 arrangement of centripetal tubules, are occasionally observed adjacent to the nucleus (Fig. 25). The plasmalemma of the vesicle and its branches is highly convoluted and appears to bleb toward the fungal cell wall (Fig. 26).

COLONIZATION

Vegetative development of *P. hyoscyami* in susceptible host tissue is highly dependent upon temperature, relative humidity, water pressure deficit, and light conditions. Optimal environmental conditions are 15–20° C, 98–100% relative humidity, and low light. In growth chambers optimal light intensity was 45 microEinsteins per square meter per second ($\mu E \cdot m^{-2} \cdot sec^{-1}$). Variations in the growth chamber conditions caused considerable changes in the rate of growth and pattern of development of the intercellular hyphae.

Initially, the intercellular hyphae grow toward the lower epidermis (McKeen and Svircev, 1984). The cause of this directional growth is not clear, but it does not appear to be due to geotropism because it occurs regardless of the orientation of the tobacco.

The pathogenic hypha reaches the intercellular spaces of the

Table 2. Time course of infection of 6-wk-old tobacco leaves by *Peronospora hyoscyami* at 20° C

Time after inoculation (hr)	Stage of fungal development
0	Inoculation
0.5–2	Sporangial germination
1.0–3	Appressorial formation
1.5–2.5	Penetration and vesicle formation
1.7–3	First growth beyond vesicle
2.5–4	Growth to bottom of epidermal cell
2.6–4.1	Entrance to intercellular space or palisade cell

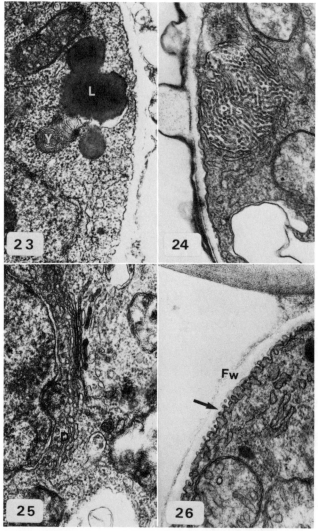

Figure 23. Transmission electron micrograph of a fungal hypha with myelin (Y) and lipid (L). (×24,000)

Figure 24. Transmission electron micrograph of a plasmalemmasome (Pls) adjacent to the fungal wall. (×26,200)

Figure 25. Section through a centriole (C) and dictyosome (D). The centriole is composed of nine groups of centripetal tubes in a cartwheel structure. The dictyosome (D) is very close to the nucleus and the centriole. (×18,700)

Figure 26. Thin section through part of an infection vesicle. Note the fungal wall (Fw) and the echinulate form of the fungal plasmalemma (arrow). (×26,200)

spongy parenchyma about 5 hr after inoculation of the upper epidermis. Dichotomously branching hyphae, about 8 μm in diameter, radiate outward from the initial penetration area (Plate 6). Intercellular hyphae occupy a small portion of the intercellular space and closely follow the contours of the mesophyll cells. Figure 27 is a scanning electron micrograph of a cross section from a healthy tobacco leaf with intercellular spaces. In places where hyphae contact mesophyll cells, an infection peg sometimes develops, penetrates, and forms a haustorium. Long segments of intercellular hyphae (up to 0.1–2.0 mm long) were frequently observed without haustoria. Host cells often contain more than one haustorium. Haustorial clusters, usually located near a stoma, originate from a single hyphal segment. This unusual arrangement of haustorial mother cells has not been reported in other downy mildews.

Actively growing intercellular hyphae of *P. hyoscyami* are characterized by numerous nuclei, mitochondria, ribosomes, rough endoplasmic reticulum, and dictyosomes, a few lipid granules, and very small vacuoles (Figs. 28 and 29). An irregular plasmalemma is

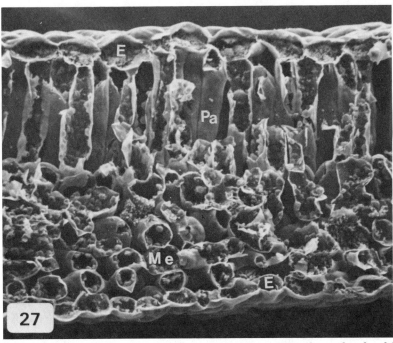

Figure 27.   Scanning electron micrograph of a section through a healthy tobacco leaf. Note the epidermal (E), palisade (Pa), and mesophyll (Me) cells. (×400)

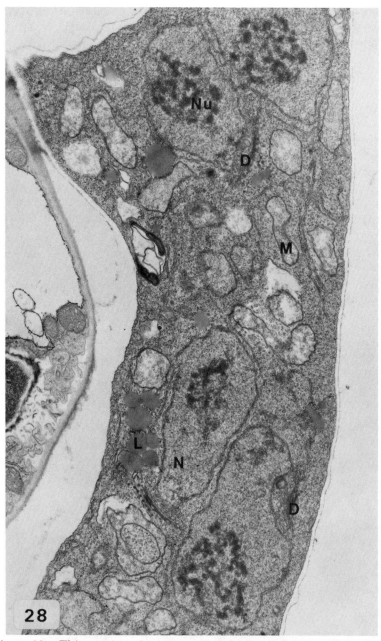

Figure 28. Thin section of a young, actively growing intercellular hypha. The hypha contains well-defined nuclei (N) and nucleoli (Nu). The cytoplasm is full of tubular mitochondria (M), dictyosomes (D), lipid bodies (L), and ribosomes. (×20,100)

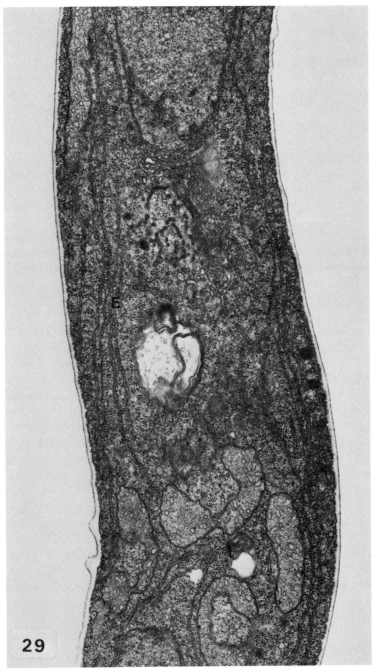

29

Figure 29. Thin section of a young hypha with much endoplasmic reticulum (E) and many nuclei and mitochondria. (×23,400)

typical at the growing hyphal tip. Older intercellular hyphae contain large vacuoles, which occupy a major portion of the hyphal tube; few organelles are present at this developmental stage.

The intercellular mycelium of *P. hyoscyami* is similar to that of *Plasmopara halstedii* (Farl.) Berl. & de Toni, the causal agent of sunflower downy mildew. The hyphae of both pathogens are irregular in size and shape. However, the hyphae of the sunflower pathogen occupy the entire intercellular space (Sackston, 1981), whereas hyphae of *P. hyoscyami* occupy a relatively small portion of the space. Filling of the intercellular space was also observed in *Glycine max* (L.) Merr. with hyphae of *P. manshurica* (Naum.) Syd. ex Gäum. (Peyton and Bowen, 1963).

HAUSTORIA

Haustoria of *P. hyoscyami* develop in the upper epidermis, palisade and spongy parenchyma, and lower epidermis of susceptible leaves. Although haustoria are present in all susceptible tobacco leaf cell layers, they are most concentrated in the spongy parenchyma and the lower epidermis. Haustoria only lie adjacent to segments of intercellular hyphae that are in contact with host cells. Contact between the host cell and the pathogen does not ensure invasion. Thus, thigmotropism does not appear to be responsible for initiation of penetration. Long segments of intercellular hyphae, 400–800 μm long, are commonly seen without haustoria forming in the adjacent cells, and occasionally clusters of haustoria were observed radiating from a single terminal portion of an intercellular hypha.

In our study of *P. hyoscyami* on the susceptible cultivar Virginia 115, no papilla formation or any ultrastructural change was evident before penetration (Svircev and McKeen, 1982). Appearance of host papillae is a common reaction in other downy mildews. They were observed in *Pisum sativum* L. inoculated with *P. pisi* Syd. (Hickey and Coffey, 1980) and *P. viciae* (Berk.) Casp. (Beakes et al, 1982). Trigiano and co-workers (1983), working with *P. hyoscyami* on susceptible tobacco cultivars, observed papillae (or wall appositions). This discrepancy may be attributed to the use of different races and/or different cultivars. Formation of papillae before invasion by the pathogen appears to be a species-specific reaction.

Penetration into a cell is accomplished by dissolution of a cylindrical portion, 1 μm in diameter, of the cell wall. Enzymatic and mechanical action appear to be involved in the passage of the pathogen into the tobacco cell. The out-curling of the host wall toward the intercellular hyphae is thought to be the result of the pressure created as the haustorium neck passes through the wall

66

(Fig. 30). Enzymatic degradation is evidenced by the reorientation of the host wall fibrils (Fig. 31). Immediately adjacent to the penetration pore, the wall fibrils are oriented at approximately 45° to the infection tube, whereas in control areas distant from the penetration pore, the wall fibrils are oriented at 90°.

The bulb-shaped incipient haustorium (Fig. 30) develops into a cane-shaped body (Figs. 32–35), which grows up to 10–15 μm in length. Branching of the cane-shaped haustorium is occasionally observed. Continued growth and development of the haustorium result in the formation of a spiraling and torulose structure that reaches lengths up to 50 μm. By seven days after inoculation, shrunken or collapsed haustoria are evident in the host tissue (Figs. 36 and 37). Shrunken haustoria are often observed adjacent to turgid haustoria in a host cell.

The haustorium cell wall is continuous with that of the inter-cellular mother hypha. Plasmalemmasomes are evident in an area adjacent to the haustorium wall, but their function and significance are not known. The young haustorium is full of cytoplasm, which contains mitochondria, nuclei, and extensive endoplasmic reticulum. Large dictyosomes are always seen adjacent to the nuclei. The juvenile haustorium is not vacuolated, but vacuoles become evident as the haustorium ages.

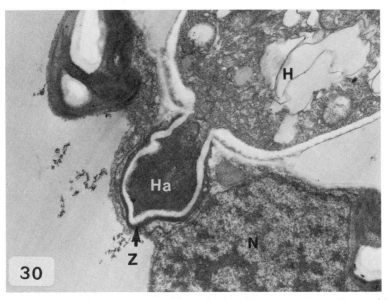

Figure 30. Thin section through a bulb-shaped haustorium (Ha) and its mother hypha (H). Immediately next to the fungal wall is an electron-opaque layer (Z). A host nucleus (N) lies adjacent to the haustorium. (×12,400)

Haustoria of *P. hyoscyami* are surrounded by two ultrastructurally distinct layers. Immediately adjacent to the haustorium cell wall is an electron-opaque layer; the outer layer is electron-transparent (Fig. 38). The electron-opaque layer, 0.3–0.5 μm thick, encases the entire haustorium, and the electron-transparent layer, up to 3 μm thick, encloses part or all of the haustorium. Dark-staining, membrane-bound vesicles are interspersed in this outer layer. This outer layer is usually somewhat thicker near the base of the haustorium, although projections from the host cytoplasm frequently contact the electron-opaque layer (Fig. 38).

The terminology used to describe these layers is extensive, varied, and confusing. Many investigators have adopted terminology used to describe seemingly similar layers found on the haustoria of the rusts and the powdery mildews. The situation was further complicated when for a given fungal species, similar haustorial layers were assigned different terms. We have adopted the terminology used by Bushnell (1972). The extrahaustorial matrix is a liquid or solid substance between the extrahaustorial membrane (or plasma membrane) and the haustorium wall. The extrahaustorial matrix is composed of two distinct layers in *P. hyoscyami*. Immediately next to the fungal wall is a dark-staining zone called the electron-opaque layer (Figs. 31–33 and 38). The electron-opaque layer has been

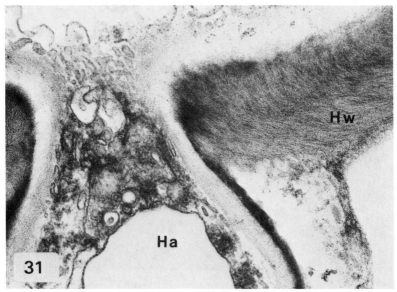

Figure 31.   High magnification of the host wall (Hw) immediately adjacent to the penetration tube of a haustorium (Ha). The wall microfibrils orient toward the hypha. (×33,600)

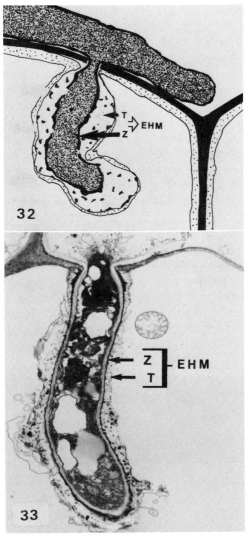

Figure 32.   Schematic diagram of a haustorium with its associated layers. The fungal wall is surrounded by an electron-opaque layer (Z). An electron-transparent layer (T) encloses the haustorium. These two layers form the extrahaustorial matrix (EHM). The host plasmalemma lies adjacent to the outer region of the electron-transparent layer. A small amount of host cytoplasm is bounded by the tonoplast and the plasma membrane.

Figure 33.   Thin section through a cane-shaped haustorium, which is constricted at its neck where it passes through the host wall. The haustorial wall is covered by a thin, electron-opaque layer (Z) that is in turn surrounded by an electron-transparent layer (T). The two layers make up the extrahaustorial matrix (EHM). A thin layer of host cytoplasm surrounds the haustorium. (×9,920)

observed in *P. manshurica* (Peyton and Bowen, 1963); *P. parasitica* (Fr.) Tul. (Chou, 1970); *P. destructor* (Berk.) Casp., *P. brassicae,* and *P. spinaciae* (Kajiwara, 1971); and *P. tabacina* (Trigiano et al, 1983). Thus the electron-opaque layer appears to be an intrinsic component of the haustoria of the downy mildews, serving an unknown function.

An additional layer lies on the outer side (toward the host) of the electron-opaque layer. This electron-transparent layer is an important zone of interaction because it is a passage area between the host and the fungus (Figs. 32, 33, and 38). Our micrographs show that the electron-transparent matrix contains membrane-bound inclusions and that the host cytoplasm invaginates into this region. The electron-transparent layer is often referred to as the encasement layer. Trigiano et al (1983), in their study of the ultrastructure of the blue mold fungus, used this term to describe the electron-transparent area of the haustorium. This term seems inappropriate, for it suggests inactivity. The electron-transparent zone stains positive for callose with aniline and possibly contains cellulose but not lignin (Trigiano et al, 1983). This electron-transparent layer does not always extend along the entire length of the haustorium; it can surround all or part of the haustorium. At present very little is

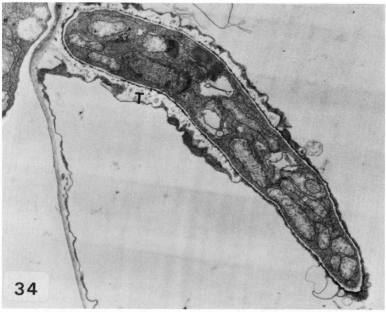

Figure 34. Longitudinal section through a haustorium partially surrounded by an electron-transparent matrix (T). (×10,000)

Figure 35. Scanning electron micrograph of a cane-shaped haustorium (Ha) inside a mesophyll cell. The intercellular hypha (H) is evident outside the cell. (×840)

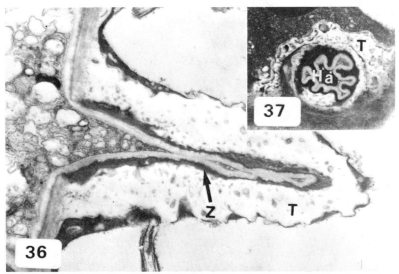

Figure 36. Longitudinal section through a collapsed haustorium that is surrounded by an electron-opaque layer (Z) and a wide electron-transparent layer (T). (×13,800)

Figure 37. Cross section of a collapsed haustorium (Ha). The electron-opaque and -transparent (T) layers that make up the extrahaustorial matrix are well defined. (×11,500)

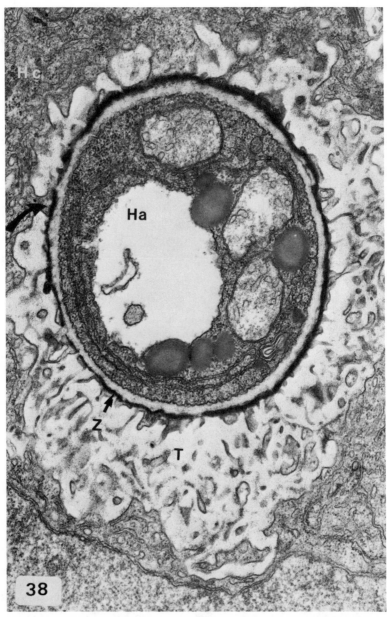

Figure 38. Cross section of a haustorium (Ha), which contains a large vacuole, mitochondria, and lipid bodies. The haustorium plasmalemma is markedly indented. The electron-opaque layer (Z) contains pores. The electron-transparent layer (T) contains numerous blebs and vacuoles. In some instances, the host cytoplasm (Hc) contacts the electron-opaque layer (curved arrow). The host cytoplasm appears to be blebbing into the electron-transparent layer of the extrahaustorial matrix. (×30,000)

known about the composition, physiology, and origin of the extrahaustorial matrix.

A unit membrane surrounds each haustorium and is continuous with the plasma membrane of the host cell. The membrane is not formed by stretching the existing host plasma membrane but rather by synthesis of a new membrane around the haustorial matrix. This new membrane is characteristic of the host-pathogen interface, and it needs a name to distinguish it from the host plasma membrane. Trigiano and co-workers (1984a) labeled the area adjacent to the haustorial electron-dense layer (toward the host) the extrahaustorial membrane. Careful examination of their electron micrographs does not provide convincing evidence of the presence of a unit membrane in this region.

Most investigators agree that the presence of dense cytoplasm in young haustoria is an indication of metabolically active protoplasm. The maturing haustorium is characterized by elongation from a cane to a coil-shaped structure. The cause of haustorial shrinkage and collapse (Figs. 36 and 37) in advanced infection is not known. These collapsed structures are often seen in cells that also contain a number of fully turgid haustoria. They may represent a natural stage in the aging of the haustorial body.

Trigiano and co-workers (1984b) examined haustorium formation in *N. tabacum* plants treated with the systemic fungicide metalaxyl. Ultrastructural changes in the fungus were evident 24 hr after the application of metalaxyl. The intercellular hyphae became highly vacuolated, and the nuclei condensed. Within 48 hr two types of haustoria were apparent. The majority (73%) were encased (= electron-transparent layer) by a single layer. The remainder exhibited a bilayer encasement composed of an inner layer, which showed the typical encasement appearance, and an outer encasement, which was composed of a membranelike structure (Trigiano et al, 1984b). This bilayered appearance of the encasement layer is not evident in the susceptible host.

HOST

The host morphological response to fungal invasion appears to be minimal even seven to eight days after inoculation, although antigenic and physiological changes (see Chapter 4) can be detected much earlier. The host protoplasm lies in a thin layer on the periphery of the epidermal, palisade, and spongy parenchyma cells, and the host mitochondria, nuclei, and chloroplastids exhibit no ultrastructural changes due to infection by *P. hyoscyami.*

Reproduction

Sporangiogenesis of *P. hyoscyami* in the susceptible host *N. tabacum* occurs four to five days after inoculation at 15/20°C day/night temperature, 12/12 hr day/night regime, and 98–100% ambient relative humidity. These conditions result in extensive spread of the fungus (Plate 3) in the host tissue and minimize the time required from inoculation to initiation of sporulation.

Sporangium production follows a diurnal cycle (Cruickshank, 1963). For sporulation to occur at optimal temperature and relative humidity, a dark period of at least 2 hr is needed. Sporangiophore and spore formation in *P. hyoscyami* is believed to result from a dark-induction phenomenon (Cruickshank, 1963). Optimal temperatures for sporulation were reported as 15–23°C (Cruickshank, 1961b; Hill and Green, 1965). Day/night temperatures of 24/20, 20/20, and 16/16°C resulted in the highest spore production on infected tissue (Hill and Green, 1965). Day temperatures of 28°C or higher and nights below 12°C retarded pathogen sporulation under field conditions (Hill, 1965, 1966).

Transpiration rates are higher in infected plants before onset of sporulation than in healthy plants (Cruickshank and Rider, 1961). Cruickshank (1963) observed that light in the blue region of the spectrum inhibits spore formation and results in deformed spores. Cohen (1976) confirmed Cruickshank's results and demonstrated that the inhibitory effect of light on sporulation was greatly influenced by temperature. Temperatures from 19 to 24°C increased the inhibition by light, whereas no inhibition was evident at 8–15°C.

Knots

One or more deviations from the optimal conditions, such as low ambient relative humidity, prevent the formation of sporangiophore initials and induce hyphal "knot" formation. While the adverse environmental conditions persist, the hyphae thicken and coil, forming knots in the substomatal chamber (Figs. 39 and 40). When optimal environmental conditions for sporangiogenesis return, sporangiophore initials emerge from the knot hyphae and grow toward the stomatal opening.

These hyphal knots are ultrastructurally distinct from other vegetative structures. The cytoplasm is similar to the cytoplasm observed in the dormant spores, for the knot cytoplasm stains intensely because of its dense and compact nature. The cytoplasmic organelles are camouflaged and are difficult to recognize in the electron micrographs. Low numbers of tiny vesicles and vacuoles are present in this pathogen structure.

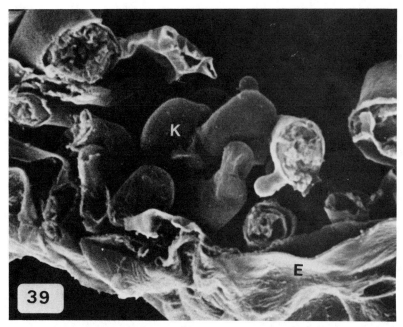

Figure 39.   Scanning electron micrograph of the spongy parenchyma and lower epidermis (E). Observe the hyphal knot (K), composed of several hyphae compressed together in the substomatal chamber. (×750)

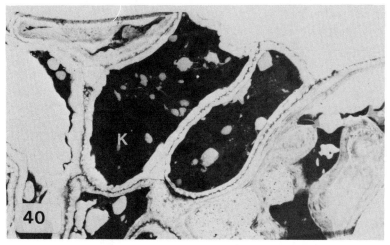

Figure 40.   Transmission electron micrograph section through a hyphal knot (K), where several large hyphae are closely pressed together. Organelles are not distinguishable because of the high electron density of the cytoplasm. (×4,500)

The location of the hyphal knots in the stomatal chamber places a large quantity of quiescent cytoplasm in a strategic position for the formation of large numbers of asexual spores once the environmental conditions become suitable for sporulation. The knots may serve a function similar to that of sporangia of *Pythium* (McKeen, 1977) and *Aphanomyces* (McKeen, 1949), as a reservoir of concentrated cytoplasm available for rapid asexual reproduction. The soil pathogens produce zoospores only if free water is available. *P. hyoscyami,* a leaf pathogen, also requires air saturated with water vapor for the development of its asexual spores. In this manner the sporangiophore serves the same function as an exit or evacuation tube in *Pythium* spp. This may represent the adaptation of the tobacco downy mildew parasite to a terrestrial habitat.

The mechanism by which the fungus senses the presence of a stomatal chamber and triggers the production of a sporangium primordium is unknown. Gradients in oxygen, carbon dioxide, or relative humidity may trigger the initial development.

Sporangiogenesis

Sporangiophore initiation is characterized by the presence of one to eight hyphae in the substomatal chamber on the lower epidermis of the tobacco leaf (Fig. 41), but in epiphytotics they also emerge through stomata on the upper surface. As the hypha pushes through the stomatal opening, it becomes constricted and approximately 1 μm in diameter (Figs. 42 and 43). The narrow tube widens into a regular funnel shape until it emerges from the stomatal aperture to produce the aerial portion of the sporangiophore.

Once on the outside, a sporangiophore stem is formed (Fig. 44) at the proximal end from the point of emergence. After the stalk reaches a length of 70 μm, it begins to branch dichotomously (Fig. 45). Spore development is initiated after a fourth or fifth dichotomy (Fig. 46). The cytoplasm in the developing sporangiophore remains uniformly electron-opaque, and the organelles are difficult to detect. The cytoplasm of the sporangiophore surges through the thick-walled stalk into the tips to form the young, spherical sporangiospores (Fig. 47, Plate 7). The developing sporangia are filled with electron-dense cytoplasm (Fig. 48). The entire process takes 4–6 hr.

Trigiano and Spurr (1987) studied the nuclear development in the young sporangium by the use of the fluorescent stain mithramycin. Initially a single nucleus migrated into a spherical spore, less than 3 μm in diameter. As this spore enlarged at 15°C to 4–10 μm, two, four, or eight nuclei were observed in each spore. Thus, at 15°C three synchronous divisions occurred. Later divisions were nonsynchronous. At 23°C only the first division was synchronous. The final number of nuclei was 14–15 per sporangium. In the blue mold

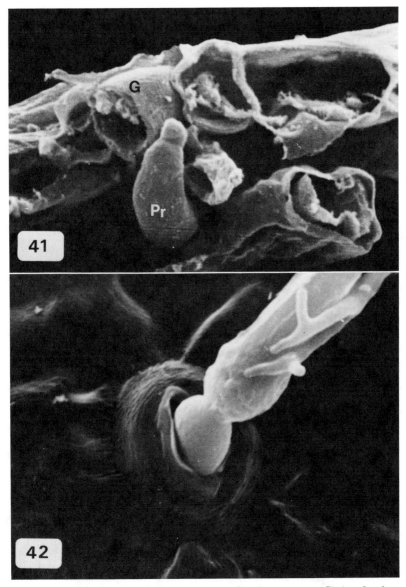

Figure 41.   Scanning electron micrograph of a stoma (G) in the lower
epidermis. The stoma contains the sporangiophore primordium (Pr).
(×1,200)

Figure 42.   Scanning electron micrograph of a sporangiophore stalk in the
stomatal opening. The constriction in the sporangiophore became evident
because the sporangiophore was partially extruded during preparation of
the specimen. (×1,200)

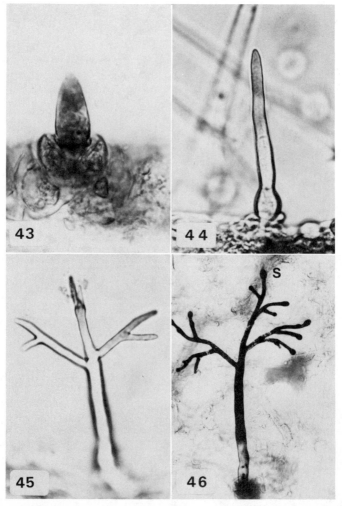

Figure 43. Light micrograph of a sporangiophore emerging through the stoma. (×640)

Figure 44. Light micrograph of a young, unbranched sporangiophore on the lower leaf surface of *Nicotiana tabacum* six days after inoculation and after 4 hr of darkness at 100% relative humidity. The constriction is caused by the guard cells. (×850)

Figure 45. Light micrograph showing the young dichotomous branches in the sporangiophore six days after inoculation and after 4–5 hr of darkness and 100% relative humidity. (×300)

Figure 46. Light micrograph of a sporangiophore six days after inoculation and after 5–6 hr of darkness and 100% relative humidity. Young sporangia (S) are present. (×170)

pathogen, sporangial nuclei appear to be derived from a single daughter nucleus and not from nuclear migration from the sporangiophore (Trigiano and Spurr, 1987). The evidence strongly indicated that most sporangia are homokaryotic.

Each sporangiophore can produce 2^5 or 2^6 sporangia per generation. This represents an enormous potential for infection of susceptible tobacco (Plate 4). The mature sporangia are released into the environment once the relative humidity drops below 98%. By a twisting action, the sporangiophore collapses and the sporangia are released into the air.

Cruickshank (Chapter 9) mentions that mechanical shock, diurnal cycle, and relative humidity play a role in sporangium release, but he does not indicate that there may also be an electrostatic mechanism. Leach (1982) showed photographs of active discharge of sporangia of *P. destructor*. Whether release of sporangia was spontaneous or was triggered by vibrations, their trajectories were parallel and were perpendicular to the leaf surface. The vertical propulsion of sporangia from onion leaves, coupled with the facts that sporangia are charged and that their velocities are influenced by the size of leaf potentials, suggested the operation of an electrostatic mechanism.

This postulated mechanism involves the repulsion of unipolarly charged sporangia from the charged surface of the same polarity. To determine whether spores were charged when liberated, a pair of

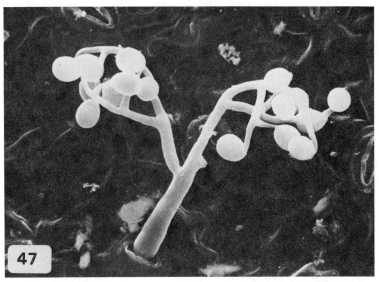

Figure 47.   Scanning electron micrograph of mature ellipsoidal sporangia on a sporangiophore. (×570)

oppositely charged electrodes were placed several centimeters from sporulating leaves. The discharged sporangia were attracted to the negatively charged electrode; that is, the spores were positively charged.

If an electrostatic mechanism is responsible for the active discharge of spores, then it is axiomatic that leaves become electrostatically charged and that this should relate to changes in atmospheric humidity and exposure to infrared light, factors known to trigger spore release. Tests showed that plant leaves do become charged in response to humidity changes and exposure to infrared light. In nature leaves remain uncharged when the humidity is near saturation. Also leaf surfaces become electrically conductive at high atmospheric humidities but not at low humidities. The polarity of leaves grown under sunny, warm, and dry conditions is consistently positive. After extended periods of rain, leaves are uncharged.

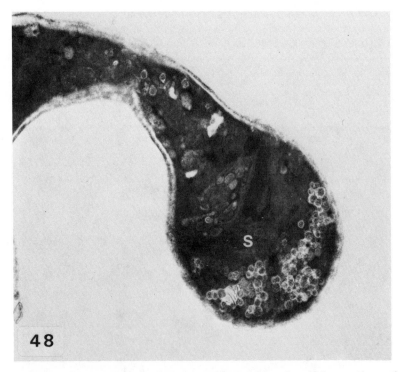

Figure 48. Transmission electron micrograph of a thin section of a developing sporangium (S). The cytoplasm at this point of development is electron-dense, and the cytoplasmic organelles are not easily distinguished. (×4,500)

Sexual structures of *P. hyoscyami* were observed in eight- to 12-day-old infected tobacco maintained in growth chambers at 20° C, 12/12 hr day/night periods, and ambient relative humidity. The immature oogonium, 46 μm in diameter, appears to conform to the shape of the intercellular space. Older oogonia are spherical, thin-walled, dark-staining structures. A small, club-shaped antheridium, 5 μm in diameter, is often observed in the vicinity of the oogonium (Fig. 49). The same leaf tissue contains oospores with at least one well-defined reserve globule, a central globular body, and a thick wall (Fig. 50).

Oogonia (Fig. 51), antheridia, and oospores were observed in the infected tissue in the first two years of our study. By the third year our field isolate of *P. hyoscyami* had lost its ability to produce sexual structures. Michelmore (1981) demonstrated that *P. parasitica* carries homothallic and heterothallic isolates. Mycelia of opposite compatibility types need to be established in the same tissue to achieve oospore formation. A similar situation may exist in *P. hyoscyami,* and the compatible mating type may have been inadvertently lost while the fungus was being maintained in growth chambers. Wolf et al (1934) postulated that *P. hyoscyami* disappeared from Florida two years after its arrival because only one heterothallic strain was present and the fungus failed to form sexual structures. Although oospores have been found in central Europe and the Soviet Union, Kröber (1969) concluded that oospores play a doubtful role in the epidemiology of blue mold.

The cytoplasm in the oogonium and oospore is amorphous and electron-opaque (Fig. 52). Ultrastructurally, the cytoplasm resembles that seen in the hyphal knot and the developing sporangiophore. Alternatively, the actively growing vegetative hyphae and germinating spores, appressoria, and primary vesicles inside the epidermal cell and haustoria contain electron-transparent cytoplasm. The opacity is not a fixation artifact because both types of cytoplasm are frequently observed in the same leaf section. The changes in cytoplasmic appearance are highly correlated with the cytoplasmic type and function. The change from the resting to an active metabolic state and vice versa results in a shift in the physical and architectural appearance of the cytoplasm.

Germination of the oospores was not observed or tested from the isolate of *P. hyoscyami* collected during the 1979 blue mold epiphytotic in Ontario. The function and importance of oospores in establishing primary infection loci have not been elucidated. Shaw (1981) pointed out that reports of germinating oospores in the downy mildews must be critically reevaluated because oospores may be attacked by hyperparasites.

Patrick and Singh (1981) reported a low concentration of oospores in field samples collected during the 1979 Ontario epiphytotic. In contrast, we observed large numbers of oospores in chlorotic leaf tissue. Our isolate of *P. hyoscyami* readily produced oospores once

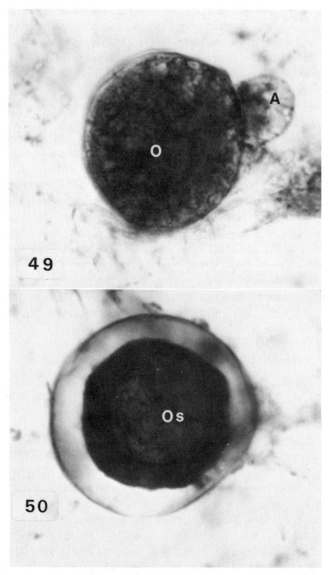

Figure 49.   Light micrograph of an oogonium (O) and an antheridium (A) from an infected tobacco leaf. (×1,100)

Figure 50.   Light micrograph of an oospore (Os) in a tobacco leaf. The oospore contains two reserve globules. (×1,200)

the conditions favoring sporulation were altered (by increasing the light intensity, decreasing the relative humidity, or both).

The establishment of oospores in leaf tissue may depend on a number of factors. Michelmore (1981) described three prerequisites for the establishment of oospores in *Bremia lactucae* Regel: compatibility types must be present; a certain level of infection must be attained; and the pattern of fungal growth in the host must ensure the spatial meeting of compatible mating types.

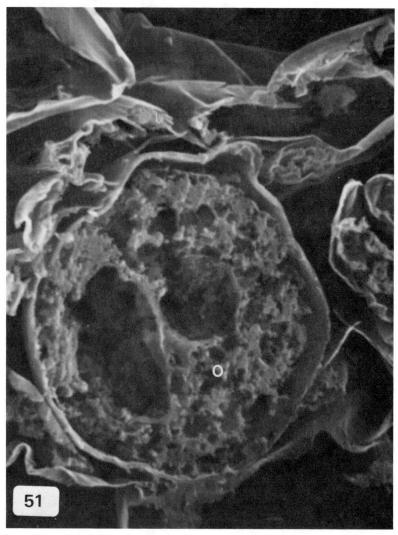

Figure 51.   Scanning electron micrograph of a section of an oogonium (O) that was embedded in plastic sections and etched to remove the plastic from around the tissue. Observe the reserve globule sites. (×1,800)

Immunocytochemistry

Immunocytochemistry is a new branch of biology that, in conjunction with electron microscopy, permits scientists for the first time to see the location of antigens even in minute organelles within plant and animal cells. Consequently, this is an elegant way of pinpointing molecules in tissues. This new procedure has enabled

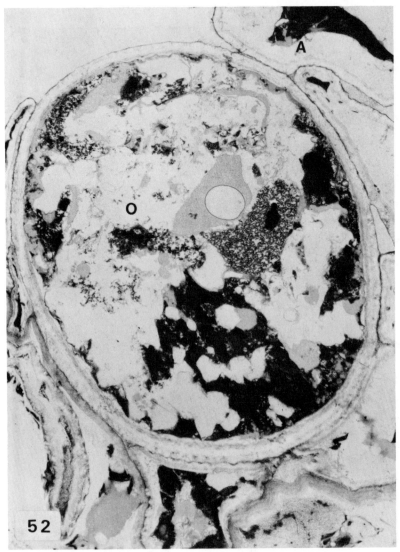

Figure 52.   Cross section of an oogonium (O) and an antheridium (A). The cytoplasm is electron-dense, and cellular organelles cannot be distinguished. (×2,000)

pathologists to locate fungal antigens, probably messengers, within diseased plant tissue and to begin to determine how communication occurs between pathogens and their host plants.

Immunocytochemistry was introduced by Roth et al (1978). The technique, described in detail by De Mey (1984), uses tiny colloidal particles, 10–15 μm in diameter, to determine the specific location of antigens. The gold particles are produced by the reaction of chlorauric acid and sodium citrate (De Mey, 1984). The colloidal gold is complexed with protein A, a surface compound on *Staphylococcus aureus* Rosenbach. The protein A-gold probe binds to the fragment-crystallizable portion of any antibody, and the antibody binds specifically with the antigen. Consequently, the precise position of the antigen in plant tissue can readily be seen in the electron microscope.

ANTIGENS

We have used the protein A-gold probe to study tobacco infected with the blue mold pathogen. Thin sections of *N. tabacum* infected by *P. hyoscyami* were cut from five-day-old infected tissue and treated with fungal antibodies and protein A-gold (Day et al, 1986). Sections of infected tissue were heavily labeled with gold particles, especially hyphal walls (Figs. 53 and 54). Healthy control tissue showed only a low level of labeling (Fig. 55).

A similar procedure was used earlier with *B. cinerea* and *Vicia faba* L. Cells in infected host tissue, but not cells in healthy tissue, were heavily labeled with gold. In many cases the labeled host cells had not been penetrated by the fungus and were some distance from the nearest hyphae (Svircev et al, 1986). Thus, a biotroph and a facultative parasite initiated the same response in diseased plant tissue.

Communication between pathogen and host has been postulated for many years by such hypotheses as the gene-for-gene theory (Flor, 1971). It has been shown that pathogens send messages into the cytoplasm in advance of their hyphae and even before penetration (McKeen and Rimmer, 1973; O'Connell and Bailey, 1986). Also many parasites are quite specific to a host and require certain stimuli to germinate and to infect (Kaminskyj and Day, 1984a, 1984b; Staples et al, 1983). The specificity of the fungal antigen would permit this individualization between host and pathogen.

Three hypotheses are proposed for these results. First, the fungus sends a messenger into the host, which causes the production of a fungal antigen in the host. Second, an antigen from the fungal sporangium, germ tube, haustorium, or hypha enters the host cells well ahead of the hypha. Third, fimbrial protein, either as dissociated subunits or as intact fibrils, enters the host.

85

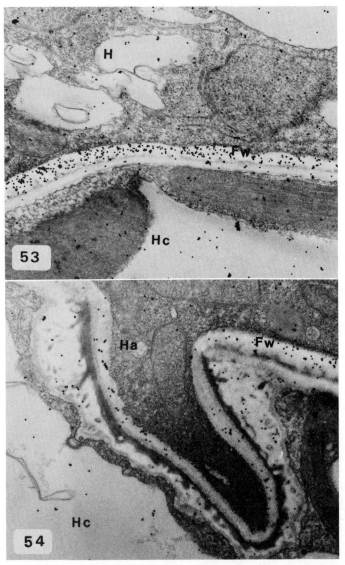

Figure 53. Thin section of a leaf of *Nicotiana tabacum* infected with *Peronospora hyoscyami*. The section was treated with antifimbrial antiserum and protein A-gold. Note the intense labeling of the fungal cell wall (Fw) and the labeling of the fungal hyphae (H) and the interior of the plant cell (HC). (×17,000)

Figure 54. Thin section of a fungal haustorium (Ha) treated with antifimbrial antiserum and protein A-gold. The fungal cell wall (Fw) is intensely labeled with the gold probe. Gold label was also located in the host cell (HC). (×18,700)

Fimbriae, which were first found on the smut fungus *Ustilago violacea* Funkel. (Poon and Day, 1974, 1975), have since been observed on many fungi, including *P. hyoscyami* (Gardiner, 1985; Gardiner and Day, 1985). The fimbriae play an essential role of communication among the sex cells of *U. violacea*.

Fimbriae of *P. hyoscyami* probably play some role, which could be information transmission (Figs. 56 and 57). The fimbriae are composed of polymerized protein subunits, and either the subunits or the intact fimbriae may pass into the host protoplasm and aid in the delicate balance between host and pathogen. There is some indication that gold particles appear in rows in infected tobacco tissue, which may indicate the presence of fimbriae. Scanning electron microscopy supports the transmission electron microscope investigations. The surface of the hyphal walls was strongly labeled with protein A-gold (Fig. 58).

Although we do not know how fungal antigens arise in the host, we are convinced that they play an active role in the host-pathogen relationship.

Starch

In infections five or more days old, increased numbers of starch granules are observed in the chloroplasts of healthy leaves. Ultra-

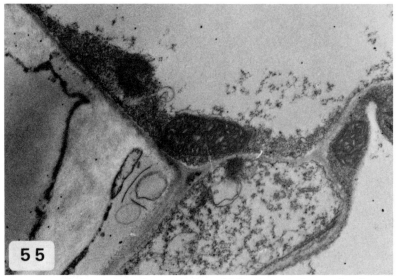

Figure 55.   Thin section of an uninfected *Nicotiana tabacum* leaf treated with antifimbrial antiserum and protein A-gold. Note the few randomly scattered gold particles, which constitute background or nonspecific labeling. (×15,000)

structural studies of early infection have shown that starch granules are present in the chloroplasts of infected leaves but not in the chloroplasts of healthy leaves following periods of darkness (Figs. 59 and 60).

Infected and healthy leaves were placed in growth chambers and provided with 150 μE of artificial light per square meter per second on a 12-hr day/night cycle. Starch was detected macroscopically using a 0.2% solution of iodine in potassium iodide (IKI). Control

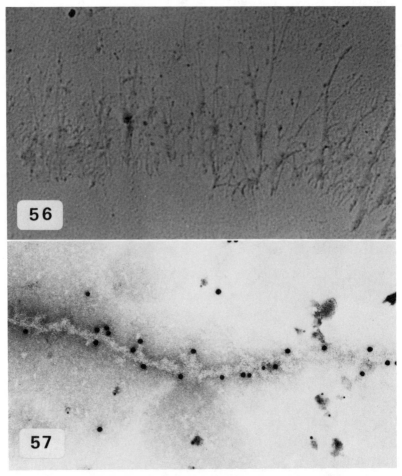

Figure 56. Transmission electron micrograph of tungsten-shadowed *Peronospora hyoscyami* fimbriae. (×50,000)

Figure 57. Fungal fimbria negatively stained with ammonium molybdate and treated with protein A-gold. Many gold particles are attached to the fimbria. (×65,000)

and infected leaves were cleared in 95% alcohol and placed in the IKI solution. The presence of starch is indicated by development of an intense blue-purple color in the leaves. This very quick technique allows the qualitative monitoring of starch levels in the healthy and diseased leaves.

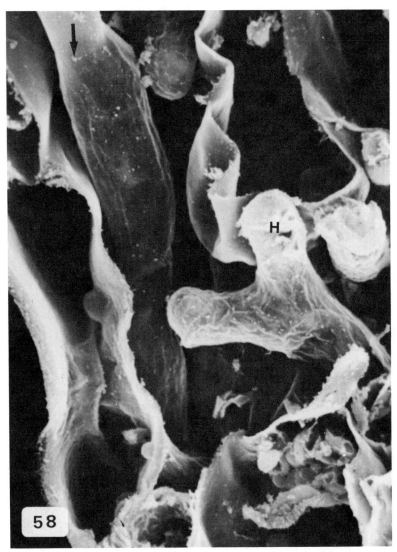

Figure 58.   Scanning electron micrograph of a tobacco leaf invaded by a *Peronospora hyoscyami* hypha (H). The material was treated with antifimbrial antiserum and labeled with protein A-gold (arrow). Note the distribution of the gold label on the fungal surface. (×9,000)

Healthy and infected tobacco leaves accumulate starch at a similar rate until five days after inoculation (Table 3). By the sixth day, starch accumulation was faster in healthy tissue than in infected tissue (Table 4). In contrast, starch degradation in leaf tissue was altered almost immediately following inoculation. Leaves inoculated with *P. hyoscyami* 2 hr after entry into darkness

Table 3. Starch formation[a] in healthy leaves and in leaves heavily infected with *Peronospora hyoscyami* up to five days postinoculation[b]

Hours in light	Healthy	Infected
0.0[b]	−	−
0.75	+	+
1.0	+	+
1.5	++	++
2.0	++	++
3.0	+++	+++
4.0	+++	+++
5.0	+++	+++

[a]Scale range intensity of iodine in potassium iodide (IKI).
[b]Before the test, plants were cleared of starch.

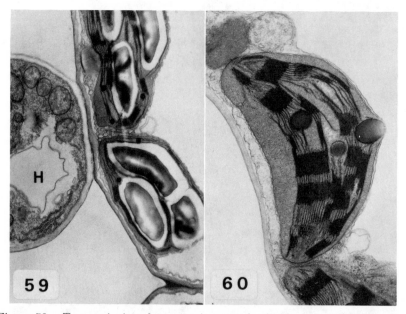

Figure 59.   Transmission electron micrograph of 16-hr infected tissue after 16 hr of darkness. Note the starch granules in the chloroplast and the hypha (H). (×7,000)

Figure 60.   Transmission electron micrograph of healthy tissue after 16 hr of darkness. Observe the lack of starch in the chloroplast. (×7,000)

retained starch 6 hr longer than the healthy controls (Table 5). By 14 hr in darkness, healthy plants were devoid of starch, whereas the infected tissue did not test negative for starch until 20 hr. In contrast, at six days postinoculation and after 8 hr of darkness, the infected leaves were devoid of starch, whereas the healthy leaves retained starch for more than 10 hr of darkness (Table 6).

A total starch assay (TSA) was used to quantify starch content of tobacco leaves (Svircev, 1984). Jensen (1962) described the starch extraction and quantification. The TSA test demonstrated significantly more starch in healthy tissue than in six-day infected tissue (Fig. 61). The accumulation of starch in healthy leaves remained significantly higher than in infected leaves (Fig. 61).

The profile of starch degradation as monitored by the TSA test was slightly different. In early infection (one to three days), total starch did not vary significantly between healthy and infected host

Table 4. Time required in light[a] for starch formation[b] in healthy leaves and leaves heavily infected with *Peronospora hyoscyami* at six days after inoculation

Hours in light[a]	Healthy	Infected
0.0	−	−
0.75	+	−
1.0	++	−
1.5	+++	+
2.0	+++	++
3.0	+++	++
5.0	+++	+++

[a]$150 \ \mu E \cdot m^{-2} \cdot sec^{-1}$.
[b]Scale range intensity of iodine in potassium iodide (IKI).

Table 5. Time required in darkness for degradation of starch[a] in healthy tobacco leaves and in leaves heavily inoculated with *Peronospora hyoscyami* 2 hr after entry into darkness

Hours in darkness	Healthy	Infected
0	+++	+++
2	+++	+++
4	+++	+++
6	++	+++
8	++	+++
10	++	+++
12	+	+++
14	−	++
16	−	++
18	−	++
20	−	−
22	−	−

[a]Scale range intensity of iodine in potassium iodide (IKI).

tissue. The difference in starch content becomes apparent six days after inoculation, when starch levels were significantly higher in healthy leaves than in infected leaves (Fig. 61).

TSA revealed higher starch levels in healthy than in infected leaf tissue. The exceptions occur at the end of each 12-hr period of darkness, particularly during the first three days after inoculation.

Table 6. Time required in darkness for degradation of starch[a] in healthy leaves and in leaves heavily infected with *Peronospora hyoscyami* at six days after inoculation

Hours in darkness	Healthy	Infected
0	+++	+++
2	+++	+++
4	+++	++
6	++	+
8	++	−
10	+	−
12	−	−

[a]Scale range intensity of iodine in potassium iodide (IKI).

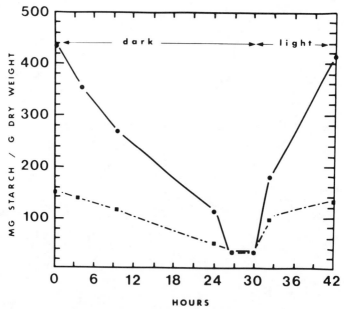

Figure 61. Quantitative determination of starch levels in tobacco leaves in late infection. In late infection, the healthy leaves (solid lines) contained more starch than the infected leaves (dashed lines) during both the starch accumulation and the starch degradation cycles. At the 1% level, Student's *t*-test showed that the quantities of starch in the infected and healthy leaves were significantly different at all times except the period from 26 to 31 hr.

If one monitors the reaction with the IKI test, a different profile is obtained. The discrepancy between the IKI and TSA tests for the level of starch in infected and healthy leaves during accumulation and degradation of starch in leaf tissue may be the result of the limited sensitivity of the IKI test and the fact that the color reaction is valid only for amylopectin and not for the other starch components. Perhaps different types of starch in leaf tissue of *N. tabacum* differ in their speeds of production and degradation.

The processes of starch degradation and regulation in plants are poorly understood (Preiss, 1982). Starch degradation and accumulation are controlled by the enzymes located in the cytoplasm and chloroplasts of plant cells (Preiss, 1982). Light also controls and regulates enzyme activation and inhibition.

Less is understood of the mechanisms involved in starch accumulation and degradation in infected plants. The preliminary data obtained with the blue mold fungus suggest that the situation is far more complex than observing the presence or absence of starch granules in infected tissue, which is often reported. Whipps and Lewis (1981) listed several factors that influence the concentration of carbohydrates in infected host tissue: intensity of infection, rate of photosynthesis of infected host tissue, rate of translocation of sucrose from the plant, activity of synthetic and degradative enzymes, and loss of soluble carbohydrates from host to fungus.

Tissues invaded by fungal parasites often undergo changes in chlorophyll content (Harding et al, 1968; Misra and Biswall, 1981), changes in levels of soluble and insoluble sugars (Inman, 1962), necrosis, and starch accumulation and/or degradation (Inman, 1962; Tomlinson and Webb, 1978; Tu, 1979). Not only are these complex differences evident between healthy and diseased tobacco plants, but also younger tobacco plants degrade starch more efficiently than older plants (Preiss, 1982).

The change in total starch content in infected leaves of *N. tabacum* compared to healthy leaves may indicate higher enzymatic activity in the infected tissue. Alternatively, the enzymes may be found in greater concentration in healthy tissue because more starch is degraded than in the infected host. The influence of the pathogen on host metabolism warrants further investigation.

Immunity and Resistance

The 1979 isolate of *P. hyoscyami* from southern Ontario was identified as form species *hybrida* because of its pathogenicity on the differential cultivar Sirone (see Chapter 1). This isolate also had the ability to sporulate in *Lycopersicon esculentum* Mill., *Capsicum annuum* L., and *Solanum tuberosum* L., but the life cycle was extended three to four weeks, and few spores were produced.

Histocytological studies of the interactions between *P. hyoscyami* and *Nicotiana* spp. carrying the genes for resistance are limited. Species within the genus *Nicotiana* exhibit a wide range of susceptibility to this obligate parasite. The genus has been intensively screened for the presence of species resistant or immune to the blue mold pathogen. The resistant-immune classification was based chiefly on the ability of the fungus to sporulate (Clayton, 1945; Izard et al, 1964; Wuttke, 1969). Species such as *N. longiflora* Cav. and *N. plumbaginifolia* are highly susceptible while plants are in early development (seven to eight weeks), but as they mature, they are no longer susceptible to blue mold. *N. exigua* Wheeler was the only species rated as immune to *P. hyoscyami* at all developmental stages (Clayton, 1945).

The resistant response to *P. hyoscyami* can be induced in the susceptible species *N. tabacum* by injecting the lowest stem internode with a sporangial suspension. The susceptible host can thus be rendered resistant to subsequent infection by *P. hyoscyami* (Lucas et al, 1985) (see also Chapter 7). Lucas et al (1985) used tissue culture regenerants from protected tissue to determine whether the induced resistance is transmissible. Transmission was not achieved; the regenerants were susceptible to foliar challenge by the blue mold pathogen. This type of experiment demonstrates that the expression of systemic-induced resistance depends on the presence of active lesions in the protected tissue (Lucas et al, 1985). However, Tuzun and Kuć found that resistance was transferred to regenerants via tissue culture (Chapter 7).

We used *N. exigua* to study the development of *P. hyoscyami* in an immune host. The upper leaf surface of the host plant was inoculated with a spore suspension. The surface of the plant was exceedingly waxy, and the droplet with spores failed to remain on the leaf surface. In all subsequent experiments, the leaves were held in a horizontal position to facilitate infection (Berry and McKeen, 1985).

The pathogen's ability to penetrate *N. exigua* depends on the concentration of sporangia in the inoculation drop. When one or two sporangia per epidermal cell were placed on the surface, penetration occurred. The host response was apparent from the immediate accumulation of cytoplasm in the lobes of the epidermal cell. The entire cell eventually became full of dark-staining cytoplasm (Fig. 62). The fungus failed to form further infection structures in the host cell.

With 10^3 sporangia per milliliter in the infection droplet, 75% of the sporangia germinated, forming exceedingly long (75 μm) germ tubes. The majority of germ tubes fail to form appressoria. When an appressorium was formed, the host epidermal cell was invaded and a small vesicle formed in the epidermal cell. This vesicle fails to develop further.

In contrast, inoculation with 10^5 sporangia per milliliter results in the formation of appressoria and penetration of the epidermal cell, leading to successful establishment of the pathogen inside the host. At 2.5 hr after inoculation, a vesicle forms in the epidermal cell. The vesicle is highly branched, with haustoriumlike appendages attached to it. The fungus exits from the epidermal cell into the palisade cell layer 8–12 hr after inoculation. The exit of the fungal mass into the second cell layer is characterized by a browning reaction. The entire area covered by the infection droplet becomes brown. Browning of the leaf surface did not occur in the control plants in which the infection droplet did not contain sporangia.

The intercellular hyphae grow in the palisade layer closely following the contour of the host cell. Intercellular hyphae invade the spongy parenchyma at 24–48 hr. The presence of the fungus in this cell layer results in a drastic host response. The cells immediately below the infection droplet collapse (Figs. 63 and 64), which is easily seen without a microscope. The radial development of the fungal hyphae is limited to the zone of collapse. Club-shaped sporangiophore primordia collect in the substomatal chamber. Under optimal environmental conditions, sporangiophores and

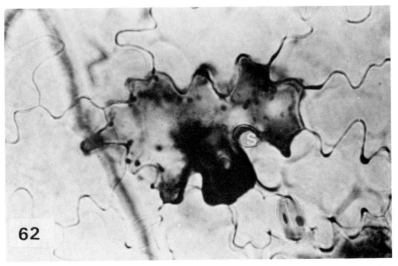

Figure 62. Light micrograph of an epidermal cell of *Nicotiana exigua* infected by a single sporangium (S). The staining reaction is restricted to the infected cell. (×400)

sporangia are formed. The sporangiophores show very limited dichotomous development, with only two or three dichotomies. Sporangia form but average only four to eight spores per sporangiophore.

The infection process in *N. exigua* is in sharp contrast to the development observed on the susceptible *N. tabacum*. The infection droplets remain on the surface of *N. tabacum* for an extended period of time, providing the water necessary for germination. In *N. exigua,* the water droplets fall from the leaf, and the fungus does not attain the conditions necessary for germination. The spores are washed off the surface, or if they remain, the lack of free water prevents germination.

The entire process of germ tube and appressorium formation depends on the spore concentration in the infection droplet. Unsuccessful penetration of *N. exigua* is marked by the unusual appearance of the germ tubes. They resemble the long structures formed when sporangia are germinated in water on glass slides. The presence of appressoria and short germ tubes seem essential for successful penetration of the host. This phenomenon has also been observed in *B. lactucae,* where short germ tubes are produced on the susceptible host and long germ tubes form on the resistant host.

The growth through the epidermal cell in *N. exigua* is slower. The primary vesicle contains numerous branches and haustoriumlike structures that are not present in the susceptible host. The presence of large numbers of intracellular hyphae in *N. exigua* may be an

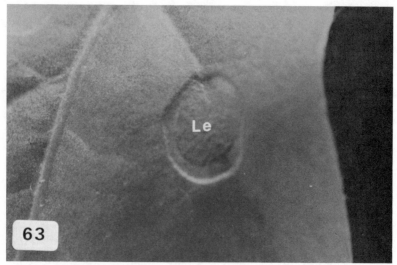

Figure 63.   Macroscopic lesion (Le) at the site of the infection droplet on a *Nicotiana exigua* leaf. (×3.5)

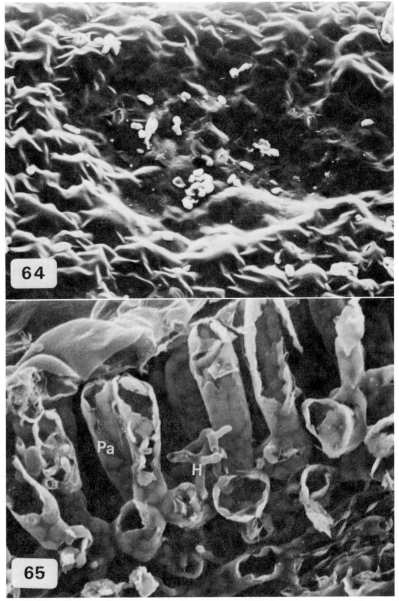

Figure 64. Scanning electron micrograph of the pitted region underneath the infection droplet on a *Nicotiana exigua* leaf. (×150)

Figure 65. Scanning electron micrograph of the epidermis and palisade (Pa) layer in *Nicotiana exigua*. The fungus (H) is mostly in the palisade layer. (×650)

indication of a different nutritional state in this host-pathogen system.

The vegetative development in *N. exigua* is unique in that the greatest portion of the mycelial mass is located in the palisade layer (Fig. 65). A distinct hypersensitive response occurs once the hyphae invade the spongy parenchyma. If the presence of browning and collapse of plant cells can be manipulated by infecting the lower or upper epidermal surface, the two events are independent of one another. Browning occurs only if the upper epidermal surface is inoculated, whereas collapse occurs when the fungal hyphae invade the spongy parenchyma, regardless of the epidermal surface inoculated.

Development of the fungus in the host tissue becomes limited once the hypersensitive reaction occurs. Hyphae collect in the substomatal chamber, forming the sporangiophore primordia. The formation of sporangiophores in *P. hyoscyami* is a tropic response independent of the host tissue composition. The fungus will sporulate in *N. exigua;* however, very few spores are produced on the sporangiophores.

The ability of *P. hyoscyami* to germinate, penetrate, develop, and form viable sporangiophores in *N. exigua* necessitates reclassification of this species. The species is resistant to *P. hyoscyami* but not immune.

Summary

The sensitivity and adaptability of *P. hyoscyami* have enabled it to survive in most tobacco-growing regions of the world; however, in Europe and North America it overwinters best in the warmer regions.

Rapid germination and infection permit this pathogen to gain protection within its host against desiccation as soon as the entry hole is plugged. However, the external environment as well as the host influences where and how it develops in the tobacco leaf. In the resistant *N. exigua* host, the blue mold pathogen develops in the palisade layer, whereas in the susceptible *N. tabacum* cultivar Virginia 115, its hyphae grow dichotomously into the intercellular spaces around the lobulate spongy parenchyma cells. Development of *P. hyoscyami* is possible because the fungus produces food-absorbing structures, haustoria. Haustoria can penetrate the cell wall, but they only invaginate the plasmalemma and protoplasm, and thus a delicate balance is permitted, which frequently is tolerated by the host under many environmental conditions.

The pathogen accumulates sufficient reserves for reproduction only after a few days if the air is humid. Under dry conditions it may take several days for this process to occur. For release of asexual reproductive bodies, the pathogen grows into the stomatal chamber. If the ambient air around the infected leaf is dry, the large, growing hyphal tips curl around each other and form a hyphal knot that contains quiescent, electron-opaque, dense protoplasm in which the organelles are camouflaged.

When the ambient air becomes humid, sporangiophores grow through stomatal openings, branch dichotomously, and rapidly produce sporangiospores, which blow away. The ability of this pathogen to produce a million spores per square centimeter of leaf enables it to reproduce rapidly in ideal weather conditions.

Oospores, which probably develop when heterosexual strains come into contact, enable the blue mold pathogen to survive for a much longer time than hyphal knots, which provide temporary survival. More information on the production, survival, and importance of the oospore is required.

Many triggers and receptors clearly participate during the development of this fungus in its host. The fungus recognizes the tobacco leaf, for the germ tube from the sporangium remains short and penetrates immediately. If the spore is placed on a glass slide or nonhost, the germ tube grows until its energy is exhausted, and it never attempts penetration.

The findings that fungal antigens are present in the host protoplasm some distance from the haustoria and that starch metabolism is altered after infection prove that messengers and chemical communication occur. Temperature and other factors have a marked influence on these messengers. During cool weather there are no symptoms, but at higher temperatures yellow and brown lesions develop.

The complex interactions between the fungus and the invaded host need further investigation. This chapter attempts to provide an insight for future investigations of the host-pathogen interactions.

Acknowledgment

Financial support for these studies was provided by the Natural Science and Engineering Research Council, Grant No. AO752.

LITERATURE CITED

Bartnicki-Garcia, S. 1968. Cell wall chemistry, morphogenesis and taxonomy of fungi. Annu. Rev. Microbiol. 22:87–108.

Beakes, G. W., Singh, H., and Dickinson, C. G. 1982. Ultrastructure of host-pathogen interface of *Peronospora viciae* in cultivars of pea which show different susceptibilities. Plant Pathol. 31:343–354.

Berry, J. W., and McKeen, W. E. 1985. Development of *Peronospora hyoscyami* f. sp. *tabacina* in the resistant host *Nicotiana exigua*. Can. J. Plant Pathol. 7:262–269.

Bushnell, W. R. 1972. Physiology of fungal haustoria. Annu. Rev. Phytopathol. 10:151–176.

Chou, C. H. 1970. An electron-microscope study of host penetration and early stages of haustorium formation of *Peronospora parasitica* (Fr.) Tul. on cabbage cotyledons. Ann. Bot. 34:189–204.

Clayton, E. E. 1945. Resistance of tobacco to blue mold (*Peronospora tabacina*). J. Agric. Res. 70:79–87.

Clayton, E. E., and Gaines, J. G. 1945. Temperature in relation to development and control of blue mold (*Peronospora tabacina*) of tobacco. J. Agric. Res. 71:171–182.

Cohen, Y. 1976. Interacting effects of light and temperature on sporulation of *Peronospora tabacina* on tobacco leaves. Aust. J. Biol. Sci. 29:281–289.

Cohen, Y., Pe'er, S., Balass, O., and Coffey, M. D. 1987. A fluorescent technique for studying growth of *Peronospora tabacina* on leaf surfaces. Phytopathology 77:201–204.

Cruickshank, I. A. M. 1961a. Germination of *Peronospora tabacina*: Effect of temperature. Aust. J. Biol. Sci. 14:58–65.

Cruickshank, I. A. M. 1961b. Environment and sporulation in phytopathogenic fungi. II. Conidia formation in *Peronospora tabacina* Adam as a function of temperature. Aust. J. Biol. Sci. 14:198–207.

Cruickshank, I. A. M. 1963. Environment and sporulation in phytopathogenic fungi. IV. The effect of light on the formation of conidia of *Peronospora tabacina* Adam. Aust. J. Biol. Sci. 16:88–110.

Cruickshank, I. A. M. 1977. Fungitoxicity of duvatrienediols associated with cuticular wax of tobacco leaves. Phytopathol. Z. 90:243–249.

Cruickshank, I. A. M., and Rider, N. E. 1961. *Peronospora tabacina* in tobacco: Transpiration, growth and related energy considerations. Aust. J. Biol. Sci. 14:45–57.

Day, A. W., Gardiner, R. B., Smith, R., Svircev, A. M., and McKeen, W. E. 1986. Detection of fungal fimbriae by protein A-gold immunocytochemical labelling in host plants infected with *Ustilago heufleri* or *Peronospora hyoscyami* f. sp. *tabacina*. Can. J. Microbiol. 32:577–584.

De Mey, J. 1984. Colloidal gold as a marker in light and electron microscopy. Electron Microsc. Soc. Am. Bull. 14:54–66.

Durbin, R. D. 1959. Factors affecting the vertical distribution of *Rhizoctonia solani* with special reference to CO_2 concentration. Am. J. Bot. 46:22–25.

Flor, H. H. 1971. Current status of the gene-for-gene concept. Annu. Rev. Phytopathol. 9:275–296.

Gardiner, R. B. 1985. Fungal fimbriae: Their structure and distribution. Ph.D. thesis. University of Western Ontario, London, Canada. 248 pp.

Gardiner, R. B., and Day, A. W. 1985. Fungal fimbriae. IV. Composition and properties of fimbriae from *Ustilago violacea*. Exp. Mycol. 9:334–350.

Harding, H., Williams, P. H., and McNabola, S. S. 1968. Chlorophyll changes, photosynthesis and ultrastructure of chloroplasts in *Albugo candida* induced "green islands" on detached *Brassica juncea* cotyledons. Can. J. Bot. 46:1229–1234.

Hemmes, D. E., and Hohl, K. R. 1969. Ultrastructural changes in direct germinating sporangia of *Phytophthora parasitica*. Am. J. Bot. 56:300–313.

Hickey, E. L., and Coffey, M. D. 1980. The effect of Ridomil on *Peronospora pisi* parasitizing *Pisum sativum*: An ultrastructural investigation. Physiol. Plant Pathol. 17:199–204.

Hill, A. V. 1965. The role of temperature in the development of blue mould (*Peronospora tabacina* Adam) disease in tobacco seedlings. II. Effect on plant growth. Aust. J. Agric. Res. 16:609–615.

Hill, A. V. 1966. Effect of inoculum, spore load, length of infection period and leaf washing on occurrence of *Peronospora tabacina* Adam (blue mould of tobacco). Aust. J. Agric. Res. 17:133–146.

Hill, A. V., and Green, S. 1965. The role of temperature in the development of blue mould (*Peronospora tabacina* Adam) disease in tobacco seedlings. I. In leaves. Aust. J. Agric. Res. 16:597–607.

Hollomon, D. W. 1973. Protein synthesis during germination of *Peronospora tabacina* A. conidia: An examination of the events involved in the initiation of germination. J. Gen. Microbiol. 78:1–13.

Ingram, D. S. 1981. Physiology and biochemistry of host-parasite interaction. Pages 143–163 in: The Downy Mildews. D. M. Spencer, ed. Academic Press, New York. 636 pp.

Inman, R. E. 1962. Disease development, disease intensity, and carbohydrate levels in rusted bean plants. Phytopathology 52:1207–1211.

Izard, C., Lacharpagne, J., and Schiltz, P. 1964. Behaviour of *Peronospora tabacina* in tissue culture, and role of the leaf epidermis. Pages 95–99 in: Annales de la Direction des Etudes et de l'Equipement. Société nationale d'exploitation industrielle des tabacs et allumettes (SEITA), Paris.

Jensen, A. W. 1962. Botanical Histochemistry, Principles and Practice. W. H. Freeman and Co., San Francisco. 408 pp.

Kajiwara, T. 1971. Structure and physiology of haustoria of various parasites. Pages 255–277 in: Morphological and Biochemical Events in Plant-Parasite Interaction. S. Akai and S. Ouchi, eds. Phytopathological Society of Japan Press, Tokyo. 415 pp.

Kaminskyj, S. G., and Day, A. W. 1984a. Chemical induction of infection structures in rust fungi. I. Sugars and complex media. Exp. Mycol. 8:63–72.

Kaminskyj, S. G., and Day, A. W. 1984b. Chemical induction of infection structures in rust fungi. II. Inorganic ions. Exp. Mycol. 8:193–201.

Kröber, H. 1969. Über das infektionsverhalten der Oosporen von *Peronospora tabacina* Adam an Tabak. Phytopathol. Z. 64:1–6.

Leach, C. M. 1982. Active sporangium discharge by *Peronospora destructor*. Phytopathology 72:881–885.

Leppik, R. A., Hollomon, D. W., and Bottomley, W. 1972. Quiesone: An inhibitor of germination of *Peronospora tabacina* conidia. Phytochemistry 11:2055–2063.

Lucas, J. A., Dolan, T. E., and Coffey, M. D. 1985. Nontransmissibility to regenerants from protected tobacco explants of induced resistance to *Peronospora hyoscyami*. Phytopathology 75:1222–1225.

McKeen, W. E. 1949. A study of sugar beet rootrot in southern Ontario. Can. J. Res. 27:284–311.

McKeen, W. E. 1977. Growth of *Pythium graminicola* Subrm. in barley roots. Can. J. Bot. 55:44–47.

McKeen, W. E., and Rimmer, S. R. 1973. Initial penetration process in powdery mildew infection of susceptible barley leaves. Phytopathology 63:1049–1053.

McKeen, W. E., and Svircev, A. M. 1981. Early development of *Peronospora tabacina* in the *Nicotiana tabacum* leaf. Can. J. Plant Pathol. 3:145–158.

McKeen, W. E., and Svircev, A. M. 1984. Vegetative development of *Peronospora hyoscyami* f. sp. *tabacina* in *Nicotiana tabacum*. Can. J. Plant Pathol. 6:40–47.

Michelmore, R. W. 1981. Sexual and asexual sporulation in the downy mildews. Pages 165–181 in: The Downy Mildews. D. M. Spencer, ed. Academic Press, New York. 636 pp.

Misra, A. N., and Biswall, U. C. 1981. Changes in chlorophylls and carotenoids during aging of attached and detached leaves and isolated chloroplasts of wheat seedlings. Photosynthetica 15:75–79.

Mitchell, D. J., and Zentmyer, G. A. 1971. Effects of oxygen and carbon dioxide tensions on growth of several species of *Phytophthora*. Phytopathology 61:787–791.

Moss, M. A., and Main, C. E. 1988. The effect of temperature on sporulation and viability of isolates of *Peronospora tabacina* collected in the United States. Phytopathology 78:110–114.

O'Connell, R. J., and Bailey, J. A. 1986. Immunogold labelling of fungal antigens in cells of *Phaseolus vulgaris*. Physiol. Mol. Plant Pathol. 28:99–105.

Patrick, Z. A., and Singh, H. 1981. Studies of the blue mold disease of flue-cured tobacco in Ontario: The oospore stage. Pages 47–61 in: Blue Mold Symposium II, 29th Tobacco Workers Conference, Lexington, Kentucky, January 19–22. F. A. Todd, compiler. 109 pp.

Peyton, G. A., and Bowen, C. C. 1963. The host-parasite interface of *Peronospora manshurica* on *Glycine max*. Am. J. Bot. 50:787–797.

Poon, N. H., and Day, A. W. 1974. "Fimbriae" in the fungus *Ustilago violacea*. Nature 250:648–649.

Poon, N. H., and Day, A. W. 1975. Fungal fimbriae. I. Structure, origin, and synthesis. Can. J. Microbiol. 21:537–546.

Preiss, J. 1982. Regulation of the biosynthesis and degradation of starch. Annu. Rev. Plant Physiol. 33:431–454.

Rast, D., Stauble, E. J., and Zobrist, P. 1976. The Krebs cycle and control of dormancy in the *Agaricus bisporus* spore. New Phytol. 76:469–477.

Reuveni, M., Tuzun, S., Cole, J. S., Siegel, M. R., and Kuć, J. 1986. The effects of plant age and leaf position on the susceptibility of tobacco to blue mold caused by *Peronospora tabacina*. Phytopathology 76:455–458.

Roth, J., Bendayan, M., and Orci, L. 1978. Ultrastructural localization of intracellular antigens by the use of protein A-gold complex. J. Histochem. Cytochem. 28:55–57.

Sackston, W. E. 1981. Downy mildew of sunflower. Pages 545–575 in: The Downy Mildews. D. M. Spencer, ed. Academic Press, New York. 636 pp.

Salt, S. D., Tuzun, S., and Kuć, J. 1986. Effects of β-ionone and abscisic acid on the growth of tobacco and resistance to blue mold. Mimicry of effects of stem infection by *Peronospora tabacina* Adam. Physiol. Mol. Plant Pathol. 28:287–297.

Shaw, C. G. 1981. Taxonomy and evolution. Pages 17–29 in: The Downy Mildews. D. M. Spencer, ed. Academic Press, New York. 636 pp.

Shepherd, C. J. 1962. Germination of conidia of *Peronospora tabacina* Adam. I. Germination in vitro. Aust. J. Biol. Sci. 15:483–509.

Shepherd, C. J., and Mandryk, M. 1963. Germination of conidia of *Peronospora tabacina* Adam. II. Germination in vivo. Aust. J. Biol. Sci. 16:77–87.

Staples, R. C., Grambow, H. J., and Hoch, H. C. 1983. Potassium ion induces rust fungi to develop infection structures. Exp. Mycol. 7:40–46.

Steele, S. D., and Fraser, T. W. 1973. Ultrastructural changes during germination of *Geotrichum candidum* arthrospores. Can. J. Microbiol. 19:1031–1034.

Stewart, G. 1983. Substrates affecting the germination of sporangiospores of *Peronospora hyoscyami* f. sp. *tabacina*. Student report, Department of Plant Sciences, University of Western Ontario, London, Canada. 30 pp.

Svircev, A. M. 1984. A study of blue mould of tobacco caused by *Peronospora hyoscyami* f. sp. *tabacina*. Ph.D. thesis. University of Western Ontario, London, Canada. 203 pp.

Svircev, A. M., and McKeen, W. E. 1982. The haustorium of *Peronospora hyoscyami* f. sp. *tabacina* in the susceptible tobacco leaf cell. Can. J. Plant Pathol. 4:119–128.

Svircev, A. M., McKeen, W. E., and Berry, J. W. 1984. Sensitivity of *Peronospora hyoscyami* f. sp. *tabacina* to carbon dioxide, compared to that of *Botrytis cinerea* and *Aspergillus niger*. Phytopathology 74:445–447.

Svircev, A. M., Gardiner, R. B., McKeen, W. E., Day, A. W., and Smith, R. J. 1986. Detection by protein A-gold of antigens to *Botrytis cinerea* in cytoplasm of infected *Vicia faba*. Phytopathology 76:622–626.

Tomlinson, J. A., and Webb, M. J. W. 1978. Ultrastructural changes in chloroplasts of lettuce infected with beet western yellows virus. Physiol. Plant Pathol. 12:13–18.

Trigiano, R. N., and Spurr, H. W., Jr. 1987. The development of the multinucleate condition of *Peronospora tabacina* sporangia. Mycologia 79:353–357.

Trigiano, R. N., Van Dyke, C. G., and Spurr, H. W., Jr. 1983. Haustorial development of *Peronospora tabacina* infecting *Nicotiana tabacum*. Can. J. Bot. 61:3444–3453.

Trigiano, R. N., Van Dyke, C. G., Spurr, H. W., Jr., and Gray, D. J. 1984a. Infection and colonization of tobacco callus by *Peronospora tabacina*. Phytopathology 74:280–285.

Trigiano, R. N., Van Dyke, C. G., and Spurr, H. W., Jr. 1984b. Effects of metalaxyl on *Peronospora tabacina* infecting tobacco. Phytopathology 74:1034–1040.

Tu, J. C. 1979. Alterations in chloroplast and cell membranes associated with cAMP induced dissociation of starch grains in clover yellow mosaic virus infected clover. Can. J. Bot. 57:360–369.

Wells, J. M., and Uota, M. 1970. Germination and growth of five fungi in low-oxygen and high-carbon dioxide atmospheres. Phytopathology 60:50–53.

Whipps, J. M., and Lewis, D. M. 1981. Patterns of translocation, storage and interconversion of carbohydrates. Pages 47–83 in: Effects of Disease on the Physiology of the Growing Plant. P. G. Ayres, ed. Cambridge University Press, Cambridge. 288 pp.

Wolf, F. A., Dixon, L. F., McLean, R., and Darkis, F. R. 1934. Downy mildew of tobacco. Phytopathology 24:337–363.

Wuttke, H. H. 1969. Different levels of resistance in blue mould resistant tobacco. Aust. J. Exp. Agric. Anim. Husb. 9:545–548.

Chapter 4

Host-Parasite Relations: Biochemistry

Aglika Edreva
Institute of Genetics
Sofia 1113, Bulgaria

> Good and Evil,
> Friend and Foe,
> Host and Perfidy
> live together,
> like the two faces of the Moon,
> and it is too difficult
> to distinguish between them.
> —Anonymous medieval Bulgarian author

The biochemical and molecular bases of interactions in the integral entity tobacco-*Peronospora hyoscyami* de Bary f. sp. *tabacina* (Adam) Skalický are still poorly understood, partly because of the difficulty of separating the two components of this system and the fact that the pathogen cannot be cultivated on artificial media because of its obligate character. On the other hand, blue mold damage has been severe and the disease has spread around the world only in the last two decades, much more recently than, for example, the "classical" rust diseases on cereals, whose pathogenesis has been better studied and elucidated from a biochemical point of view.

Many authors have reported profound changes in the chemical composition of blue mold-infected tobacco leaves leading to deterioration in quality and technological properties. These changes are clearly the final result of the dramatic perturbations in the entire metabolism of tobacco caused by blue mold infection.

"The war against blue mold," as proclaimed by Lucas (1980), has a multilateral strategy. Theoretically, however, one approach may prove particularly promising, namely the biochemical study of the preinfection state of the plant and the metabolism of the parasite. This approach includes the investigation of the biochemical responses of the host to *P. hyoscyami* infection, the search for characteristic features of blue mold pathogenesis useful in the biochemical diagnostics of the disease, the understanding of recognition and resistance phenomena, and the finding of resistance-related characters that could serve as markers and tools in directed tobacco breeding for blue mold resistance.

Preinfection Resistance Factors

Wittmer (1968) found a highly positive correlation between nicotine content and blue mold resistance, which was not confirmed by Iskender (1975) for Turkish tobacco cultivars. Koelle's (1970) data and those of Edreva et al (1970) are in accordance with Iskender's, showing that highly resistant wild *Nicotiana* species contain less nicotine than susceptible tobacco cultivars. The amounts of free basic amino acids and some neutral amino acids (Berbec et al, 1966; Oczos, 1969; Shaldjan and Avundjan, 1974) as well as the protein content (Oczos, 1969, 1971; Pashenko, 1982) have also been suggested to be related to blue mold resistance. There are also some data on the implication of growth-stimulating substances (Avundjan and Shaldjan, 1974).

The relationship between the level of peroxidase activity of noninfected plants and disease resistance has been exhaustively studied because many functions of peroxidase (EC 1.11.1.7) could be involved in plant pathogenesis: oxidation of polyphenols in the system polyphenols-peroxidase, and consequent formation of toxic products; biosynthesis of lignin, which acts as a barrier to infection; oxidation of aromatic residues in membrane structures of pathogenic origin; and participation in the control of the level of free radicals, an important factor in cell damage (Gaspar et al, 1982). Thus, a higher level of peroxidase activity in the healthy plant could imply a greater potential for plant responses to pathogen invasion. The interest in this topic dates from the 1930s (Grechushnikov, 1939), persists to this day (Reuveni and Bothma, 1985), and covers different couples of plants and bacterial, viral, and fungal pathogens. In most cases, a positive relationship between peroxidase activity and resistance has been established, although in some systems this has not been observed (Rubin et al, 1975).

My and my co-workers' experiments on blue mold resistance have also demonstrated its positive relation to peroxidase activity. The difference between susceptible and resistant plants was observed at the early ontogenetic stages and was especially pronounced at the late stages, that is, when the resistance genes were completely derepressed. This finding is based on the study of a wide range of experimental material: hybrids of resistant and susceptible cultivars, interspecific hybrids of resistant wild *Nicotiana* species and susceptible tobaccos, *N. tabacum* cultivars of Oriental and Virginia type, and a number of wild *Nicotiana* species with and without blue mold resistance genes (Bailov and Edreva, 1964; Bailov et al, 1963, 1967; Edreva et al, 1970; Palakarcheva et al, 1978) (Fig. 1). Pashenko (1975) confirmed our results by investigating the inheritance of blue mold resistance and peroxidase activity in hybrids of resistant and susceptible Oriental cultivars. Collaborative experiments on the peroxidase activity in Mg^{2+}-grown tobacco seedlings, which are characterized by complete expression of blue mold resistance genes (Edreva et al, 1983–1984b), also lend support to our previous conclusions.

Polyphenols, as substrates of the oxidative enzymes and precursors of lignin polymers, were also implicated in plant pathogenesis and were studied as possible resistance markers, taking into account their fungistatic and fungitoxic action. Abundant data are available on the importance of preinfection total phenolic level as well as the importance of the presence of individual phenolics for disease resistance, although opposite results are also in hand (Friend, 1981; Rubin et al, 1975). The resistance of tobacco to blue mold is not related to the total content of polyphenols (Pashenko, 1978) or to the amounts of the major tobacco leaf polyphenols—chlorogenic acid and rutin—as shown by the screening of a wide range of cultivars, hybrids, and wild species (Bailov and Edreva, 1964; Bailov et al, 1967; Edreva, 1966; Edreva et al, 1970; Palakarcheva et al, 1978; Sheen, 1970).

Washings from noninfected tobacco leaves (containing some polyphenols) have a slight inhibitory effect on the germination of *P. hyoscyami* conidia. This effect is not connected, however, with the resistance of the investigated species (Pashenko, 1978; Shepherd and Mandryk, 1962, 1963). In particular, the amount of germination inhibitors on the leaves of the blue mold-immune *N. debneyi* is very low compared to that on the leaves of the very susceptible *N. tabacum* cultivar Virginia Gold. Washed tobacco leaves are generally more susceptible to blue mold than unwashed leaves, probably because of the leakage of some germination inhibitors. This could explain blue mold epiphytotics in rainy weather, especially when inoculum concentration is low (Hill, 1969a, 1969b; Shepherd and Mandryk, 1963). This possibility was substantiated by a later finding, pointing to the existence of two fungitoxic isomeric macrocyclic diterpenes (4,8,13-duvatriene-1,3-diols) identified in cuticular wax of tobacco leaves. These inhibitory

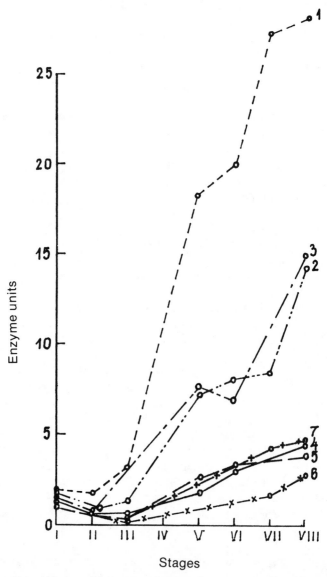

Figure 1. Peroxidase activity (enzyme units) in leaves of the resistant wild species *N. debneyi* (1), *N. exigua* (2), and *N. megalosiphon* (3), the susceptible wild species *N. longiflora* (4) and *N. glutinosa* (5), and the susceptible *N. tabacum* cultivars Virginia Gold (6) and Harmanliska basma 163 (7). Development stages are crossing (I), ears (II), transplanting (III), 14th leaf (IV) (for *N. tabacum* only), before bud formation (V), bud formation (VI), anthesis (VII), and pods (VIII). (Reprinted, by permission, from Edreva et al, 1970)

108

compounds are thought to have a role in blue mold epidemiology but not in genetic resistance (Cruickshank et al, 1977).

ENVIRONMENT AND RESISTANCE

Gene expression is influenced by environmental factors (Tobin and Silverthorne, 1985), especially in cases of polygenically governed characters such as blue mold resistance, as was extensively studied by Schiltz and Coussirat (1978). Light deficiency strongly reduces the expression of blue mold resistance, which is of great importance in tobacco production. The effect is supposed to be mediated by the regulatory action of light on RNA polymerase activity, RNA biosynthesis, and polyribosome formation processes. Growth regulators such as kinetin have a similar effect on resistance expression and were shown to compensate partly for light deficiency, probably by some interactions at a nucleolar level (Schiltz et al, 1970).

Mineral nutrition also influences blue mold resistance expression. According to Oczos (1969), it is quite possible to reduce disease severity by applying optimal NPK ratios. Smith et al (1979) reported a definite increase in disease severity when increased rates of nitrogen were applied to sandy soil.

An intriguing phenomenon discovered at the Bergerac Tobacco Institute was the importance of magnesium ions in gene expression (Schiltz and Coussirat, 1969, 1978). These ions, when used as the sole nutrient source for cultivating tobacco seedlings, induce the complete expression of blue mold resistance genes much earlier (while plants are still at the cotyledonary stage) than under normal field conditions, where this event takes place several months later. Mg^{2+}-grown seedlings therefore are ontogenetically equivalent to adult tobacco plants. This discovery allowed the development of an excellent laboratory test for screening for blue mold resistance.

The mechanism of magnesium action on hereditary structures is still not clear. It is supposed to be related mainly to polyribosome formation and protein biosynthesis, because magnesium ions are necessary for binding the ribosome subunits into a functionally active assembly. In fact, magnesium-grown tobacco seedlings contain more protein than seedlings grown in Knop medium (Edreva et al, 1983–1984a). Peroxidase activity in Mg^{2+}-grown seedlings is also higher, and its molecular pattern is more complex, which is another indication of the more advanced ontogenetic stage of these plants (Edreva et al, 1983–1984b). As shown by chemiluminescence (Mollé et al, 1983–1984) and electron paramagnetic resonance studies (J. C. Coussirat, R. Delon, A. Edreva, and R. Karjieva, unpublished), magnesium ions enhance the energetic level of the biomembranes. The age factor has a similar effect. It is

109

logical, therefore, to assume that magnesium ions act on some common primary cell sites related to ontogenetic mechanisms.

Tobacco Plant Responses to *P. hyoscyami* Infection

An understanding of the biochemical responses of the tobacco plant to *P. hyoscyami* infection is essential to establish host-pathogen relationships. The main problem, as in every system involving obligate parasites, is to distinguish between the behavior of plant cells and fungal hyphae in the invaded areas. In our work we overcome this difficulty by applying, along with biochemical methods, an experimental cytochemical approach, localizing the cell components in situ without damaging cell and tissue integrity. In this way, the responses of the infected plant cells cannot be confounded with the reactions of the fungal structures.

We investigated leaves of adult tobacco plants. In the susceptible cultivars (Virginia and Oriental types), we examined three stages of pathogenesis, differing in the severity of tissue injury: early (mild symptoms), intermediate, and late (necrosis). The pathological process develops for several days. In the resistant cultivars (Bel 61-9, Bel 61-10, and the resistant 98 and 134 cultivars developed at the Institute of Genetics, Sofia, Bulgaria, by Dr. M. Palakarcheva), pathogenesis is much faster, and necrosis occurs shortly after infection. In these cases we studied only the early and necrotic stages. In addition, tobacco seedlings grown on a medium containing Mg^{2+} ions were used as a model system, in which complete expression of the blue mold resistance genes occurred. For this purpose we used the resistant cultivar PBD6 and the susceptible cultivar Paraguay 48.

OXIREDUCTION PROCESSES

The importance of oxireduction processes in plant pathogenesis is well known (Rubin et al, 1975; Stahmann, 1983). It can be accounted for by the involvement of oxireduction in the main metabolites and energy-producing systems and by the significance of host cell redox potential in pathogen development. Thus, in the case of host-obligate parasite systems, an increase in oxidative enzymes was observed. The accumulation of oxidized metabolites and the formation of active oxygen species, deleterious to the host cells, would also contribute to the pathogen damage.

Numerous data are available on the enhancement of respiration and the activity of peroxidase, polyphenoloxidase, and lipoxygenase in plants infected by obligate parasites. Peroxidase, whose role is to create an oxidative state in the host cells and for necrosis formation, is particularly important in discussions of plant pathogenesis and resistance (Gaspar et al, 1982; Stahmann, 1983). An elevated respiration rate was reported in blue mold-infected leaves (Bailov et al, 1962; Boceski, 1963), especially in resistant tobaccos (Oczos, 1973). This effect could account for the energy needed for increased transpiration, which is established in leaves before sporulation of *P. hyoscyami* (Cruickshank and Rider, 1961).

Peroxidase activity was strongly augmented in blue mold-infected tobacco leaves (Bailov et al, 1962; Cohen, 1976; Edreva, 1974a; Pashenko, 1975). This rise may be due to synthesis de novo and/or release from bound or zymogenic form. The latter explanation is more logical, as the peroxidase increase depends on the degree of tissue damage; the increase is maximal in heavily injured tissues and in necrotic zones. The destruction of the chloroplast pigments connected with leaf damage and peroxidase enhancement (Edreva, 1974a) supports this supposition.

Cytochemical tests have proved that the peroxidase rise is a proper response of the plant to infection and is not due to the presence of the enzyme in the hyphae of the pathogen (Edreva et al, (1989). The rise in peroxidase occurs much earlier and is greater in resistant plants than in susceptible plants (Edreva, 1975c). Strong localization and high intensity of the peroxidase response around the sites of infection are characteristic of Mg^{2+}-grown resistant tobacco seedlings (Edreva et al, 1987).

All molecular components of peroxidase increase their activity following infection, especially those with relative electrophoretic mobilities of 0.17 and 0.25. No new peroxidase isoforms specific for blue mold pathogenesis or resistance have been established (Edreva, 1975a).

Polyphenoloxidase (EC 1.10.3.1), which is implicated in polyphenol oxidation and necrosis formation, behaves in a similar manner to peroxidase (Bailov et al, 1962; Edreva, 1974a; Pashenko, 1975). Quinones, which are products of polyphenol oxidation, were detected and identified in blue mold-infected leaves (Edreva and Georgieva, 1984).

Cohen et al (1981) reported an increase in lipoxygenase activity of tobacco leaves following *P. hyoscyami* infection. Lipoxygenase (EC 1.13.11.12) is responsible for the oxidation of the unsaturated fatty acids in the lipid constituents of cell membranes. As a result of its action, lipid peroxidases are formed. The formation of lipid peroxidases is considered to be the first event in membrane injury (Mead, 1976) and necrosis formation (Kato and Misawa, 1975; Ruzicka et al, 1983). Accumulation of lipid peroxidases along with tissue damage has been established in blue mold-infected leaves (Edreva et al, 1988). It is more pronounced and occurs earlier in resistant plants.

Catalase (EC 1.11.1.6), whose function is to destroy the H_2O_2 toxic to the cell, exhibits characteristic changes depending on the pathogenesis stage and resistance. In susceptible plants, the early stage is marked by a spurt of catalase activity (Bailov et al, 1962; Boceski, 1963). In the later stages, when damage is severe, catalase activity declines (Bailov et al, 1962). A decreased catalase level is also detected in resistant plants (Pashenko, 1975). These variations correspond to a drop in H_2O_2 content during the early pathogenesis stage in susceptible plants. H_2O_2, which is responsible for cell damage, accumulates during the final stages of infection in both susceptible and resistant plants.

A similar situation is established with superoxide dismutase (EC 1.15.1.1). Cell protective functions ascribed to this enzyme have been intensively studied in recent years. Superoxide dismutase catalyzes the reaction $O^{x-} + O^{x-} + 2H^+ \rightarrow H_2O_2 + O_2$, that is, the dismutation of superoxide radicals, which are extremely injurious to the cell. In resistant Mg^{2+}-grown tobacco seedlings, superoxide dismutase activity (responsible for the accumulation of superoxide radicals) drops in the initial disease stages. This drop can be associated with damage to the infected tissue and consequently the damage and localization of the pathogen. The drop is followed by an elevation in the activity related to the survival of the plant. The opposite behavior of the enzyme in the susceptible cultivar permits the pathogen to develop normally and invade the host tissues (J. C. Coussirat, R. Delon, and A. Edreva, unpublished).

Malate dehydrogenase (EC 1.11.1.37) and isocitrate dehydrogenase (EC 1.1.1.42), which catalyze metabolic steps in the Krebs cycle, also vary significantly in blue mold pathogenesis. In susceptible cultivars, a rise in their activity and the appearance of new isoenzymes of malate dehydrogenase are observed at the early pathogenic stage, followed by an activity decrease and disappearance of isoforms in the later stages (Edreva, 1975b). In the resistant plants, only a sharp decrease in both enzyme activities is found, contributing to the shift of the redox potential toward oxidation. This course of activity of the dehydrogenases can be partly explained by their sensitivity to oxidized polyphenol metabolites (A. Edreva, unpublished), which are intensively produced in the pathological process. Cytochemical tests have shown that the dehydrogenase increase is a host response to *P. hyoscyami* infection (A. Edreva and J. D. Georgieva, unpublished).

The drop in the content of free and protein-bound sulfhydryl (SH) groups during blue mold pathogenesis (A. Edreva, unpublished) also contributes to the increment in the redox potential.

We also investigated the energetic state of cells in conditions of blue mold infection, using some new approaches such as chemiluminescence (Abeles, 1986) and electron paramagnetic resonance (EPR) (Alger, 1968). The induced chemiluminescence is indicative of the energetic level of the biomembranes, revealed by the passage of ions through the ion channels (Sandblom, 1980). The EPR signals, a measure of the concentration of free radicals, characterize the energetic state of the molecules. Both techniques have been applied in studies of host-parasite relations in plants (Michalov and Komar, 1984; Savin et al, 1981). Higher rates of both induced chemiluminescence and EPR were recorded in our resistant tobacco seedlings compared to the susceptible ones upon infection (Mollé et al, 1983–1984; R. Karjieva, A. Edreva, J. C. Coussirat, and R. Delon, unpublished). This situation reflects an enhancement in the energetic level of the molecules and biomembranes, consequently a labilization of the cell structures. The variations in chemiluminescence, as a membrane property, could be connected with the peroxidation of the membrane lipid constituents, as shown by the lipid peroxidase tests of infected leaf disks (Edreva et al, 1988).

The data summarized here suggest that early reactions and a more oxidized and labilized state (i.e., a more damaged state) depict the response of resistant tobaccos to *P. hyoscyami* infection. A delayed response is characteristic of susceptible plants.

POLYPHENOL METABOLISM

Many biochemical processes in plants, such as oxidation-reduction, energy production, enzyme regulation, and photochemical responses, involve the participation of polyphenol compounds. One important biological property of polyphenols is their antimicrobial activity, related to conformational interactions with proteins, enzymes, nucleic acids, and membrane structures of the microorganisms. Their involvement in lignin building, metabolism of growth substances, and necrosis formation is also essential. Thus, the importance of polyphenols in phytopathogenesis, along with the role of oxidative enzymes, is a subject of steadily increasing interest (Friend, 1981; Kosuge, 1969).

We investigated some of the main enzymes of polyphenol biosynthesis—phenylalanine ammonia lyase (EC 4.1.3.5) (PAL), glucose-6-phosphate dehydrogenase (EC 1.1.1.49), and 6-phosphogluconate dehydrogenase (EC 1.1.1.44)—in blue mold pathogenesis. PAL catalyzes the deamination of 1-phenylalanine, which is the first step for biosynthesis of the phenylpropanoid skeleton in higher plants. Phenylpropanoid gives rise to activated cinnamic acids, which are precursors of a large variety of secondary constituents. The two dehydrogenases are key enzymes of the pentose phosphate pathway (PPP), producing intermediates for the formation of

113

shikimic acid, a central metabolite in polyphenol biosynthesis. The levels of PAL and PPP enzymes may fluctuate significantly in response to a wide range of stimuli, including pathogenic agents (Jones, 1984; Legrand, 1983).

An increase in both PPP enzymes, glucose-6-phosphate dehydrogenase and 6-phosphogluconate dehydrogenase, was recorded in the leaves of susceptible and resistant tobacco plants after infection with *P. hyoscyami*. This response occurred earlier in resistant cultivars (A. Edreva, unpublished). Moreover, a great increase of PAL activity was also observed following infection of tobacco seedlings by *P. hyoscyami* and was more important in the resistant cultivar (J. C. Coussirat, R. Delon, and A. Edreva, unpublished).

These events could account for the significant changes in the polyphenol pattern in blue mold pathogenesis. It has been shown that extracts from blue mold-infected leaves inhibit germination of *P. hyoscyami* conidia. Extracts from healthy leaves do not have such an effect (Pashenko, 1978; Shepherd and Mandryk, 1962). This is supposed to be related to the polyphenols formed in the diseased leaves (Pashenko, 1978). In effect, chlorogenic acid and its isomers accumulate as a result of *P. hyoscyami* infection. These polyphenols are predominantly localized in the infected areas of the leaves as well as in the adjacent tissues. The process takes place in the early disease stages; during necrotizing, a drop in the chlorogenic acid content was recorded (Edreva, 1974b) (Fig. 2A). These changes proceed faster in the resistant plants than in the susceptible ones (Edreva, 1975c). The variations in the flavonoid rutin are similar to those in chlorogenic acid (Edreva, 1974b). Scopoletin, an aglycone of scopolin (6-methoxy, 7-hydroxycoumarin 6-glucoside), also accumulates (Cohen, 1976), especially in heavily damaged tissues (Edreva, 1974b), accounting for the blue fluorescence of tobacco leaves infected with *P. hyoscyami* (Mayr et al, 1963). The accumulation of scopoletin could be related to lignification processes, which are of great importance in phytopathogenesis. Infection also provokes the appearance of some unidentified polyphenols that are absent from healthy leaves (Edreva, 1974b).

The accumulation of chlorogenic acid, scopoletin, and scopolin in diseased plants has frequently been reported (Clarke, 1973; Uritani, 1982). It is part of the widespread phenomenon of accumulation of phenol compounds, known as tissue "aromatization," which is a plant response to attacks from fungal, bacterial, and viral pathogens (Farkas and Kiraly, 1962). The biological meaning of this phenomenon in blue mold pathogenesis could be seen in terms of the phenol functions outlined above, as well as in formation of necroses.

Whether cell death, or the hypersensitive response of plants to pathogens, is the cause or the consequence of resistance has been the subject of lengthy discussions and much speculation (Heath, 1976; Kiraly et al, 1972; Martin and Martin-Tanguy, 1981; Tomiyama, 1983). In the case of the tobacco-*P. hyoscyami* system, differing views have also been developed (Izard et al, 1961; Mandryk, 1971; Shepherd and Mandryk, 1967; Ternovskii and Dashkeeva, 1963). Light and electron microscopy (Kröber, 1970; Kröber and Petzold, 1972) have shown that leaf cells in the resistant cultivar are destroyed immediately after invasion by the fungus. The damage is confined to several cells. In the suscept, only a few cells are destroyed several days after invasion. Nevertheless, it has been suggested that in the necroses the fungus does not seem to be damaged by a shortage of nutrients, but rather by a toxic principle induced after the infection. Thus, the rapid necrotization of the invaded resistant host cells is supposed to be only a concomitant phenomenon and not the cause of resistance.

The nature of the biochemical processes involved in necrosis formation is not quite clear. An increase in the level of oxidative enzymes, diminishment of dehydrogenase activity, oxidation of

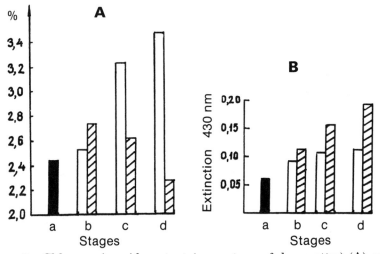

Figure 2. Chlorogenic acid content (percentage of dry matter) (A) and intensity of brown color of water extracts (extinction 430 nm) (B) of tobacco leaves (susceptible cultivar Pembe) in different stages of blue mold development. Stage a is the control (healthy leaves). Stages b–d are stages of blue mold; b = early, c = intermediate, d = late (necrosis). Hatched columns refer to infected tissues; open columns refer to adjacent tissues. (Part A reprinted, with permission, from Edreva, 1974b; part B reprinted, by permission, from Edreva, 1974c)

115

polyphenols, and brown pigment formation are considered to be the main events in necrotizing in plant infections (Rubin et al, 1975). This was confirmed in blue mold pathogenesis (Edreva, 1977).

Information is scanty, however, about the precursors and the composition of brown pigments formed in necrobiosis. The brown pigments are suggested to be "toxic melanin-like products," "resin-like polymers of quinones impregnating the tissues to form a barrier against infection" (Hare, 1966), or "products of interaction of phenols with carbohydrates, aromatic acids, etc." (Rubin et al, 1975), but no reliable experimental evidence for these suggestions has been provided.

Quinones, produced in the polyphenol-polyphenoloxidase and/or polyphenol-peroxidase systems, are also supposed to form during necrotic reactions and to accumulate in a free state as inhibitors of both plants and pathogens (Metlizki, 1968; Oku, 1964). Being highly reactive compounds, they are hypothesized to be the most probable precursors of brown pigments in diseased plants (Friend, 1979; Stahmann, 1983), but this is evidenced only by common histochemical tests (Farkas et al, 1960; Herr, 1975; Oku, 1964).

In blue mold pathogenesis, attempts to elucidate the composition and the precursors of brown pigments emphasize the reduction in chlorogenic acid content in the necroses, which parallels the increase in brown color intensity (Edreva, 1974b, 1974c) (Fig. 2).

Quinones interact covalently with -NH$_2$, -SH, and =NH groups of amino acids and proteins to form polymeric products, as shown in model experiments (Pierpoint, 1969a, 1969b). This is the basis for the supposition that a similar process consuming chlorogenic acid may occur in blue mold necrotizing. In fact, the brown pigments isolated from necrotized tobacco leaves have been proved by acidic and alkaline hydrolytic breakdown to be polymers built up of chlorogenic acid and proteins. Fraction ratio, size, and distribution of the molecular weights of brown pigments, determined by gel filtration, point to the presence of products with different degrees of polymerization covering a wide range of molecular weights (3,000–80,000) (Edreva, 1974c, 1977).

Moreover, the presence of quinones of chlorogenic acid in diseased tissue has been demonstrated (Edreva and Georgieva, 1984). The presumably highly reactive quinones are studied as stable sulfone derivatives. The interaction of chlorogenoquinones with benzenesulfinic acid (Pierpoint, 1966), yielding stable crystallized sulfones, has been used for this purpose. The sulfone character of the compound produced in vitro from chlorogenic acid, oxidative enzymes, and benzenesulfinic acid has been shown using reliable chemical and physical methods, such as ultraviolet and infrared spectroscopy, thin-layer chromatography, and specific color reactions. This model sulfone (compound 1) is identical to the sulfone isolated from blue mold-infected leaves treated with benzenesulfinic acid (compound 2) (Table 1, Plate 8). Thus, the presence of chlorogenoquinones in blue mold-infected leaves has been proved.

The mechanism of necrotizing in blue mold pathogenesis can be examined, therefore, as an interaction of chlorogenic acid with proteins (via chlorogenoquinone as intermediate) and the formation of brown pigments. The role of brown pigments can be seen as one of stabilizing cell walls and membranes (Beckman et al, 1974; Glazener, 1982), making them more rigid—that is, more resistant to chemical and physical breakdown and to subsequent infection. Cytochemical tests indicating localization of quinones predominantly in cell walls in blue mold pathogenesis (Edreva and Georgieva, 1984) lend support to this hypothesis.

The reactions described above clearly cannot take place in a normal cell. Possibly, quinones arise and accumulate as a sequence of nonregulated contacts of phenols and oxidative enzymes that are localized in the vacuoles and cytoplasm, respectively. Disturbances in the regulation of tonoplast permeability may be a primary event in plant cell anomalies; hence quinones can be regarded as stress metabolites and an alarm signal of cell damage.

The interaction of the chlorogenoquinone with host plant proteins, resulting in brown pigment formation, shows the phytotoxic action of chlorogenic acid, leading to the localization of the effect of damage stimuli. Usually, the role of chlorogenic acid in phytopathogenesis is related to its direct toxic effect on the pathogens as well as to the fungitoxic effect of the chlorogenoquinone (Friend, 1979; Metlizki et al, 1972). The phytotoxicity of chlorogenic acid suggests that the biological meaning of its accumulation in blue mold pathogenesis may be the provision of enough substrates for the forthcoming necrotizing reactions. The higher rate of these reactions could be related to disease resistance.

HYDROLYTIC ENZYMES

According to the lysosomal concept of pathophysiology (Wilson, 1973), hydrolytic enzymes play an important role in plant pathogenesis. Information about the involvement of hydrolases in plant-obligate parasite systems, however, is insufficient.

We followed the variations in the activity of acid phosphatase, esterase, and glycosidases in blue mold pathogenesis. Esterase (EC 3.1.1.6) hydrolyzes various esters, including esters of short-chain fatty acids, thus supplying small carbon fragments for acetyl coenzyme A formation and a range of biosyntheses. It catalyzes the transfer of acyl groups toward amino acid esters, thereby also being

Table 1. Chromatographic, fluorescence, and infrared (IR) and ultraviolet (UV) spectral characteristics and Hoepfner's reaction of sulfones of chlorogenoquinone[a]

Substance	IR bands (cm⁻¹) for sulfone groups $\geq\!S\!\leq^O_O$	Max in UV (nm)	R_f solvents A[b]	R_f solvents B[c]	Fluorescence in UV −NH₃	Fluorescence in UV ⁺NH₃	Hoepfner's reaction
Compound 1[d]	1140, 1300	255, 308	0.72	0.74	Blue-green	Yellow-green	Orange
Compound 2[e]	1140, 1300	255, 308	0.73	0.75	Blue-green	Yellow-green	Orange
Chlorogenic acid	—	295, 324	0.57	0.60	Blue	Blue-green	Red
Benzenesulfinic acid	—	261, 265, 272	—	—	—	—	—

[a] Source: Edreva and Georgieva (1984).
[b] n-Butanol-ethanol-water (4:1:2).
[c] n-Butanol-acetic acid-water (4:1:1).
[d] Sulfone of chlorogenoquinone produced in vitro from chlorogenic acid, benzenesulfinic acid, and horseradish peroxidase.
[e] Sulfone of chlorogenoquinone from blue mold-infected tobacco leaves.

involved in certain synthetic processes. The functions of acid phosphatase (EC 3.1.3.2), hydrolyzing phosphate esters, are related to the active transport of sugars between the cells and in the conducting tissues, the biosynthesis of polysaccharides, the mobilization of food reserves, and the release of phosphate groups for adenosine triphosphate (ATP) synthesis. Thus, the catabolic action of the two enzymes is closely connected with anabolic cell processes.

Both enzymes behave similarly in blue mold-infected leaves (Edreva and Georgieva, 1977; Edreva et al, 1979, 1980a). Their activity increases in the early disease stage and decreases in the final stages. The conidia and the hyphae of *P. hyoscyami* also contain highly active acid phosphatase and esterase. Cytochemical tests have proved, however, that the augmented activity of these enzymes is a host response to *P. hyoscyami* infection and is not due to the parasite structures per se. These data suggest that some activation of the anabolic processes of the invaded plant takes place during the initial stages of blue mold and is followed by disturbances of the anabolic functions during the later stages of the disease.

Glycosidases catalyze the breakdown of glycosidic bonds in disaccharides and oligosaccharides building up polymeric cell surface components. Thus, these enzymes are implicated in the regulation of the relationship between the host and the parasite at their interface, as well as in the recognition phenomena (Bateman and Basham, 1976; Cline and Albersheim, 1981; Netzer and Kritzman, 1979; Nichols et al, 1980). The glycosidases also catalyze the transfer of glycosyl groups and hydrolyze the phenyl glycosides (releasing free phenol aglycones), thus participating in phenol metabolism.

The involvement of glycosidases in blue mold pathogenesis has been studied for several years (Edreva, 1984; Edreva and Georgieva, 1980; Edreva et al, 1980b, 1986). The activity of the following enzymes has been investigated: α- and β-glucosidase, α- and β-galactosidase, α- and β-mannosidase (EC 3.2.1.20–25), and α- and β-xylosidase (EC 3.2.1.36–37). The activity of all of these enzymes is enhanced in tobacco leaves infected with blue mold. The increase is especially dramatic for α- and β-glucosidase and β-xylosidase, where about a 20-fold augmentation in activity has been recorded. Cohen (1976) also reported an enhancement of β-glycosidase in blue mold-diseased tissue.

We compared the effect of *P. hyoscyami* infection with other pathogenic and nonpathogenic damages to tobacco leaves. Only endoparasitic fungi (*P. hyoscyami, Phytophthora parasitica* var. *nicotianae, Alternaria tenuis,* and *Fusarium* sp.) induce an increase in glycosidase activity. The obligate ectoparasitic fungus *Erysiphe cichoracearum,* the bacterium *Pseudomonas syringae* pv. *tabaci,* and viruses (tobacco mosaic virus, cucumber mosaic virus, tomato spotted wilt virus, and potato virus Y) do not provoke the same event. Senescence and nonpathogenic stress factors such as excess manganese, γ-irradiation, and excess water (the cause of the physiological disease "sharilka") have no effect. This finding distinguishes endoparasitic fungi from all other factors. The behavior of β-glucosidase is especially characteristic in this respect (Edreva and Georgieva, 1980) (Fig. 3).

β-Xylosidase activity shows a marked increase only in the tobacco-*P. hyoscyami* system, not in systems involving other tobacco pathogens or damage factors. This specificity of β-xylosidase variations underlies the test proposed by Edreva (1984) for the biochemical diagnosis of blue mold. The test implies the use of *p*-nitrophenyl-β-D-xylopyranoside as a substrate of β-xylosidase action. The hydrolysis of the substrate by extracts of tobacco leaves releases *p*-nitrophenol, which is easily quantified by an optical density measurement.

Cytochemical evidence indicates that both fungal hyphae and invaded host cells contribute to the enhancement of β-glucosidase in blue mold-infected leaves. The response of the host cells to infection is faster and more pronounced in resistant cultivars (Fig. 3). This is spectacularly demonstrated in Mg^{2+}-grown resistant tobacco seedlings, where islets of host cells with very high β-glucosidase activity localized under ungerminated conidia are observed. These islets can be examined as a barrier to infection. The phenomenon is not found in susceptible cultivars (Edreva et al, 1986) (Plate 9).

These data imply the participation of glycosidases in the regulation of blue mold pathogenesis and possibly in the resistance mechanisms of tobacco to *P. hyoscyami* invasion. Host glycosidases may act in the release of fungitoxic phenol aglycones, or in the processing of the parasitic structures that is necessary for host-pathogen recognition, or in the interaction with fungal glucan elicitors and/or compatibility factors related to triggering phytoalexin production. Glycosidases of pathogenic origin could also be important as a tool for penetration in host tissues. The exact nature of glycosidase involvement in tobacco-*P. hyoscyami* relationships is still obscure, and this field is open to investigation.

ALIPHATIC DIAMINES AND POLYAMINES

The regulatory and structural functions of aliphatic diamines and polyamines (ADPA) are well known (Smith, 1985). These cationic molecules play an important role in maintaining the helicoidal structure of nucleic acids, in membrane and cell wall integrity, and

Plate 1.   A tobacco leaf infected with blue mold.

Plate 2.   A tobacco leaf with many blue mold lesions (light green spots).

Plate 3. A tobacco leaf with numerous young, sporulating lesions, which have a downy appearance. The lesion tissue is green.

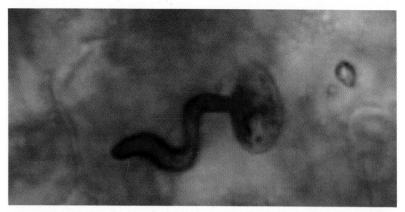

Plate 4. A partially empty sporangium with a relatively long, curved germ tube.

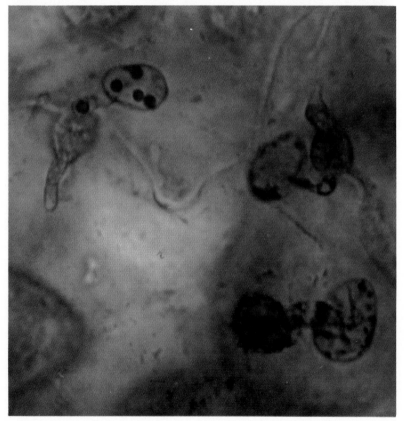

Plate 5. Three sporangia which have infected and produced large vesicles inside tobacco epidermal cells.

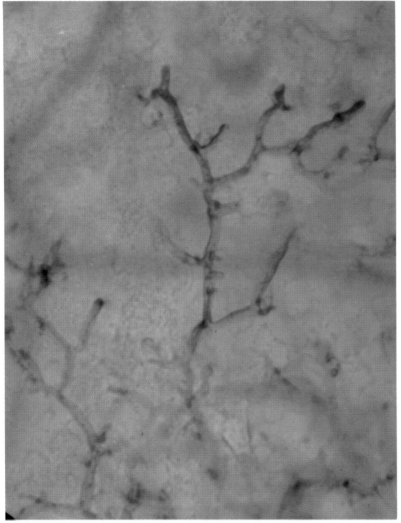

Plate 6. Dichotomously branching vegetative hyphae in the spongy mesophyll intercellular spaces of a tobacco leaf.

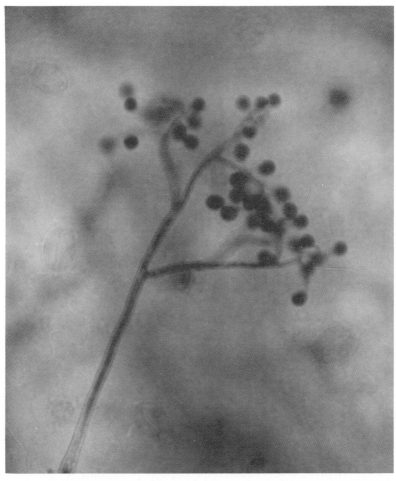

Plate 7. A dichotomously branched sporangiophore with numerous nonpapillate sporangia attached to acute tips.

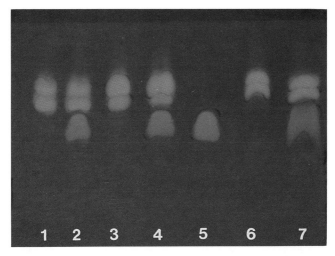

Plate 8. Thin-layer chromatogram (in ultraviolet light plus NH₃) of sulfone derivatives of chlorogenoquinones (solvent ethanol-acetic acid-water, 4:1:1; cellulose layer, 0.1 mm, Merck). 1, Sulfone of chlorogeno-quinone (CQ) produced in vitro from chlorogenic acid (CA), tobacco leaf polyphenoloxidase, and benzenesulfinic acid (BSA); 2, as in 1 plus CA; 3, sulfone of CQ produced in vitro from CA, horseradish peroxidase, and BSA; 4, as in 3 plus CA; 5, CA; 6, sulfone of CQ from blue mold-infected tobacco leaves; 7, as in 6 plus CA.

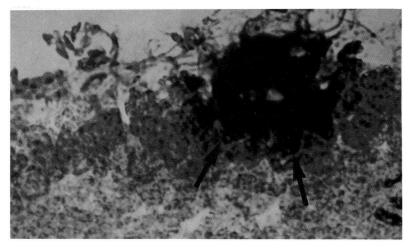

Plate 9. Frozen sections of Mg^{2+}-grown blue mold-infected tobacco seedlings of the resistant cultivar PBD6. High β-glucosidase activity is observed in islets of cells (arrows) of the upper epidermis and palisade parenchyma underlying ungerminated conidia of *Peronospora hyoscyami*. The phenomenon is not observed in the susceptible tobacco cultivar Paraguay 48. (×340) (Reprinted, by permission, from Edreva et al, 1986 [reference in Chapter 4])

Plate 10.   A cartoon of the 1979 blue mold epiphytotic in Ontario. (Drawn by M. R. Tingley, cartoonist for *The London Free Press*)

in ion homeostasis. In plants, growth and development promoter functions are ascribed to these compounds, and senescence phenomena are closely related to their metabolism (Altman and Bachrach, 1981). Both ethylene, a plant senescence hormone, and ADPA are derived from S-adenosylmethionine; that is, they compete for a common precursor. This could explain the reduction in the ADPA content observed during senescence of plant tissues (Roberts et al, 1984). Little information is available, however, about

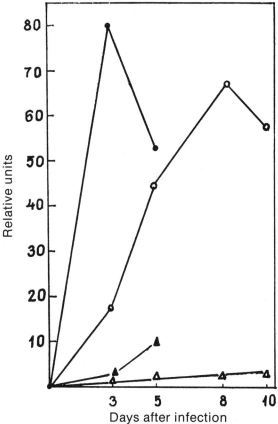

Figure 3. Relative activity of β-glucosidase in the resistant tobacco cultivar 134 and the susceptible cultivar Nevrokop 5 in different stages of blue mold development (activity in healthy leaves = 1.0). The graph shows activity in infected (•) and adjacent (▲) tissues in the resistant cultivar and in infected (o) and adjacent (Δ) tissues in the susceptible cultivar. A very important rise in β-glucosidase activity is also observed in tobacco infected by *Alternaria tenuis, Phytophthora parasitica* var. *nicotianae,* and *Fusarium* sp. No rise is found with infections by *Erysiphe cichoracearum* or *Pseudomonas syringae* pv. *tabaci* or in nonpathogenic damage or senescence. (Reprinted, by permission, from Edreva and Georgieva, 1980)

121

the possible implication of ADPA in phytopathogenesis.

Edreva and Hadjiska (1985) investigated the pattern and the level of both free and bound ADPA in leaves affected by blue mold. Spermidine, putrescine, and traces of cadaverine are found in a free form. These same compounds are identified in a bound state as amides of caffeic and ferulic acids. ADPA patterns in infected and healthy leaves are identical. However, in infected leaves, a decrease is observed in the content of both free and bound spermidine and putrescine. The extent of this decline depends on the degree of damage and the minimal ADPA titer being established in heavily damaged tissues. These data point to the participation of ADPA in the regulatory control of blue mold. The infection appears to accelerate the senescence process, leading to a reduction in ADPA at the expense of enhanced ethylene production. In fact, ethylene formation was recorded in blue mold-infected leaves (A. Edreva, unpublished).

b-PROTEINS

The b-proteins are one of the most fascinating and intensively studied compounds in plant pathophysiology in the last 15 years (Gianinazzi et al, 1970; Van Loon and Van Kammen, 1970) because they appear and accumulate in plants in response to pathological conditions. They are not degradation products or by-products of metabolism but rather are macromolecules actively synthesized de novo (Jamet et al, 1985). Many investigations have attempted to elucidate their induction, origin, properties, and physiological importance; different views have evolved about their implication in disease resistance. The opinion that b-proteins are strongly related to resistance has given way to the view that they are commonly related to plant pathogenesis. This new view accounts for the new term *pathogenesis-related proteins* (Van Loon, 1985). Recent work has shown, however, that b-proteins are not necessarily related to pathogenesis but may also be elicited by a range of nonpathogenic stimuli (Ohashi and Matsuoka, 1985).

In tobacco, which serves as a model plant for b-protein investigation, b-proteins appear as a sequel of viral, fungal, and bacterial infections. Noninfectious processes leading to profound changes in metabolism and genome organization, such as flowering and interspecific hybridization (Ahl and Gianinazzi, 1982; Fraser, 1981), also result in b-protein formation. The b-proteins also appear in response to water stress, which is the cause of the "sharilka" physiological disorder of Oriental tobacco (Edreva, 1988), and in manganese toxicity (Edreva and Apostolova, 1988).

Coussirat (1983-1984) exhaustively examined the problem of b-proteins in tobacco blue mold pathogenesis. Several findings underline the importance of his work. The b-proteins form following *P. hyoscyami* infection in leaves of adult tobacco plants as well as in young seedlings, but there is no relationship between this phenomenon and resistance. Thus, susceptible and resistant genotypes respond similarly to infection with regard to both time of appearance and rate of accumulation of b-proteins. Treatment with fungicides (Acylon) that confer resistance to blue mold does not induce b-protein accumulation. In contrast, polyacrylic acid elicits b-protein formation, which is not accompanied, however, by induction of resistance. Moreover, b-proteins accumulate in nonpathogenic stress conditions, such as disturbances in hormonal and nutritive balance such as flowering, stem cutting, and specific Mg^{2+} nutrition. Mg^{2+} ions, when used as the sole nutrient source for tobacco seedlings, provoke premature gene expression, and b-proteins accumulate. This reaction is not observed when seedlings are grown in the normal Knop nutritive medium.

Meanwhile, Coussirat's data suggest a similarity of b-proteins with other abnormal molecules, namely the phenyldiamines, which appear in tobacco leaves following infection, flowering, and stem cutting (Cabanne et al, 1977).

These results lend support to the view that b-proteins are common stress metabolites, which are synthesized and accumulated in response to profound perturbations in plant metabolism of both pathogenic and noninfectious origin. On this basis, it is proposed that these proteins be called stress proteins rather than pathogenesis-related proteins (Ohashi and Matsuoka, 1985).

Applying immunoelectrophoresis and immunodiffusion methods, Masiak (1983) investigated whether new specific proteins were formed as a result of infection of tobacco plants by *P. hyoscyami* and whether the presence of such new proteins was related to resistance to blue mold. Plants susceptible to blue mold were found to have similar protein patterns before and after inoculation. However, *N. exigua,* which is resistant to *P. hyoscyami,* responds to infection by producing a specific protein component, which is supposed to condition resistance to blue mold. Macromolecules other than b-proteins are probably implicated in this case.

Metabolism of *Peronospora hyoscyami*

The metabolism of obligate parasites has been investigated less than that of saprophytes and facultative parasites because of specific requirements for experimental work with obligate parasites. Knowledge has accumulated on rust fungi concerning chemical composition of spores and hyphae, enzyme activities and heterogeneity, metabolic pathways, self-inhibition and control of dormancy of conidia, induction of differentiation in sporulation and germination as well as mechanisms of these events, race and species enzyme molecular patterns, and resistance or compatibility elicitors in recognition phenomena.

HYPHAE

As stated in the preceding section, hyphae developing intercellularly can be distinguished from the leaf tissue by cytochemical methods. Staining tests reveal the presence of peroxidase, polyphenoloxidase, nicotinamide adenine dinucleotide (NAD)-malate dehydrogenase, NAD phosphate (NADP)-isocitrate dehydrogenase, alcohol dehydrogenase, NAD-glutamate dehydrogenase, glucose-6-phosphate dehydrogenase, 6-phosphogluconate dehydrogenase, acid phosphatase, esterase, and β-glucosidase (Edreva et al, 1980a). The activity of the hydrolases in the hyphae is more pronounced than that of the oxireductases. The cytoplasm of hyphae is also characterized by a high content of RNA and basic proteins (Georgieva and Edreva, 1974), which is characteristic of actively dividing cells (Davenport and Davenport, 1965).

CONIDIA

The metabolism and the composition of conidia are better understood than those of hyphae because conidia can be readily isolated from tobacco leaves. Shepherd and Tosic (1966) established the presence of riboflavin in conidia of *P. hyoscyami*. Shepherd and Muller (1967) reported the existence of two pools of free amino acids and sugars, one outer, or readily water-extractable, and one inner, or alcohol-extractable. Both contain glutamine, glutamic acid, α-amino butyric acid, α-alanine, and proline. Some 98% of the sugars is glucose. Trehalose and mannitol, common in other fungal spores, have not been detected. Conidia contain threonine, serine, aspartic acid, histidine, arginine, tryptophan, organic acids of glucose, α-alanine, and glutamic acid (Edreva, 1968).

Activity of α- and β-glucosidase, α- and β-xylosidase, α- and β-mannosidase, α- and β-galactosidase, catalase, and PAL has been detected in conidia. The enzyme activities were also detected in hyphae (Edreva et al, 1980a). Cohen (1976) also reported the presence of β-glucosidase in conidia of *P. hyoscyami*. Electrophoretic studies have demonstrated the molecular heterogeneity of these enzymes (Edreva et al, 1980a). These data indicate that *P. hyoscyami* performs a variety of metabolic functions and operates with multimolecular enzyme forms, a tool for fine metabolic regulation and adaptation to changing environmental factors. Special attention should be given to the presence of PAL (an

124

enzyme of the aromatic metabolism), reported in an obligate parasite for the first time. All of these findings are important as a basis for understanding sporulation, germination, and penetration events in *P. hyoscyami*.

SPORULATION AND GERMINATION

By applying different metabolites and antimetabolites to sporulating tobacco leaf disks, Shepherd and Mandryk (1964) found that a range of metabolites, including sugars, amino acids, vitamins, phosphates, and nitrogen- and carbon-containing compounds, have little effect on the amount of sporulation, thus demonstrating that nutrient deficiency is not a limiting factor for this process.

The uracil analogues have a strong inhibitory effect on sporulation. The inhibition is reversed by the addition of uracil, which shows its involvement in sporulation. The ornithine cycle is also involved, as proved by the inhibition of sporulation by canavanine and its reversal by arginine, citrulline, and ornithine. A tyrosine oxidizing system is also operative. The light-dependency of sporulation (Uozumi and Kröber, 1967) could be related to the functioning of PAL, a light-regulated enzyme, in *P. hyoscyami* conidia.

Factors influencing germination of conidia of *P. hyoscyami* were also examined. The removal of the outer amino acid pool did not influence the rate of germination but reduced germ tube growth, whereas the size of the inner pool strongly affected germination (Shepherd and Muller, 1967).

Shepherd (1962) tested the in vitro effect of 141 metabolites and antimetabolites (vitamins, amino acids, sugars, purine and pyrimidine bases, nucleotides and their analogues, as well as inorganic ions and inorganic carbon and nitrogen sources) on germination and germ tube elongation. He found that both processes are enhanced by the presence of carbon and nitrogen nutrients, phosphates, and calcium and magnesium cations; calcium and magnesium cations are specifically required for normal germination and germ tube growth. The riboflavin level has proved to be the most important limiting factor, whereas the other vitamins (mainly B group) have had no stimulatory effect. Sugars produce stimulation or inhibition. Most of the amino acids are stimulatory, but no requirement for a specific amino acid has been recorded. The inhibitory effect of the ornithine analogue, canavanine, points to the participation of an ornithine cycle in germination. No generalizations can be made from the results obtained with purines and pyrimidines and their analogues showing either stimulation or inhibition. The importance of uracil in germination and sporulation was recorded also.

Hollomon (1969, 1970, 1971, 1973) made a comprehensive in vitro investigation of the biochemical mechanisms controlling germination in *P. hyoscyami*. Protein and RNA syntheses during the differentiation of spores were examined. A strong radioactively labeled amino acid incorporation preceded germ tube appearance, showing that de novo protein synthesis was necessary for this event. This was substantiated by the fact that actidione inhibited both germination and protein synthesis. Inhibition of RNA synthesis has no effect on germination, indicating that spore differentiation does not require RNA synthesis. The proteins that are located in germ tubes appear therefore to be synthesized on a template of stable messenger RNA present in dormant conidia. Alteration of this RNA in such a way that it becomes able to act as a template for protein synthesis may be the first step in germination processes. It has been suggested that control of germination may be at the translation level.

The mechanism of the penetration of *P. hyoscyami* infection tubes through tobacco host cell walls is not well understood. This event is supposed to occur in a mechanical and/or a biochemical way. On the basis of ultrastructural studies, Trigiano et al (1983) concluded that penetration might be achieved by enzymatic processes. Data indicating the presence of highly active hydrolases, including glycosidases, in *P. hyoscyami* hyphae (Edreva et al, 1980a) lend support to this view.

AUTOINHIBITION

Self-inhibition is an essential mechanism in the control of dormancy and population size in fungal spores (Allen and Dunkle, 1971). Autoinhibitors, which act as regulatory constituents of dormant conidia, maintain dormancy and prevent germination, and their leakage facilitates germination. Shepherd and Mandryk (1961, 1962), Izard (1961), Izard and Gradouteaud (1962), and Schiltz (1967) have reported autoinhibition within *P. hyoscyami*.

Inhibitory substances were extracted from conidia and separated chromatographically. They are water-soluble and fluoresce blue in ultraviolet light. The same inhibitory compounds, as judged from their solubility, chromatographic behavior, and biological activity, also were found in blue mold-infected leaves and healthy leaves growing on stems inoculated with blue mold (Shepherd and Mandryk, 1962). It was suggested that these inhibitors in the leaves may be fungal in origin. Leppik et al (1972) substantiated this suggestion by isolating a potent inhibitor of *P. hyoscyami* germination from blue mold-infected tobacco leaves and from *P. hyoscyami* conidia. The compound, named quiesone (from the

Latin *quiescere,* to sleep), has been assigned the structure 5-iso-butyroxy-β-ionone. Thus, quiesone is structurally related to ionone-type compounds known to control developmental changes in organisms. Abscisic acid, which also contains an ionone skeleton, belongs to the same class and participates not only in abscission but also in maintaining seed and bud dormancy (Libbert, 1974). When injected into stems, ionone compounds bring about developmental and morphological changes in tobacco plants, such as accelerated growth and senescence and loss of apical dominance (Salt and Kuć, 1984). These data are in accordance with previous results (Izard, 1961; Izard and Gradouteaud, 1962) showing a developmental effect in young tobacco plants and oat coleoptiles when inhibitory substances from water extracts of conidia were applied.

Ionone-type compounds have also been shown to influence sporulation of the fungus. Injection of these compounds into tobacco stems reduces sporulation of *P. hyoscyami* but not the lesion area (Salt and Kuć, 1984). Schiltz (1974) reported that β-ionone sprayed on tobacco seedlings 24 hr before inoculation had a preventive inhibitory effect on conidiophore formation; the effect was more pronounced with the virulent *P. hyoscyami* strain. In some cases, a curative effect is also observed. These findings are discussed in terms of the direct action of β-ionone compounds on fungal metabolism not mediated via the host. Two points must be stressed. First, quiesone is not fungitoxic, as its inhibitory effect on germination is completely reversible. Second, it is very specific; closely related ionone-containing compounds do not inhibit germination, and quiesone fails to inhibit spore germination of fungal species not related to *P. hyoscyami* (Leppik et al, 1972).

Investigations of *P. hyoscyami* metabolism enrich our knowledge of the biochemistry of obligate parasitism in fungi. They could also be useful in the search for antimetabolites and enzyme inhibitors and hence for a means of blue mold control.

Host-Pathogen Compatibility in the System *Nicotiana tabacum-Peronospora hyoscyami*

In the past decade, much knowledge has been gained and many hypotheses evolved concerning the molecular basis of host-parasite interaction and recognition (Daly, 1984; Keen, 1982). Schemes of molecular events occurring during the primary stages of host-obligate pathogen interactions have been proposed (Chakravorty and Shaw, 1977a, 1977b). They imply derepression of genes, complementation of enzymes in the host and the pathogen and, in some cases, complementation between host-specific and pathogen-specific polypeptides leading to the formation of catalytically different enzymes whose functions are essential for the continuation of the host-parasite relationship. The basic tenets of these schemes are transfer of nucleic acids, synthesis of new RNA and proteins, subunit interactions and formation of hybrid enzymes, and enzyme complementation during host-parasite interactions. The complementation of specific gene products, fungal elicitors and host receptors, is discussed in terms of molecular mechanisms of plant-parasite recognition. Pathogen molecule suppressors or compatibility factors are suggested to be essential for triggering compatibility phenomena (Bushnell and Rowell, 1981; Metlizki and Ozerezkovskaia, 1984; Ouchi and Oku, 1982; Roby et al, 1985).

The role of proteins and enzymes in these interactions has been extensively discussed and reviewed (Aksenova and Rubin, 1976; Albersheim and Anderson-Prouty, 1975). The high homology of molecular forms of proteins and enzymes in the host plant and in the invading pathogens is considered to be one of the features of compatible relations between the two "partners" (Jurina, 1981; Kartashova and Zolotuhina, 1977; Stahmann et al, 1968).

Edreva (1972) compared the molecular heterogeneity of several enzymes in both components of the couple *N. tabacum-P. hyoscyami*. Noninfected leaves of a number of susceptible *N. tabacum* cultivars and conidia of *P. hyoscyami* isolated from the same host plants were investigated. The isoforms of the following enzymes were electrophoretically separated: peroxidase, NAD-malate dehydrogenase, NAD-glutamate dehydrogenase, glucose-6-phosphate dehydrogenase, esterase, and glutamate oxalacetate transaminase. The polymorphism of these enzymes is commonly used as a tool for resolving populational and taxonomic problems (Burdon and Marshall, 1983). The experimental results show that the molecular patterns of peroxidase, malate dehydrogenase, glucose-6-phosphate dehydrogenase, and esterase vary slightly among susceptible *N. tabacum* cultivars studied and among the isolates of *P. hyoscyami*. Moreover, close similarity is observed between the host tobacco suscepts and *P. hyoscyami* (Table 2). With respect to the molecular patterns of glutamate oxalacetate trans-aminase and glutamate dehydrogenase, a complete identity is observed both among suscepts and among conidial isolates, as well as between the two counterparts. This can be accounted for by the low polymorphism and the evolutionary and developmental stability of these enzymes catalyzing key metabolic reactions.

It is essential to note that the isoenzyme patterns of *P. hyoscyami* conidia originating from France and Bulgaria are very similar (A. Edreva and R. Delon, unpublished).

By contrast, when enzyme polymorphism is studied in a

Table 2. Relative electrophoretic mobility of the peroxidase and glutamate oxalacetate transaminase (GOT) isoenzymes in leaves of *Nicotiana tabacum* 'VSP$_{26}$' and in conidia of *Peronospora hyoscyami* f. sp. *tabacina* and *Phytophthora parasitica* var. *nicotianae*[a]

Source	Peroxidase												GOT	
N. tabacum	0.05	0.06	0.09	0.17	0.25	0.49	0.52	0.57	0.61	0.66	0.68	0.70	0.36	0.46
Peronospora hyoscyami isolated from														
France	0.04	0.06	0.09	0.17	0.25	0.50	0.52	0.57	0.61	0.65			0.38	0.47
Bulgaria		0.06	0.09	0.17	0.25	0.50	0.53	0.58	0.62	0.65	0.68		0.37	0.46
Phytophthora parasitica														
Bulgaria					0.40								0.41	

[a] Reprinted in part, by permission, from Edreva (1972).

facultative parasite, *Phytophthora parasitica* var. *nicotianae* (tobacco isolate), the molecular patterns of the fungus are distinct from those of the host tobacco plant (A. Edreva and I. Kutova, unpublished) (Table 2).

Thus, the host tobacco plant and the obligate parasite *P. hyoscyami* are closely related in terms of enzyme molecular heterogeneity, in contrast to the distinction between host and nonspecific parasites. This reveals part of the mechanism constituting the quasisymbiotic character of the relationships in a plant-obligate parasite system, characterized by the close dependence of the pathogen on the host, and substantiates the hypothesis of Stahmann et al (1968) that obligate pathogens can develop successfully on a plant only if there is sufficient similarity between the enzymes of the partners. The exact structural and functional bases of these interactions are not yet completely understood.

Conclusion

In the field of the biochemistry of blue mold pathogenesis, few mechanisms are well understood, including the unanswered question of whether the hypersensitive response is a cause or consequence of resistance, the hypothetical toxic principle in the necroses, and phytoalexin formation in blue mold-infected leaves. What are the temporal sequence, spatial localization, and structural organization of the events constituting the blue mold disease? At which interface do the critical contacts between plant and parasite take place—cell walls, plasmalemma, or tonoplasts? What molecules are involved in recognition (elicitors, receptors, suppressors), and what is the exact role of glycosidases? What are the bases of pathogen race specificity as the finest expression of molecular evolution? How are resistance and susceptibility responses triggered? What mechanism underlies the induced resistance to and cross protection by *P. hyoscyami*? And, finally, what is the role of magnesium ions in provoking a premature and complete gene expression of blue mold resistance? Can it be explained in terms of the protein biosynthetic apparatus, or more profoundly, at a transcriptional level? Resolving this last problem would help us understand gene expression in tobacco. Joint efforts of biochemists, geneticists, and plant pathologists are necessary to answer these questions, and fascinating progress in molecular biology would be made as a result of these efforts.

LITERATURE CITED

Abeles, F. B. 1986. Plant chemiluminescence. Annu. Rev. Plant Physiol. 37:49–72.

Ahl, P., and Gianinazzi, S. 1982. b-Protein as a constitutive component in highly (TMV) resistant interspecific hybrids of *Nicotiana glutinosa* × *Nicotiana debneyi*. Plant Sci. Lett. 26:173–181.

Aksenova, V. A., and Rubin, B. A. 1976. The role of proteins in plant-parasite interaction. Skh. Biol. (Agric. Biol.) 11:807–815. (In Russian)

Albersheim, P., and Anderson-Prouty, A. 1975. Carbohydrates, proteins, cell surfaces and the biochemistry of pathogenesis. Annu. Rev. Plant Physiol. 26:31–52.

Alger, R. S. 1968. Electron Paramagnetic Resonance. Interscience, London. 580 pp.

Allen, P. J., and Dunkle, L. D. 1971. Natural activators and inhibitors of spore germination. Pages 23–58 in: Morphological and Biochemical Events in Plant-Parasite Interactions. S. Akai and S. Ouchi, eds. Phytopathological Society of Japan, Tokyo. 415 pp.

Altman, A., and Bachrach, U. 1981. Involvement of polyamines in plant growth and senescence. Pages 365–375 in: Advances in Polyamine Research, Vol. 3. C. M. Caldarera, V. Zappia, and U. Bachrach, eds. Raven Press, New York. 512 pp.

Avundjan, E. S., and Shaldjan, M. M. 1974. Growth-stimulatory and inhibitory substances in tobacco leaves susceptible, resistant and immune to blue mold. Fiziol. Rast. (Plant Physiol.) 21:837–843. (In Russian)

Bailov, D., and Edreva, A. 1964. On the relationship between some biochemical characters and blue mold resistance of tobacco. Rastenievud. Nauki (Plant Sci.) 1(9):43–56. (In Bulgarian)

Bailov, D., Istatkov, S., Edreva, A., and Secenska, M. 1962. Untersuchungen über manche biochemische und physiologische vorgänge in den blattern der von *Peronospora tabacina* Adam befallenen Tabakpflanzen. C. R. Acad. Bulg. Sci. 15:427–430.

Bailov, D., Istatkov, S., Edreva, A., and Secenska, M. 1963. On certain biochemical indicators of tobacco elucidating the nature of its resistance to *Peronospora tabacina* Adam. Pages 85–95 in: Proc. World Tob. Sci. Congr., 3rd, Salisbury, Rhodesia. Tobacco Research Board of Rhodesia and Nyasaland, Salisbury. 644 pp.

Bailov, D., Edreva, A., Palakarcheva, M., and Nicolov, S. 1967. A biochemical study of amphidiploids *N. tabacum* × *N. debneyi* (2n = 96). Rastenievud. Nauki (Plant Sci.) 4(12):3–15. (In Bulgarian)

Bateman, D. F., and Basham, H. G. 1976. Degradation of plant cell walls and membranes by microbial enzymes. Pages 316–355 in: Encyclopedia of Plant Physiology, Vol. 4. R. H. Heitefuss and P. H. Williams, eds. Springer-Verlag, Berlin. 890 pp.

Beckman, C. H., Mueller, W. C., and Mace, M. E. 1974. The stabilization of artificial and natural cell wall membranes by phenolic infusion and its relation to wilt disease resistance. Phytopathology 64:1214–1220.

Berbec, I., Oczosiowa, A., and Drzas, E. 1966. Differences in the occurrence

131

of free amino acids in the species and varieties as well as hybrids of tobacco resistant and susceptible to *Peronospora tabacina*. Rocz. Nauk Roln. (Ann. Agric. Sci.) 92:53–62. (In Polish)

Boceski, D. 1963. Catalase activity and ability of Oriental type of tobacco to absorb O_2 from the air when infected with *Peronospora tabacina* A. Pages 119–122 in: Proc. World Tob. Sci. Congr., 3rd, Salisbury, Rhodesia. Tobacco Research Board of Rhodesia and Nyasaland, Salisbury. 644 pp.

Burdon, J. J., and Marshall, D. R. 1983. The use of isoenzymes in plant disease research. Pages 401–412 in: Isozymes in Plant Genetics and Breeding, Part A. S. D. Tanksley and T. Y. Orton, eds. Elsevier Science Publishers, Amsterdam. 516 pp.

Bushnell, W. R., and Rowell, J. B. 1981. Suppressors of defense reactions: A model for roles in specificity. Phytopathology 71:1012–1014.

Cabanne, F., Martin-Tanguy, J., and Martin, C. 1977. Phenolamines associées à l'induction florale et à l'état reproducteur du *Nicotiana tabacum* var. *Xanthi* n.c. Physiol. Veg. 15:429–443.

Chakravorty, A. K., and Shaw, M. 1977a. The role of RNA in host-parasite specificity. Annu. Rev. Phytopathol. 15:135–151.

Chakravorty, A. K., and Shaw, M. 1977b. A possible molecular basis for obligate host-pathogen interactions. Biol. Rev. 52:147–179.

Clarke, D. D. 1973. The accumulation of scopolin in potato tissue in response to infection. Physiol. Plant Pathol. 3:347–358.

Cline, K., and Albersheim, P. 1981. Host-pathogen interactions. XVII. Hydrolysis of biologically active fungal glucans by enzymes isolated from soybean cells. Plant Physiol. 68:221–228.

Cohen, Y. 1976. Enzyme activity in downy mildew-infected tobacco plants and its probable role in scopoletin accumulation. (Abstr.) Phytoparasitica 4:67.

Cohen, Y., Grossman, S., and Lupu, R. 1981. Elevation in endogenous antioxidant level: A possible mechanism governing the induced resistance of tobacco infected with *Peronospora tabacina* against *Erysiphe cichoracearum*. Phytoparasitica 9:247–248.

Coussirat, J. C. 1983–1984. Induction par *Peronospora tabacina* A. de protéines solubles (b) chez les Nicotianae traités ou non avec certaines fongicides et avec l'acide polyacrylique. Ann. Tab. SEITA (Sect. 2) 18:107–122.

Cruickshank, I. A. M., and Rider, N. E. 1961. *Peronospora tabacina* in tobacco: Transpiration, growth, and related energy considerations. Aust. J. Biol. Sci. 14:45–57.

Cruickshank, I. A. M., Perrin, D., and Mandryk, M. 1977. Fungitoxicity of duvatrienediols associated with the cuticular wax of tobacco leaves. Phytopathol. Z. 90:243–249.

Daly, J. M. 1984. The role of recognition in plant disease. Annu. Rev. Phytopathol. 22:273–307.

Davenport, R., and Davenport, J. C. 1965. Cytoplasmic basic proteins in the oocytes of three species of molluscs. (Abstr.) Exp. Cell Res. 39:74–80.

Edreva, A. 1966. Investigation on the chlorogenic acid content in tobacco as connected to *Peronospora tabacina* A. Pages 713–716 in: Proc. Int. Tob. Sci. Congr., 4th, Athens. National Tobacco Board of Greece, Athens.

1,114 pp.

Edreva, A. 1968. An investigation into the metabolism of *Peronospora tabacina* Adam. C. R. Acad. Sci. Agric. Bulg. 1(1):49–52.

Edreva, A. 1972. A study of the isoenzyme composition of peroxidase and malate dehydrogenase in *Peronospora tabacina* Adam and its host *Nicotiana tabacum* L. C. R. Acad. Sci. Agric. Bulg. 5(2):121–125.

Edreva, A. 1974a. A biochemical study of tobacco blue mould pathogenesis. I. The activity of certain oxidative enzymes and chloroplast pigment content. C. R. Acad. Sci. Agric. Bulg. 7(2):73–76.

Edreva, A. 1974b. Biochemical study of tobacco blue mould pathogenesis. II. Changes in the pattern of phenolic compounds. C. R. Acad. Sci. Agric. Bulg. 7(3):17–21.

Edreva, A. 1974c. Biochemical study of tobacco blue mould pathogenesis. III. Mechanism of necrosis formation. C. R. Acad. Sci. Agric. Bulg. 7(4):55–58.

Edreva, A. 1975a. A biochemical study of tobacco blue mould pathogenesis. IV. Isoenzyme pattern of the peroxidase. C. R. Acad. Sci. Agric. Bulg. 8(1):23–26.

Edreva, A. 1975b. A biochemical study of tobacco blue mould pathogenesis. V. Isoenzyme pattern of the malate dehydrogenase and glutamate dehydrogenase. C. R. Acad. Sci. Agric. Bulg. 8(2):5–10.

Edreva, A. 1975c. A biochemical study of tobacco blue mould pathogenesis. VI. On some resistance factors. C. R. Acad. Sci. Agric. Bulg. 8(3):55–58.

Edreva, A. 1977. Comparative biochemical studies of an infectious disease (blue mould) and a physiological disorder of tobacco. Physiol. Plant Pathol. 11:149–161.

Edreva, A. 1984. The β-xylosidase reaction—A possible test for blue mould diagnosis. Pages 115–116 in: Bull. Inf. CORESTA. Int. Tob. Sci. Congr., 8th, 7–12 Oct., Vienna. 160 pp.

Edreva, A. 1988. b-Protein: Factors in pathogenesis or markers of stress in plants? Section 5.2.13 in: Natl. Congr. Biochem. Biophys., 4th, 3–9 May, Varna, Bulgaria. Biochemical and Biophysical Society Press, Sofia, Bulgaria. (In Bulgarian)

Edreva, A., and Apostolova, E. 1988. Manganese toxicity in tobacco: A biochemical investigation. Agrochimica 32:(In press)

Edreva, A. M., and Georgieva, J. D. 1977. Biochemical and cytochemical study of the acid phosphatase during infectious disease, physiological disorder and senescence of tobacco leaves. C. R. Acad. Bulg. Sci. 30:1193–1196.

Edreva, A., and Georgieva, J. D. 1980. Biochemical and cytochemical investigations of α- and β-glucosidase activity in an infectious disease, a physiological disorder and senescence of tobacco leaves. Physiol. Plant Pathol. 17:237–243.

Edreva, A., and Georgieva, J. D. 1984. Investigation on the chlorogenic acid and its quinone in different damage phenomena of tobacco leaves. C. R. J. Int. Etude Polyphenols 12:222-228.

Edreva, A. M., and Hadjiska, E. J. 1985. Study of the aliphatic di- and polyamines in different stress phenomena of tobacco leaves. Section VI.3.1 in: Natl. Congr. Biochem. Biophys., 3rd, 19–25 May, Varna,

Bulgaria. Bulgarian Biochemical and Biophysical Society Press, Sofia, Bulgaria. (In Bulgarian)

Edreva, A., Bailov, D., and Nikolov, S. 1970. Contribution to the biochemical characteristics of certain wild species of *Nicotiana* with a view to their use in interspecific hybridization. C. R. Acad. Sci. Agric. Bulg. 3(1):55–62.

Edreva, A. M., Georgieva, J. D., and Vitkova, A. A. 1979. Biochemical and cytochemical study of esterase in infectious disease, physiological disorder and senescence of tobacco. C. R. Acad. Bulg. Sci. 32:1113–1116.

Edreva, A. M., Cholakova, N. J., and Georgieva, J. D. 1980a. Biochemical and cytochemical study of some enzymes in *Erysiphe cichoracearum* DC. and *Peronospora tabacina* A., obligatory tobacco parasites. C. R. Acad. Bulg. Sci. 33:1137–1140.

Edreva, A., Georgieva, J. D., and Cholakova, N. J. 1980b. Biochemical and cytochemical study of some glycosidases in infectious and physiological disease and in senescence of tobacco. Page 124 in: Natl. Congr. Biochem. Biophys., 2nd, 18–23 May, Varna, Bulgaria. Bulgarian Biochemical and Biophysical Society Press, Sofia, Bulgaria. 251 pp. (In Bulgarian)

Edreva, A., Mollé, E., Schiltz, P., and Coussirat, J. C. 1983–1984a. Etude biochimique du tabac éprouvé dans les conditions du "test cotylédons": Effet du magnésium, réactions des plantes résistantes et sensibles à *Peronospora tabacina*. I. Teneur en protéines solubles chez des *N. tabacum* non contaminés. Ann. Tab. SEITA (Sect. 2) 18:161–164.

Edreva, A., Mollé, E., Schiltz, P., and Delon, R. 1983–1984b. Etude biochimique du tabac éprouvé dans les conditions du "test cotylédons": Effet du magnésium, réactions des plantes résistantes et sensibles à *Peronospora tabacina*. II. Activité péroxydasique chez des *N. tabacum* non contaminés. Ann. Tab. SEITA (Sect. 2) 18:165–169.

Edreva, A., Georgieva, J., Coussirat, J. C., and Delon, R. 1986. Etude biochimique du tabac éprouvé dans les conditions du "test cotylédons": Effet du magnésium, réactions des plantes résistantes et sensibles à *Peronospora tabacina*. IV. Etude biochimique et cytochimique de la β-glucosidase. Ann. Tab. SEITA (Sect. 2) 20:69–79.

Edreva, A., Georgieva, J. D., and Coussirat, J. C. 1987. Etude biochimique du tabac éprouvé dans les conditions du "test cotylédons": Effet du magnésium, réactions des plantes résistantes et sensibles à *Peronospora tabacina*. V. Etude biochimique et cytochimique de la péroxydase. Ann. Tab. SEITA (Sect. 2) 21:39–50.

Edreva, A., Georgieva, J., and Cholakova, N. 1989. Pathogenic and nonpathogenic stress effects on peroxidases in leaves of tobacco. Environ. Exp. Bot. 29: (In press)

Farkas, G., and Kiraly, Z. 1962. Role of phenolic compounds in the physiology of plant diseases and disease resistance. Phytopathol. Z. 44:105–150.

Farkas, G., Kiraly, Z., and Solymosy, F. 1960. Role of oxidative metabolism in the localization of plant viruses. Virology 12:408–421.

Fraser, R. S. S. 1981. Evidence for the occurrence of the "pathogenesis-related" proteins in leaves of healthy tobacco plants during flowering. Physiol. Plant Pathol. 19:69–76.

Friend, J. 1979. Phenolic substances and plant disease. Pages 557–588 in: Recent Advances in Phytochemistry, Vol. 12. T. Swain, J. B. Harborne, and C. F. Van Sumere, eds. Plenum Press, New York. 651 pp.

Friend, J. 1981. Plant phenolics, lignification and plant disease. Pages 197–265 in: Progress in Phytochemistry, Vol. 7. L. Reinhold, J. B. Harborne, and T. Swain, eds. Pergamon Press, Oxford. 344 pp.

Gaspar, T., Penel, C., Thorpe, T., and Greppin, H. 1982. Peroxidases 1970–1980. A Survey of Their Biochemical and Physiological Roles in Higher Plants. Université de Genève, Centre de Botanique, Geneva. 324 pp.

Georgieva, J., and Edreva, A. 1974. Cytological and cytochemical changes in the blue-mould infected tobacco leaves. C. R. Acad. Sci. Agric. Bulg. 7(1):25–30.

Gianinazzi, S., Martin, C., and Vallée, J. C. 1970. Hypersensibilité aux virus, temperature et protéines solubles chez Nicotiana xanthi n.c. Apparition de nouvelles macromolecules lors de la repression de la synthèse virale. C. R. Hebd. Seances Acad. Sci. Ser. D 270:2383–2387.

Glazener, J. A. 1982. Accumulation of phenolic compounds in cells and formation of lignin-like polymers in cell walls of young tomato fruits after inoculation. Physiol. Plant Pathol. 20:11–25.

Grechushnikov, A. J. 1939. Importance of the peroxidase in the resistance of potato to Phytophthora infestans de Bary. Dokl. Acad. Nauk SSSR (Proc. Acad. Sci. USSR) 25:685–689. (In Russian)

Hare, R. 1966. Physiology of resistance to fungal diseases in plants. Bot. Rev. 32:95–137.

Heath, M. C. 1976. Hypersensitivity, the cause or the consequence of rust resistance? Phytopathology 66:935–936.

Herr, L. J. 1975. Histopathology and histochemistry of sugar beet seedlings resistant and susceptible to Aphanomyces cochlioides. Can. J. Bot. 53:284–294.

Hill, A. V. 1969a. Factors affecting viability of spore inoculum in Peronospora tabacina A. and lesion production in tobacco plants. I. The inoculum. Aust. J. Biol. Sci. 22:393–398.

Hill, A. V. 1969b. Factors affecting viability of spore inoculum in Peronospora tabacina A. and lesion production in tobacco plants. II. Lesion production. Aust. J. Biol. Sci. 22:399–411.

Hollomon, D. W. 1969. Biochemistry of germination in Peronospora tabacina Adam conidia: Evidence for the existence of stable messenger RNA. J. Gen. Microbiol. 55:267–274.

Hollomon, D. W. 1970. Ribonucleic acid synthesis during spore germination. J. Gen. Microbiol. 62:75–87.

Hollomon, D. W. 1971. Protein synthesis during germination of Peronospora tabacina A. conidia. Arch. Biochem. Biophys. 145:643–649.

Hollomon, D. W. 1973. Protein synthesis during germination of Peronospora tabacina A. conidia: An examination of the events involved in the initiation of germination. J. Gen. Microbiol. 78:1–13.

Iskender, G. 1975. Determination of alkaloids in Turkish tobacco resistant to mildew. Istanbul Univ. Eczacilik Fak. Mecm. (J. Fac. Pharm. Istanbul Univ.) 11:27–37. (In Turkish)

Izard, C. 1961. Sur l'inhibition de croissance provoquée par les extraits de conidies de *Peronospora tabacina* A. C. R. Hebd. Seances Acad. Sci. Ser. D 253:2756–2759.

Izard, C., and Gradouteaud, J. 1962. Sur les propriétés inhibitrices de croissance et toxiniques des extraits de conidies de *Peronospora tabacina*. C. R. Hebd. Seances Acad. Sci. Ser. D 255:1773–1774.

Izard, C., Schiltz, P., and Hitier, H. 1961. Note sur la résistance à *Peronospora tabacina* A. Bull. Inf. CORESTA 1961(3):18–21.

Jamet, E., Kopp, M., and Fritig, B. 1985. The pathogenesis-related proteins of tobacco; their labelling from (^{14}C) amino acids in leaves reacting hypersensitively to infection by tobacco mosaic virus. Physiol. Plant Pathol. 27:29–41.

Jones, D. H. 1984. Phenylalanine ammonia-lyase: Regulation of its induction and its role in plant development. Phytochemistry 23:1349–1359.

Jurina, E. V. 1981. Molecular heterogeneity of the oxidative enzymes in rust uredospores. Skh. Biol. (Agric. Biol.) 16:760–763. (In Russian)

Kartashova, E. R., and Zolotuhina, E. U. 1977. Formation of hybrids of malate dehydrogenase of host plant and parasite in vitro. Skh. Biol. (Agric. Biol.) 12:439–443. (In Russian)

Kato, S., and Misawa, T. 1975. Hypersensitive reaction of cowpea leaves to cucumber mosaic virus. Tohoku J. Agric. Res. 26:49–60.

Keen, N. T. 1982. Mechanisms conferring specific recognition in gene-for-gene plant-parasite systems. Pages 67–84 in: Active Defence Mechanisms in Plants. R. K. S. Wood, ed. Plenum Press, London. 391 pp.

Kiraly, Z., Barna, B., and Ersek, T. 1972. Hypersensitivity as a consequence, not the cause, of plant resistance to infection. Nature (London) 239:456–457.

Koelle, G. 1970. The importance of nicotine in research on tobacco. Dtsch. Tabakbau 5:34–35.

Kosuge, T. 1969. The role of phenolics in host response to infection. Annu. Rev. Phytopathol. 7:195–223.

Kröber, H. 1970. Host-parasite relationship in leaves of tobacco plants susceptible and resistant to blue mold. Bull. Inf. CORESTA 1970(3-4):46.

Kröber, H., and Petzold, H. 1972. Licht- und elektronen-mikroskopische untersuchungen über wirt-parasit-beziehungen bei anfälligen und gegen *Peronospora* spp. resisten gezüchteten sorten von Tabac und Spinat. Phytopathol. Z. 74:296–313.

Legrand, M. 1983. Phenylpropanoid metabolism and its regulation in disease. Pages 367–383 in: Biochemical Plant Pathology. A. Callow, ed. John Wiley & Sons, New York. 484 pp.

Leppik, R. A., Hollomon, D. W., and Bottomley, W. 1972. Quiesone: An inhibitor of *Peronospora tabacina* conidia. Phytochemistry 11:2055–2063.

Libbert, E. 1974. Lehrbuch der Pflanzenphysiologie. Gustav Fischer Verlag, Jena, German Democratic Republic. 471 pp.

Lucas, G. B. 1980. The war against blue mold. Science 210:147–153.

Mandryk, M. 1971. Resistance of solanaceous and non-solanaceous species to *Peronospora tabacina* as shown by necrotrophic reactions. Aust. J. Exp. Agric. Anim. Husb. 11:94–98.

Martin, C., and Martin-Tanguy, J. 1981. Polyamines conjuguées et limitation de l'expansion virale chez les végétaux. C. R. Hebd. Seances Acad. Sci. Paris Ser. III 293:249–251.

Masiak, D. 1983. The role of proteins in tobacco plants resistant to *Peronospora tabacina* race Pt-2. Biul. Cent. Lab. Przem. Tyton. (Bull. Cent. Lab. Tob. Ind.) 1-4:39–46. (In Polish)

Mayr, H. H., Diskus, A., and Beck, W. 1963. Scopoletinanreicherung in den durch *Peronospora tabacina* befallenen Geweben von *Nicotiana tabacum* L. Phytopathol. Z. 47:95–97.

Mead, J. F. 1976. Mechanisms of free radical damage of lipids and its importance for cell membranes. Pages 50–68 in: Free Radicals in Biology, Vol. 1. W. A. Pryor, ed. Academic Press, New York. 303 pp.

Metlizki, L. V. 1968. On the defensive role of the system polyphenols-polyphenoloxidase in phytoimmunity. Pages 290–296 in: Phenol i ih Biologiceskie Funkcii (Phenolics and Their Biological Functions). A. L. Kursanov and M. N. Zaprometov, eds. Nauka, Moscow. 408 pp. (In Russian)

Metlizki, L. V., and Ozerezkovskaia, O. L. 1984. Cell wall substances in *Phytophthora infestans*—Inductors and suppressors of the defense reactions in potato. Dokl. Akad. Nauk SSSR (Proc. Acad. Sci. USSR) 274:1020–1024. (In Russian)

Metlizki, L. V., Saveleva, O. N., Ozerezkovskaia, O. L., Balnauri, V. D., Stom, D. J., and Timofeeva, S. S. 1972. Fungitoxicity of the products of enzyme oxidation of chlorogenic and caffeic acids. Pages 58–72 in: Imunitet i Pokoi Rastenii (Immunity and Dormancy in Plants). L. V. Metlizki, ed. Nauka, Moscow. 266 pp. (In Russian)

Michalov, J., and Komar, J. 1984. The influence of *Ustilago maydis* upon free radicals concentration in the reproduction organs of maize. Phytopathol. Z. 109:204–207.

Mollé, E., Edreva, A., Batschev, S., and Schiltz, P. 1983–1984. Etude biochimique du tabac éprouvé dans les conditions du "test cotylédons": Effet du magnésium, réactions des plantes résistantes et sensibles à *Peronospora tabacina*. III. Chimioluminescence induite chez des *N. tabacum* contaminés ou non par le mildiou. Ann. Tab. SEITA (Sect. 2) 18:171–175.

Netzer, D., and Kritzman, G. 1979. β-(1,3) Glucanase activity and quantity of fungus in relation to Fusarium wilt in resistant and susceptible near-isogenic lines of muskmelon. Physiol. Plant Pathol. 14:47–55.

Nichols, J. E., Beckman, J. M., and Hadwiger, L. A. 1980. Glycosidic enzyme activity in pea-*Fusarium solani* interactions. Plant Physiol. 66:199–204.

Oczos, A. 1969. Influence of mineral nutrition (NPK) on the chemical composition of leaves and the degree of susceptibility of two tobacco varieties (resistant and susceptible) to *Peronospora tabacina* A. Pamiet. Pulawski (Warsaw Inst. Plant Soil Fert. Sci. Pulavski) 36:251–280. (In Polish)

Oczos, A. 1971. Investigations on the importance of nitrogen metabolism in the resistance of tobacco to *Peronospora tabacina* A. Pamiet. Pulawski (Warsaw Inst. Plant Soil Fert. Sci. Pulavski) 43:99–125. (In Polish)

Oczos, A. 1973. Respiration and oxidation-reduction potential of tobacco varieties resistant and susceptible to *Peronospora tabacina*. Pamiet. Pulawski (Warsaw Inst. Plant Soil Fert. Sci. Pulavski) 56:115–132.

Ohashi, Y., and Matsuoka, M. 1985. Synthesis of stress protein in tobacco leaves. Plant Cell Physiol. 26:473–480.

Oku, H. 1964. Host-parasite relation in Helminthosporium leaf spot disease of rice plant from the viewpoint of biochemical nature of the pathogen. Pages 183–192 in: Host-Parasite Relations in Plant Pathology. Z. Kiraly and G. Ubrizsy, eds. Symposium held at the Hungarian Academy of Science, 19–22 Oct., Budapest. Research Institute for Plant Protection, Budapest. 257 pp.

Ouchi, S., and Oku, H. 1982. Physiological basis of susceptibility induced by pathogens. Pages 117–136 in: Plant Infection: The Physiological and Biochemical Basis. Y. Asada, W. R. Bushnell, S. Ouchi, and C. P. Vance, eds. Japan Scientific Society Press, Tokyo; Springer-Verlag, Berlin. 392 pp.

Palakarcheva, M., Edreva, A., Cholakova, N., and Noveva, S. 1978. Morphological, cytological and biochemical studies of the amphidiploid *Nicotiana goodspeedii* W. × *Nicotiana tabacum* L. Z. Pflanzenzuecht. 80:49–63.

Pashenko, I. N. 1975. Activity of the oxidative enzymes, a character related to blue mold resistance of tobacco. Mikol. Fitopatol. (Mycol. Phytopathol.) 9:66–68. (In Russian)

Pashenko, I. N. 1978. The role of phenolics in the blue mold resistance of tobacco. Mikol. Fitopatol. (Mycol. Phytopathol.) 12:343–346. (In Russian)

Pashenko, I. N. 1982. Nitrogen metabolism in tobacco varieties and hybrids differing in blue mold resistance. Tabak (Moscow) (Tobacco) 3:40–41. (In Russian)

Pierpoint, W. S. 1966. The enzymic oxidation of chlorogenic acid and some reactions of the quinone produced. Biochem. J. 98:567–581.

Pierpoint, W. S. 1969a. *o*-Quinones formed in plant extracts. Their reactions with amino acids and peptides. Biochem. J. 112:609–617.

Pierpoint, W. S. 1969b. *o*-Quinones formed in plant extracts. Their reaction with bovine serum albumin. Biochem. J. 112:619–630.

Reuveni, R., and Bothma, G. C. 1985. The relationship between peroxidase activity and resistance to *Sphaerotheca fuliginea* in melons. Phytopathol. Z. 114:260–267.

Roberts, D. R., Walker, M. A., Thompson, J. E., and Dumbroff, E. B. 1984. The effects of inhibitors of polyamine and ethylene biosynthesis on senescence, ethylene production and polyamine level in cut carnation flowers. Plant Cell Physiol. 25:315–322.

Roby, D., Toppan, A., and Esquerré-Tugayé, M. T. 1985. Cell surfaces in plant-microorganism interaction. V. Elicitors of fungal and of plant origin trigger the synthesis of ethylene and of cell wall hydroxyproline-rich glycoprotein in plants. Plant Physiol. 77:700–704.

Rubin, B. A., Arzichovskaia, E. V., and Aksenova, V. A. 1975. Biochimia i Fiziologia Immuniteta Rastenii. (Biochemistry and Physiology of Plant Immunity.) Vishaia shkola, Moscow. 320 pp. (In Russian)

Ruzicka, P., Gombos, Z., and Farkas, G. 1983. Modification of the fatty acid composition of phospholipids during the hypersensitive reaction in tobacco. Virology 128:60–64.

Salt, S. D., and Kuć, J. 1984. Effects of ionone-type compounds on growth of tobacco and resistance to blue mold. (Abstr.) Phytopathology 74:873.

Sandblom, J. 1980. Electrical properties of ionic channels. Ingenjoersvetenskapsakad. Medd. 182:155–156.

Savin, V. N., Alekseeva, D. J., and Nicolaenko, V. F. 1981. Investigation on the rust resistance of wheat by the chemiluminescence method. Dokl. Vses. Akad. Skh. N. I. Lenin (C. R. Acad. Agric. Lenin, USSR) 1:13–14. (In Russian)

Schiltz, P. 1967. Création de N. tabacum résistants à Peronospora tabacina. Analyse histologique et biologique de la résistance. Ann. Tab. SEITA (Sect. 2) 4:5–147.

Schiltz, P. 1974. Action inhibitrice de la β-ionone au cours du développement de Peronospora tabacina A. Ann. Tab. SEITA (Sect. 2) 11:207–217.

Schiltz, P., and Coussirat, J. C. 1969. Mise en évidence de la résistance des Nicotianae aux lignées virulentes de Peronospora tabacina et détermination du pouvoir pathogène du parasite. Ann. Tab. SEITA (Sect. 2) 6:145–162.

Schiltz, P., and Coussirat, J. C. 1978. Influence exercée par le magnésium sur les manifestations héréditaires de la plante de tabac. Annee Biol. 17:169–174.

Schiltz, P., Coussirat, J. C., and Abedi, H. 1970. Action de la lumière et de la kinétine sur les manifestations de résistance à Peronospora tabacina A. Ann. Tab. SEITA (Sect. 2) 7:181–191.

Shaldjan, M. M., and Avundjan, E. S. 1974. A comparative study of the amino acid composition in tobacco leaves, susceptible, resistant and immune to blue mold. Biol. J. Arm. (Arm. Biol. J.) 8:34–40. (In Russian)

Sheen, S. J. 1970. Comparative quantities of polyphenols and oxidases in Nicotiana species. Tob. Sci. 14:16–20.

Shepherd, C. J. 1962. Germination of conidia of Peronospora tabacina Adam. I. Germination in vitro. Aust. J. Biol. Sci. 15:483–508.

Shepherd, C. J., and Mandryk, M. 1961. Autoinhibitors of Peronospora tabacina Adam and their relation to disease resistance. Aust. Tob. Res. Conf., Canberra. Aust. Agric. Counc., Melbourne 9:1–6.

Shepherd, C. J., and Mandryk, M. 1962. Autoinhibitors of germination and sporulation in Peronospora tabacina Adam. Trans. Br. Mycol. Soc. 45:233–244.

Shepherd, C. J., and Mandryk, M. 1963. Germination of conidia of Peronospora tabacina Adam. II. Germination in vivo. Aust. J. Biol. Sci. 16:77–87.

Shepherd, C. J., and Mandryk, M. 1964. Effect of metabolites and antimetabolites on the sporulation of Peronospora tabacina Adam on tobacco leaf disks. Aust. J. Biol. Sci. 17:878–891.

Shepherd, C. J., and Mandryk, M. 1967. A necrotrophic reaction in Nicotiana species induced by Peronospora tabacina A. Aust. J. Biol. Sci. 20:1161–1168.

Shepherd, C. J., and Muller, A. 1967. Metabolites in blue mould spores. Aust. CSIRO Div. Plant Ind. Annu. Rep. 115:6.

Shepherd, C. J., and Tosic, L. 1966. The role of riboflavin and inhibitors in conidial germination in *Peronospora tabacina* Adam. Aust. J. Biol. Sci. 19:335–337.

Smith, A. 1985. Polyamines. Annu. Rev. Plant Physiol. 36:117–143.

Smith, W. D., Whitty, E. B., and Kucharek, T. A. 1979. Blue mold incidence in tobacco as affected by nitrogen fertilization. Soil Crop Sci. Soc. Fla. Proc. 39:2–4.

Stahmann, M. A. 1983. Biochemistry of oxidase enzymes as related to the etiology of and resistance to plant diseases, the hemorrhagic sweet clover disease, farmer's lung disease, or food or feed production. Pages 237–250 in: The New Frontiers in Plant Biochemistry. T. Akazawa, T. Asahi, and H. Imaseki, eds. Martinus Nijhoff and Dr. W. Junk Publishers, The Hague; Japan Scientific Society Press, Tokyo. 257 pp.

Stahmann, M. A., Woodbury, W., Lovrekovich, L., and Macko, V. 1968. The role of enzymes in the regulation of disease resistance and host-pathogen specificity. Pages 263–274 in: Biochemical Regulation in Diseased Plants or Injury. T. Hirai, ed. Phytopathological Society of Japan, Tokyo. 351 pp.

Ternovskii, M. F., and Dashkeeva, K. N. 1963. Reaction of different *Nicotiana* species to blue mold infection. Dokl. Akad. Nauk SSSR (Proc. Acad. Sci. USSR) 150:931–934. (In Russian)

Tobin, E. M., and Silverthorne, J. 1985. Light regulation of gene expression in higher plants. Annu. Rev. Plant Physiol. 36:569–593.

Tomiyama, K. 1983. Research on the hypersensitive response. Annu. Rev. Phytopathol. 21:1–12.

Trigiano, R. N., Van Dyke, C. G., and Spurr, H. W., Jr. 1983. Haustorial development of *Peronospora tabacina* infecting *Nicotiana tabacum*. Can. J. Bot. 61:3444–3453.

Uozumi, T., and Kröber, H. 1967. Der Einfluss des Lichtes auf die Konidienbildung von *Peronospora tabacina* Adam an Tabakblättern. Phytopathol. Z. 59:372–384.

Uritani, I. 1982. Biochemical approaches to general principles in plants underlying plant disease phenomena. Pages 345–358 in: Plant Infection: The Physiological and Biochemical Basis. Y. Asada, W. R. Bushnell, S. Ouchi, and C. P. Vance, eds. Japan Scientific Society Press, Tokyo; Springer-Verlag, Berlin. 392 pp.

Van Loon, L. C. 1985. Pathogenesis-related proteins. Plant Mol. Biol. 4:111–116.

Van Loon, L. C., and Van Kammen, A. 1970. Polyacrylamide disc electrophoresis of the soluble leaf proteins from *N. tabacum* var. "Samsun NN." II. Changes in protein constitution after infection with TMV. Virology 40:199–211.

Wilson, C. L. 1973. A lysosomal concept for plant pathology. Annu. Rev. Phytopathol. 11:247–272.

Wittmer, G. 1968. Correlations of characteristics in tobacco: Resistance to *Peronospora tabacina* A. and alkaloid content. Atti Assoc. Genet. Ital. 13:272–282. (In Italian)

Chapter 5

Genetics of Host Resistance to Tobacco Blue Mold

R. C. Rufty
Department of Crop Science
North Carolina State University
Raleigh, North Carolina 27695-7620

Tobacco blue mold, also known as downy mildew of tobacco, is caused by the fungus *Peronospora hyoscyami* de Bary (syn. *P. tabacina* Adam). The disease was first reported in the Queensland region of Australia in 1890 (Hill, 1966a; Wuttke, 1972). By 1900, blue mold had spread thousands of miles to other regions of Australia, becoming a destructive disease wherever tobacco was grown.

In the United States, blue mold was first recorded on cultivated tobacco in 1921 in Florida and Georgia, but the disease apparently did not become established at that time (Hill, 1966b). Blue mold reappeared in the same region in 1931 and spread north into North Carolina, Virginia, and Maryland. In subsequent years, blue mold spread farther into the burley tobacco-producing areas of Kentucky and Tennessee and reached Canada by 1938 (Stover and Koch, 1951).

In Europe, *P. hyoscyami* occurred for the first time in England in 1958, and severe losses were reported from eastern and southern European countries in 1960 (Schiltz, 1981; Wuttke, 1972). By 1961–1962, blue mold had reached the Middle East and North Africa (Marani et al, 1972; Wuttke, 1972).

Blue mold appeared on tobacco in Brazil in 1938 and in Argentina the following year, but the disease does not appear to have persisted in South America or to be of economic importance there (Hill, 1966b). In contrast, blue mold has been a serious tobacco disease in Central America and Caribbean countries in recent years (Robinson, 1983; Todd, 1983).

Although blue mold generally occurs sporadically (Gayed, 1980, 1985; Hill, 1966b), economic losses can be severe when the disease reaches epidemic proportions. Before the development of dithio-carbamate fungicides, losses of up to 80% of a given tobacco crop were common in Australia (Wark, 1970). Losses from the 1979 epidemic in the United States and Canada amounted to over $250 million despite the availability by then of dithiocarbamate fungicides (Lucas, 1980; McKeen, 1981; Nesmith, 1983).

Controlling blue mold with contact fungicides is difficult. The disease is currently controlled very effectively by the systemic fungicide metalaxyl (Ridomil). However, strains of *P. hyoscyami* resistant to this compound have been reported in Mexico and the Caribbean (Todd, 1983). Because of cost and other limitations inherent in chemical control of blue mold, several breeding programs have been initiated worldwide with the aim of developing blue mold-resistant tobacco cultivars. This chapter reviews research conducted over the last 50 years concerning certain aspects of blue mold resistance.

Races of *P. hyoscyami*

Chapter 1 examines strains of *P. hyoscyami* in detail. Neverthe-less, a word is necessary here with regard to variability in the *P. hyoscyami* population since this has a direct impact on the durability of host resistance.

The blue mold fungus has great potential for variability because of the presence of sexual reproduction, which provides ample opportunity for recombination. In addition, sporangiospores contain eight to 24 nuclei (Schiltz, 1981), which may provide a high degree of phenotypic plasticity. In this context, a race is defined on the basis of host reaction. However, a variant in the fungal population can attack previously resistant host genotypes and cause inconsistency in results.

Three races or pathotypes of *P. hyoscyami*—APT1, APT2, and APT3—have been recognized in Australia (Hill, 1963, 1966a; Wark, 1970; Wark et al, 1976). Australian *P. hyoscyami* 1, or APT1, is the wild strain common to all tobacco-growing areas in Australia. Resistance to APT1 is expressed in seedlings and in mature plants and was derived from *Nicotiana goodspeedii*. The Australian cultivars Sirone and Sirogo possess resistance to APT1 (Wark, 1970; Wark et al, 1976).

A second strain, APT2, which caused considerable damage to tobacco cultivars resistant to the common strain APT1, was described in 1966 (Hill, 1966a). Strain APT2 is reported to have a slower growth rate in the host and to produce fewer spores than APT1 (Wark et al, 1976). All lines are reported to be susceptible to APT2 in the seedling stage, but a few lines have been developed with

142

field resistance to both APT1 and APT2: Beerwah H and Beerwah GG, with resistance derived from *N. debneyi;* GA 955, with resistance derived from *N. excelsior;* and KA 596, with resistance derived from *N. velutina* (Gillham et al, 1977; Wark et al, 1976). Resistance to APT2 is thought to be polygenic (Gillham et al, 1977; Wark, 1963).

A third strain of the pathogen, APT3, was detected on the resistant Australian species *N. velutina* (Hill, 1966a, 1966b; Wuttke, 1972). Strain APT3 also produces fewer spores than APT1 and does not appear to be a problem on commercial tobacco (Wuttke, 1972).

Highly virulent strains of *P. hyoscyami* have also been observed in Europe in seedbeds planted to a resistant cultivar, but these strains have not been given a specific race identification (Mihajlova et al, 1977; Nadazdin, 1976; Schiltz, 1979, 1981; Schiltz et al, 1977). No evidence of host-specific strains has been reported in the United States, Mexico, Central America, or the Caribbean.

Because of the tremendous reproductive capacity and consequent potential for variability in *P. hyoscyami,* plant breeders should strive to produce cultivars possessing horizontal resistance. Horizontal resistance may not provide a very high level of protection against the disease but is more likely to be long-lasting. Immune reactions, or resistance controlled by single genes (vertical resistance), offer a high degree of disease control but can be easily overcome by the pathogen. It may be possible, however, to provide durable resistance using single genes, if genes of diverse origin are combined in a given cultivar (gene pyramiding).

Sources of Resistance

Nicotiana germ plasm was first evaluated for resistance to tobacco blue mold in Australia in 1932. Angell and Hill (1932) reported that seedlings of 16 species of *Nicotiana* native to the American continent were all susceptible to *P. hyoscyami.* Smith-White et al (1936) tested a more extensive series of plants, including over 250 genotypes of *N. tabacum,* 35 strains of *N. rustica* of worldwide origin, several accessions of American *Nicotiana* species of diverse geographical origin, and numerous accessions of Australian species of *Nicotiana.* Evaluations were made under greenhouse conditions on seedlings. *N. tabacum* cultivars Criollo Correntino from Argentina and Cavala 39 (of unknown origin) were found to possess a slight degree of tolerance, which was insufficient for a breeding program. Some accessions of *N. rustica* were found to possess a greater degree of tolerance than *N. tabacum,* but their tolerance also was deemed inadequate. American species evaluated included *N. acuminata* var. *grandiflora, N. alata, N. bigelovii,*

N. glauca, N. paniculata, N. repanda, N. sylvestris, N. glutinosa, N. langsdorfii, and others, and all were found to be highly susceptible. In contrast, high resistance (and apparent immunity) was found in several Australian species, namely *N. exigua, N. velutina, N. excelsior, N. goodspeedii,* and three accessions of *N. debneyi* collected from different regions of Australia. The 24-chromosome species *N. debneyi* was not infected and was considered the best source of blue mold resistance because it most closely resembled the American species in morphological characteristics (Smith-White et al, 1936). Resistance of *N. suaveolens, N. hesperesis, N. rosulata, N. simulans, N. amplexicaulis,* and *N. cavicola* has also been reported (Matthews, 1981; Wark, 1963).

The prevalence of resistance to blue mold in the Australian species could mean that virulent strains of *P. hyoscyami* originated in Australia and that resistance is the result of coevolution of host and pathogen in that part of the world (Smith-White et al, 1936; Wark, 1963). Likewise, the absence of resistance among the American species could mean that the blue mold fungus was introduced into America relatively recently and that selection pressure for resistance has not yet taken place.

In the early 1930s, a search for resistance to blue mold in the genus *Nicotiana* was initiated in the United States (Clayton, 1945). More than 1,000 tobacco introductions (TIs) from different parts of the world, but in particular from Mexico and Central and South America, and several *Nicotiana* species of American and Australian origin were evaluated. Artificially inoculated seedlings five to eight weeks old were evaluated in the plant bed and the greenhouse. With few exceptions, the results corroborated earlier results obtained in Australia. In addition, *N. tabacum* line TI 57 from Argentina was found to tolerate moderate but not heavy blue mold infestations in the plant bed. TI 57 was later crossed with susceptible cultivars, but its full resistance was never recovered. Resistance in TI 57 was deemed to be controlled by multiple genes (Clayton, 1945).

Clayton (1945) also found several *Nicotiana* species to be immune or highly resistant (no evidence of disease) to blue mold: *N. debneyi, N. exigua, N. goodspeedii, N. maritima, N. megalosiphon, N. rotundifolia, N. longiflora,* and *N. plumbaginifolia.* The latter two species are the only ones not native to Australia. *N. acuminata, N. caesia* (syn. *N. acuminata* var. *multiflora*), *N. gossei, N. paniculata,* and *N. rustica* were classified as moderately resistant, because a slight amount of disease developed. Other species were classified as slightly resistant or tolerant because abundant disease developed but the seedlings were rarely completely defoliated and usually recovered. The tolerant group included *N. alata, N. otophora, N.*

repanda, N. tomentosa, N. sylvestris, and others. The remainder of the species were classified as very susceptible (Clayton, 1968).

Further germ plasm evaluations were made in Australia in the 1960s (Hill and Mandryk, 1962). The investigators inoculated seedlings growing in the greenhouse with a defined isolate of *P. hyoscyami* from the Canberra region of Australia. As in previous experiments, Australian species were found to be immune to highly resistant. In contrast with Clayton's (1945) experiments, however, *N. longiflora* and *N. plumbaginifolia* were found to be highly susceptible. Similarly, *N. tabacum* cultivar Chileno Correntino, previously classified as resistant (Smith-White et al, 1936), also was judged susceptible. The different reactions of the same species when tested in different countries were thought to be due to the use of different accessions within a given species or to the occurrence of different strains of the pathogen (Hill and Mandryk, 1962). Interestingly, one accession of *N. goodspeedii* that had been multiplied in the United States for many years was more susceptible than other accessions of the same species collected from Australia (Hill and Mandryk, 1962). Varying degrees of resistance among *N. debneyi* lines collected from different countries have also been reported (Wark, 1963). Likewise, lines of *N. megalosiphon* collected from different areas of Australia exhibited varying degrees of resistance (Hill and Mandryk, 1962). These results indicate that there is a wide range of reactions to blue mold within resistant species.

Evaluations of seedlings of *Nicotiana* spp. under greenhouse conditions in the Soviet Union (Vinogradov et al, 1975) were similar to those previously reported in other countries (Clayton, 1945; Hill and Mandryk, 1962; Smith-White et al, 1936; Wark, 1963). All species reported resistant in the United States and Australia proved to be resistant to the fungal strains present in the Soviet Union. In addition, *N. ingulba* and *N. didebta* were found to be resistant (Vinogradov et al, 1975).

Grosso (1976) reevaluated the entire TI collection for blue mold resistance because new lines had been added to the collection that had not been previously evaluated. As before, experiments were undertaken in the greenhouse using seedlings in the four- to five-leaf stage. Most TIs were judged susceptible, but two lines appeared highly resistant: TI 657 and TI 1506, both of which were virtually immune. Tobacco introduction 657 had been collected as a mixture of cultivars (origin not mentioned), possessing a high proportion of blue mold-resistant plants in the original heterogeneous population (Grosso, 1976). It was subsequently found to be susceptible when tested under field conditions in Europe (Schiltz, 1979). Tobacco introduction 1506 is commonly known as Chemical Mutant; its

145

resistance was induced by D. C. Wark in Australia in 1958 by treating seeds of flue-cured tobacco cultivar Virginia Gold with triethylene iminotrazine (Marani et al, 1972). The high level of blue mold resistance in Chemical Mutant has been corroborated numerous times under diverse conditions throughout the world (Corbaz, 1962, 1976; Marani et al, 1972; S. V. Byrne, C. E. Main, and R. Delon, unpublished).

Transfer of Blue Mold Resistance: Breeding Methods

Resistance to *P. hyoscyami* in commercial tobacco lines, as discussed earlier, originated from wild *Nicotiana* species. Incorporations of this resistance into *N. tabacum* represent classic examples of interspecific hybridization to improve a cultivated species. Much of the work was done by Clayton (1967, 1968) and Clayton et al (1967a, 1967b) (described further in the next section). The initial interspecific hybridization was *N. debneyi* × *N. tabacum* 'Hicks'. Abundant F_1 seeds were produced, which germinated well and developed normally until the cotyledonary stage, at which point most of the seedlings died. Approximately one in 500 alloploid seedlings (DDTT) continued to grow normally and was self-sterile but cross-fertile. A systematic backcross program was initiated using cultivar Hicks as the recurrent parent. Alloploid plants were never as resistant as *N. debneyi*, but a few lines in BC_3 possessed adequate resistance. However, some of those plants reverted to susceptibility upon selfing, and resistance could not be stabilized. Eventually, a few stable resistant plants were obtained, but their resistance could not be transmitted in crosses. Clayton later resorted to using a "synthetic" tobacco, a $4n$ alloploid *N. sylvestris* × *N. tomentosiformis* (SSTmTm), in which a gene system for all vital functions is completely duplicated in each of its subgenomes. Clayton believed that the failure of resistance to stabilize was the result of a semilethal condition in homozygous resistant plants; that is, vital tobacco genes not duplicated in the segment had been displaced during incorporation of blue mold resistance. Present-day tobacco is thought to have undergone extensive diploidization during its domestication, so that certain characters are now controlled by a single gene. Thus, crossing to SSTmTm provided needed duplicate genes, and resistance could be transferred by backcrossing to various types of tobacco. Eventually, a cigar-wrapper F_1 hybrid was developed from a cross of a resistant and a susceptible line. This cultivar, C-74, had field resistance to blue mold, yielded well, and was superior in quality to the available susceptible commercial cultivars. Commercial production of C-74 began in 1958 (Clayton, 1967, 1968; Clayton et al, 1967a, 1967b).

Clayton (1968) also developed several burley and flue-cured blue mold-resistant tobacco lines. Line Bel 61-10, possessing the *N. debneyi* factor, has been used throughout the world as a source of blue mold resistance and is believed to have been developed by Clayton. However, documentation of its pedigree was not available to me. Unfortunately, the whereabouts of most of Clayton's blue mold-resistant burley and flue-cured lines are at present unknown.

In contrast to Clayton's difficulties in transferring blue mold resistance of interspecific origin by backcrossing, success has been reported by Australian scientists (Lea, 1961, 1963; Wark, 1963, 1970). The cultivar Resistant-Hicks was produced by obtaining the $4n$ amphidiploid *N. debneyi* × *N. tabacum* and backcrossing it to tobacco cultivar Hicks four times. Hicks was used as the female parent. Subsequent selections were made in the field for blue mold resistance, yield, and quality. Initially, two lines, A_1 and A_2, were developed, and eventually Resistant-Hicks was released for commercial production. This cultivar possessed a major gene that conferred a moderate level of field resistance (Lea, 1963). Leaf quality of Resistant-Hicks was unsatisfactory, however, and further selection led to the development of cultivars Beerwah H and Beerwah GG (Matthews, 1981; Wark et al, 1976; Wuttke, 1972).

An additional interspecific transfer of *P. hyoscyami* resistance from *N. debneyi* to tobacco has been reported (Lea, 1963; Wark, 1963). Resistant line SO_1 was obtained by forming the amphidiploid $4n$ (*N. debneyi* × *N. tabacum*) in 1954, then backcrossing five times to tobacco and self-pollinating. Line SO_1 became available for distribution in Australia in 1960 (Lea, 1963).

Interspecific transfers of blue mold resistance from *N. good-speedii* have also been obtained (Wark, 1970). The initial sterile F_1 hybrid *N. goodspeedii* × *N. tabacum* 'Vamorr-48' was treated with β-indolyl acetic acid applied to the pistil to encourage seed set. In addition, a 1% colchicine solution containing 5% glycine was applied to the axillary buds daily for four days to produce fertile amphiploids. One fertile branch was produced and used as the pollen parent in a backcross to the flue-cured cultivar Virginia Gold. After selfing, the progeny (BC_1-F_2 generation) were inoculated with *P. hyoscyami* and selected for resistance and plant type. This procedure was repeated four times, and several plants in this generation (BC_5-F_2) were evaluated in the field. Plants in the next generation (BC_5-F_3) displaying resistance in natural field infestations were crossed with cultivar Hicks to further improve their agronomic characteristics. Progeny from this cross (BC_6) were selfed, and further single-plant selections were made from the BC_6-F_2 generation. Eventually, two blue mold-resistant commercial cultivars, Sirone and Sirogo, were released from these programs (Anonymous, 1969). Both cultivars compared favorably with the commercially grown cultivar Hicks in yield, quality, and other properties. Sirone and Sirogo were reported to give complete blue mold control in the presence of the common Australian strain of *P. hyoscyami* (APT1) without the use of fungicides. However, Wark (1970) reported that while these cultivars develop less blue mold than susceptible cultivars in the presence of strain APT2, their cultivation in areas where APT2 is prevalent must be supplemented with fungicides.

Other researchers have reported additional interspecific hybridizations between *N. debneyi, N. excelsior, N. velutina, N. suaveolens,* and *N. tabacum,* with subsequent successful transfer of blue mold resistance genes (Bailov et al, 1966; Lea, 1963; Manolovi, 1978; Palakarcheva et al, 1983; Ternovskii et al, 1977; Wuttke, 1969, 1972). The use of in vitro fertilization and ovule culture to overcome interspecific incompatibility between *N. tabacum* hybridized with *N. debneyi, N. maritima, N. noctiflora,* or *N. goodspeedii* has also been reported in the transfer of blue mold resistance (Palakarcheva and Dorosiev, 1983; Palakarcheva et al, 1983; Ternovskii and Lar'kina, 1978).

The success of interspecific hybridization in transferring blue mold resistance into *N. tabacum* has enabled breeders in various countries to use these materials in crosses with local, adapted cultivars using conventional methods such as selfing and backcrossing (Gillham et al, 1977; Lea, 1982; Marani et al, 1972; Schiltz, 1981; Schweppenhauser, 1974; Sficas, 1966; Sficas and Ioannidis, 1980). Burley cultivars Bu S51 and Bu S62, with blue mold resistance derived from Bel 61-10, were developed in this manner and were released in Europe in 1975 and 1978, respectively (Corbaz, 1981–1982).

Nonconventional breeding methods such as in vitro anther culture have also been used in the development of blue mold-resistant germ plasm (Gillham et al, 1977; Robinson, 1983; Rufty et al, 1985). Rufty et al (1985) crossed both flue-cured and burley cultivars with Ovens 62, a flue-cured tobacco cultivar developed in Australia with resistance derived from *N. velutina.* Anthers of F_1 hybrids from resistant × susceptible crosses were cultured to produce an array of haploid plantlets segregating for blue mold resistance. Haploid plantlets were suspended in a 4% colchicine solution for 4 hr to produce fertile, double-haploid (DH) lines. Several hundred DH lines were tested for blue mold resistance under field conditions, and two superior lines were selected for their high degree of resistance and acceptable agronomic characteristics after repeated evaluation. These lines were released by the North

148

Carolina Agricultural Research Service in 1987 under the designations NC-BMR 42 and NC-BMR 90. NC-BMR 42 is a flue-cured tobacco derived from the cross of susceptible cultivar MacNair 944 × Ovens 62. NC-BMR 42 possesses good field resistance to blue mold and is comparable to popular commercial cultivars in yield and in nicotine and reducing sugars in the cured leaf. NC-BMR 90 was derived from the cross of burley cultivar Kentucky 17 × Ovens 62 and is thus a "half-burley" line; it resembles Kentucky 17 phenotypically but possesses the dominant green color of the Ovens 62 parent. Blue mold resistance of NC-BMR 90 is excellent.

The development of blue mold-resistant somatic hybrids has also been reported (Pandeya et al, 1986). Hybrids were obtained by fusing protoplasts derived from cell suspension cultures of *N. rustica* var. *chlorotica* and of an albino mutant of *N. tabacum.* Somatic hybrids were backcrossed to tobacco three times, and several of the progeny were tested for blue mold resistance using leaf disks placed in petri dishes. Reactions to *P. hyoscyami* ranged from immunity to susceptibility. Neither *N. rustica* nor *N. tabacum* involved in the original somatic hybridization and subsequent back-crossing is known to be resistant to *P. hyoscyami,* so the origin of resistance is unknown. Pandeya et al (1986) ascribed the resistance to genetic complementation between the nuclear genomes of *N. rustica* and *N. tabacum,* recombination of mitochondrial genomes, or interaction between nuclear and cytoplasmic genes. No verification of resistance on whole plants in greenhouse or field conditions was reported. Conclusions regarding the resistance of a given genotype based on reactions of leaf disks are tenuous and must be further demonstrated.

Most breeding efforts have been devoted to the production of blue mold-resistant inbred lines. Nevertheless, a few investigators have examined the possibility of using F_1 hybrids derived from resistant × susceptible crosses, with the expectation of providing adequate blue mold resistance plus superior agronomic characteristics.

Extensive commercial trials have been reported in which F_1 hybrids showed excellent field resistance along with good levels of tolerance in the seedbed (Clayton, 1968). As mentioned earlier, the male-sterile F_1 hybrid of cigar-wrapper tobacco C-74 consistently showed high resistance to blue mold in the field; disease development was limited to a scattering of small, white lesions. C-74 was also very high-yielding and of high quality, indicating that blue mold resistance did not impart any detrimental characteristics (Clayton, 1967). Similarly, male-sterile hybrids with sufficient field resistance to blue mold (from an *N. debneyi* source) have been developed for Oriental and burley tobacco in Greece. Hybrids resistant to blue mold were reported to have higher yields and better

149

quality than the susceptible parent. Heterosis values for resistance to blue mold were reported to range from 59 to 95% (Sficas and Ioannidis, 1980).

In contrast, some authors report that F_1 hybrids derived from diverse resistant × susceptible crosses do not show a high level of blue mold resistance but are generally intermediate in reaction and develop greater resistance as plants mature (Corbaz, 1962; Dean et al, 1968; Wuttke, 1972). Dean et al (1968) tested several F_1 hybrids of cigar tobacco derived from resistant × susceptible crosses and found that most hybrids were intermediate in sensitivity relative to parental lines, but some were more susceptible than the midparent. When a given resistant line was crossed to different susceptible lines, the F_1 hybrids varied greatly in reaction, suggesting that susceptible lines contribute complementary or modifying factors that interact favorably with the major blue mold resistance genes. In cases where F_1 hybrids do not express a very high level of resistance, they may still be used in conjunction with fungicides to provide adequate blue mold control.

Inheritance of Resistance

Many contradictory reports on the mode of inheritance of blue mold resistance have been published over the years. Discrepancies can be caused by many factors (as will be discussed in detail later), including the source of resistance, variation in environmental conditions under which plants are evaluated, plant age, physiological condition of plants, and criteria used for assessing resistance.

In Australia, Wark (1963) studied the inheritance of blue mold resistance in the Australian species *N. goodspeedii* and *N. debneyi*. In one population, Wark crossed a resistant *N. goodspeedii* line, T.S. 115, with a susceptible line from the United States, line 1083. A separate population was derived from crosses between two lines of *N. debneyi*: T.S. 98, a highly resistant line from Australia, and line 1288, a less resistant line from New Caledonia. In both populations, parental lines, F_1, F_2, and backcrosses of the F_1 to both resistant and susceptible parents (BC$_1$ and BC$_2$) were grown at the same time, inoculated, and evaluated for blue mold resistance as six-week-old seedlings. The population derived from *N. goodspeedii* was assessed for blue mold reaction by determining the number of plants with and without sporulating lesions. In the *N. debneyi* population, a scale of 0 to 5 was used to evaluate resistance, in which 0 = no disease and 5 = systemic necrosis and plant death.

Results from the *N. goodspeedii* population indicated that all F_1 (T.S. 115 × line 1083) plants were completely resistant to blue mold.

The F_2 generation segregated in a 3:1 ratio of resistant to susceptible plants, and the BC_2 generation ($F_1 \times$ line 1083) segregated in a 1:1 ratio. All plants of BC_1 ($F_1 \times$ T.S. 115) were resistant. From these results, Wark (1963) concluded that resistance to blue mold in *N. goodspeedii* was controlled by a single, dominant gene.

In the *N. debneyi* population, most F_1 plants from T.S. 98 × line 1288 were classified in resistant classes 0 and 1. Plants of the F_2 generation and BC_2 ($F_1 \times$ line 1288) were classified in nearly all disease categories (no distinct ratios), although the majority of plants were in the resistant classes. Plants of BC_1 ($F_1 \times$ line 98) were all classified in resistant categories 0 and 1. From these data, Wark (1963) concluded that blue mold resistance in *N. debneyi* was of a polygenic nature. Resistance to blue mold in *N. velutina* was also reported to be controlled by multiple genes (Wark, 1963).

Based on these experiments, Wark (1963) postulated that several genes are necessary for full resistance at the seedling stage but that one gene may be sufficient to condition resistance in adult plants where the environment is relatively unfavorable to the pathogen. Under conditions highly favorable for disease development, additional genes with additive effects would be necessary for full expression of resistance (Wark, 1963).

The single gene that may condition adult plant resistance to tobacco blue mold is believed to have been incorporated on the same *N. tabacum* chromosome after introduction from either *N. debneyi* or *N. goodspeedii* (Wark, 1963). This would indicate that there must be a relationship between the regions of the alien chromosome carrying the major gene for resistance and a region in one of the *N. tabacum* chromosomes where segmental substitution occurs.

In the United States, Clayton worked for over 30 years to transfer blue mold resistance from *N. debneyi* to *N. tabacum* and to discern the mode of inheritance controlling resistance (Clayton, 1968). In his initial studies, Clayton backcrossed 4n *N. debneyi* × *N. tabacum* (DDTT) to tobacco cultivar Hicks and other desirable tobacco cultivars but for 10 years failed to produce a homozygous blue mold-resistant tobacco line. Clayton observed in cytological studies that plants selected with good resistance had eight or more *N. debneyi* chromosomes and concluded that the inheritance of resistance was polygenic. Pairing between *N. debneyi* and tobacco chromosomes must have occurred in rare instances, and eventually stable resistance was incorporated into tobacco. Nevertheless, these resistant lines were inferior to tobacco in yield and quality and possessed what Clayton termed "defective heredity"—that is, resistance was difficult to recover in backcrosses to tobacco cultivars, and segregation and recombination were abnormal. Earlier, Clayton had solved a similar problem with root-knot nematode resistance by backcrossing to the alloploid $4n$ $N.$ $sylvestris \times N.$ $tomentosiformis$ (SSTmTm) (Clayton, 1968). Therefore, a blue mold-resistant line, Beltsville 771, was crossed with the blue mold-susceptible lines alloploid SSTmTm and flue-cured cultivar Virginia Gold. Parental, F_1, and F_2 generations were evaluated for blue mold resistance in both plant bed and field conditions in northern Florida in spring and early summer when environmental conditions favored disease development.

Data collected included a disease index (a measure of the percentage of the leaf area damaged by the disease), a sporulation index, the percentage of plants that were killed, and the weight of the leaves. Results showed that although both the alloploid and Virginia Gold were highly susceptible, the cross of line 771 $\times$ SSTmTm produced 15 times as many resistant as susceptible plants in the F_1 and F_2 generations. F_3 and BC_1-F_2 lines derived from selected resistant F_2 plants appeared to have homozygous resistance. Furthermore, it was possible to backcross to susceptible tobacco and obtain numerous resistant plants with homozygous resistance. In the F_2 generation, Clayton found that diseased leaf area ranged from 0 to 100%; that is, there was a continuous distribution of disease reactions, yet a high frequency of resistant plants was recovered. Clayton concluded that resistance, although not controlled by one factor, had to be relatively simple and was not highly polygenic as previously believed.

To further elucidate the number of genes controlling resistance, Clayton (1968) performed intensive studies over a three-year period using a series of stable lines with resistance derived from $N.$ $debneyi$. From these studies, Clayton postulated four distinct levels of resistance. Three genes from $N.$ $debneyi$ were said to provide three different levels of resistance, indicating that this resistance was based on three chromosomal segment transfers. A fourth and still higher level of resistance was believed to be provided by the addition of a major gene found in tobacco. Resistance levels were defined as follows:

$Level I$—Full $N.$ $debneyi$ resistance plus a major gene from tobacco. Example: line 292 ($D_1D_1D_2D_2D_3D_3T_1T_1$). Level I resistant line crossed with susceptible lines produced F_1 hybrids resistant to blue mold at all stages of development.

$Level II$—Full $N.$ $debneyi$ resistance. Example: line 15 ($D_1D_1D_2D_2$-D_3D_3). F_1 of level II resistant lines $\times$ susceptible lines showed resistance as adult plants but susceptibility at the seedling stage.

$Level III$—Reduced $N.$ $debneyi$ resistance. Example: Australian line

152

A2 ($D_1D_1D_2D_2$). Level III resistant lines per se are susceptible at the seedling stage but resistant as adult plants.

Level IV—(D_1D_1). Lines in level IV were more resistant than susceptible tobacco but less resistant than plants in level III.

Many other researchers have studied the mode of inheritance controlling blue mold resistance using *N. tabacum* lines as parental material, that is, resistance of interspecific sources backcrossed to tobacco, rather than using the species per se, as Wark (1963) and Clayton (1968) did.

Wuttke (1969) conducted inheritance studies in Australia, using as parental material selfed seeds of 25 advanced lines deriving their resistance from *N. debneyi* or *N. goodspeedii* and backcrossed to flue-cured cultivar Hicks seven times. Parental lines were evaluated as seedlings in boxes placed outdoors and exposed to natural blue mold infection (strain APT1). Blue mold was assessed on a scale of 0 to 10, in which 0 = no reaction and 10 = a high degree of susceptibility. Several breeding lines were found to be homozygous for resistance. Others appeared to be segregating for a major gene for resistance. In some crosses, segregation did not depart significantly in chi-squared tests from a 3:1 ratio, as expected for a single, dominant gene. However, other families showed an excess of resistant plants. These results were interpreted as evidence for the presence of additional genes for resistance in progenies of *N. debneyi* and *N. goodspeedii* (Wuttke, 1969).

Lea (1963), also of Australia, found results similar to those obtained by Wark (1963) and Wuttke (1969). He studied the inheritance of blue mold resistance in the cultivar Resistant-Hicks derived from *N. debneyi* and concluded that a major dominant gene conferred field resistance but that other genes in addition to the major gene were necessary to ensure the expression of resistance under environmental conditions favorable to the pathogen.

Sficas (1966), working in Greece, conducted inheritance studies using *N. debneyi*-derived resistant lines Hicks Fixed A_1, Hicks Fixed A_2, SO_1, Bel 61-10, Bel 61-12, and V-Gold 1-4-2. Resistant lines were crossed to a number of Oriental and semi-Oriental tobaccos. Plants of F_2, BC, and F_3 generations were evaluated under field conditions at one location, and F_4 plants were evaluated at three locations. Disease was rated on a qualitative scale based on the number of infected plants. Data from F_2 and BC generations revealed significant differences in the transmission of resistance among susceptible cultivars crossed to the same resistant line. Unfortunately, data on the reaction of both susceptible and resistant parental lines were not presented, and it is not clear whether the experiment was replicated. Hence, one cannot discern variation in disease reaction due to genetic effects as opposed to environmental variation. In some cases, segregation ratios in F_2 generations gave more than one-fourth susceptible plants and in others less than one-fourth but in most cases more than one-sixteenth. Backcrosses in general had fewer than 50% resistant plants, and most segregating F_3 families had a 3:1 ratio. From these data, Sficas (1966) concluded that a dominant gene was mainly responsible for the transmission of blue mold resistance but that additional factors also made an important contribution.

Results of experiments in Switzerland disagree with those described above (Corbaz, 1962). Corbaz (1962) evaluated the resistance of several lines developed in Australia and derived from *N. goodspeedii, N. debneyi, N. suaveolens, N. velutina, N. knightiana,* and *N. exigua.* Swiss cultivars were hybridized with pollen of the resistant lines, and an intermediate degree of resistance occurred in the F_1 seedlings. These results suggest that resistance in the Australian materials was incompletely dominant. Evaluations of other generations were not reported.

Schweppenhauser (1974) also studied the inheritance of resistance in line Hicks A_2, reported as having dominant resistance to blue mold from *N. debneyi.* Hicks A_2 was self-pollinated and crossed with susceptible cultivar Kutsaga 51. There was no family structure in these tests; instead, different selections were compared and then reevaluated in subsequent generations. Experimental lines were artificially inoculated in plant beds and in the field at two locations in Italy. Evaluations were also made in Germany using the "cotyledon test" (Schiltz and Izard, 1962; see also Chapter 2). Materials were also subsequently evaluated under field conditions in Switzerland. Selected lines derived from A_2 crossed to Kutsaga 51 varied in their degree of resistance to blue mold, regardless of whether evaluations were based on the percentage of infected plants or the percentage of infected cotyledons. Schweppenhauser (1974) interpreted the variation in resistance among selections as indicative of the presence of modifying factors for resistance in addition to a single, dominant gene.

Marani et al (1972), in Israel, investigated the inheritance of resistance in lines Chemical Mutant and Bel 61-10, derived from *N. debneyi.* Both resistant lines were crossed with each other and with the susceptible cultivar Mikhal. Seedlings of parental, F_1, F_2, and F_3 generations, and F_1 and F_2 of backcrosses were evaluated under natural disease conditions and assessed for blue mold reaction on a scale of 0 to 6. Plants rated 0 to 4 were classified as resistant, and those rated 5 or 6 were classified as susceptible. All plants in the F_1 and F_2 generations of crosses Bel 61-10 × Chemical Mutant, including reciprocals, were found to be resistant to blue mold; that is, there was no segregation for disease reactions.

Marani et al (1972) concluded from these tests that the genetic basis for resistance in the two lines was identical. However, the probability that a resistance allele derived from mutation breeding occurred at the same locus as the resistance allele derived from interspecific crosses is very small. A simpler explanation would be inadequate disease development in the experimental plots. No disease ratings were given for plots of the susceptible cultivar, so this point cannot be ascertained. Marani et al (1972) expressed the possibility that a seed of a resistant line originating from *N. debneyi* or some other resistant species had been accidentally mixed with seed that produced Chemical Mutant. If such a mixture had occurred, however, it could have been easily detected because of the distinct phenotypic characteristics of Chemical Mutant (small, upright leaves; shriveled seed capsules; etc.), which readily distinguish it from other tobacco genotypes (R. C. Rufty, unpublished).

In crosses of resistant × susceptible lines, most (but not all) plants in F_1 generations were highly resistant regardless of the source of resistance (Marani et al, 1972). Ratios in the F_2 generation approximated a 3:1 segregation pattern of resistant and susceptible genotypes. Backcross progeny for crosses to the susceptible parent segregated approximately in a 1:1 ratio. Results from the backcross to the resistant parent approximated a 3:1 ratio, as expected if resistance is controlled by a single, dominant gene. Nevertheless, in some cases there were statistically significant deviations from these ratios because of excess numbers of susceptible plants in some families. Marani et al (1972) offered several explanations for the presence of susceptible plants in the F_1 generation and the deviations from expected ratios in other generations: the discrepancies may be due to the presence of additional genetic factors affecting the degree of resistance; dominance of the major gene may be incomplete; deviations could be caused by preferential fertilization—that is, pollen carrying the gene for resistance is less effective than that carrying the gene for susceptibility; and/or the level of resistance may be affected by the environment.

Because the expression of resistance may be affected by both genetic and environmental factors, Marani et al (1972) estimated heritability values for the degree of resistance using parent-offspring regression analyses. Heritability values were found to be 0.54 for F_3 progeny and 0.23 for backcross F_2 progeny. These relatively low values reflect the importance of environmental effects and consequent low efficiency of selection for blue mold resistance.

Rufty et al (1985) investigated the inheritance of resistance in

Australian cultivar Ovens 62 derived from *N. velutina*. Ovens 62 was crossed with susceptible flue-cured and burley cultivars, and F_1 plants were subjected to anther culture. Haploids were produced whose chromosome numbers were doubled with colchicine to produce double-haploid (DH) lines. DH lines were evaluated in replicated plots as adult plants under field conditions following artificial inoculation. The percentage of leaf area damaged was determined two to three weeks after inoculation. There was a continuous distribution of reactions to blue mold among DH lines ranging from susceptibility equal to that of the susceptible parent to resistance equal to or greater than that of the resistant parent. Disease reactions did not appear to fit discrete ratios. Calculated heritability values ranged from 0.41 to 0.75.

Rufty et al (1985) concluded from these data that a major gene for resistance was probably derived from *N. velutina* but that modifier genes were present in *N. tabacum* which enhanced the effect of the major gene. Simultaneous transfer of multiple factors of interspecific origin into *N. tabacum* is unlikely. Furthermore, the frequency of resistant plants was high, suggesting that the mode of inheritance was not exceedingly complex.

Several investigators have demonstrated that no significant differences in resistance reactions arise from reciprocal crosses. Therefore, inheritance does not appear to be controlled by cytoplasmic factors but rather is under the control of nuclear genes (Dean et al, 1968; Marani et al, 1972; Sficas, 1966).

EXPRESSION OF DISEASE REACTIONS

It is clear from the foregoing discussion that several hypotheses have been proposed with respect to the mode of inheritance controlling blue mold resistance. The interactions between the tobacco plant and *P. hyoscyami* are exceedingly complex; consequently, disease reactions are highly variable, unpredictable, and often irreproducible. Many factors influence disease reactions, which in turn can have a profound effect on interpretations of genetic studies.

It has been well documented that resistance increases with plant age, particularly in *N. tabacum* (Clayton, 1945, 1967, 1968; Hill and Mandryk, 1962; Vinogradov et al, 1975; Wark, 1963). For example, tobacco plants of certain resistant lines have been reported to be moderately susceptible when 19 and 28 days old, whereas older plants were highly resistant (Clayton, 1968). In contrast, plants of *N. debneyi, N. goodspeedii,* and *N. exigua* appear to be resistant at all stages of growth (Clayton, 1945; Rayner and Hopkins, 1962).

The vigor of the host plant and nitrogen fertilization also have marked effects on resistance. Fast-growing, succulent plants grown under optimal conditions are more susceptible than slow-growing plants or plants that have been stressed (Clayton, 1945; Oczos, 1971). Environmental conditions such as light, temperature, and relative humidity also profoundly affect disease reactions (Clayton, 1967; Marani et al, 1972; Matthews, 1981; Wark, 1963; Wuttke, 1972). Even slight variations in environmental conditions or in the physiological status of the plant can alter disease reactions.

Morphological and chemical differences among plants also contribute to differential expression of disease reactions. This is particularly apparent when materials derived through interspecific hybridization are compared with tobacco. Leaves of *N. debneyi* and *N. exigua* are very waxy, leathery, and less wettable than leaves of *N. tabacum*. Thus, quick drying of the leaf surface may confer resistance (Berry and McKeen, 1985; Clayton, 1968). Canopy architecture, leaf thickness, leaf surface chemistry, and leaf position may also influence resistant reactions (Clayton, 1945, 1968; Hill and Mandryk, 1962; Vinogradov et al, 1975).

The effect of inoculum density on disease reactions is also an important consideration when studying inheritance of blue mold resistance. Certain genotypes appear resistant under moderate inoculum concentrations but succumb readily to the disease under heavy spore loads and environmental conditions favorable for disease development (Clayton, 1945; Hill and Mandryk, 1962; Sficas, 1966). Other genotypes are insensitive to inoculum pressure and remain resistant under field conditions regardless of the level of inoculum (R. C. Rufty, unpublished).

ASSESSMENT OF RESISTANCE

Finally, the criteria used to assess resistance or susceptibility are tremendously important in genetic studies. Nearly every experimenter whose work has been reviewed above used a different assessment scale. Some workers use a quantitative scale, others adopt a descriptive scale composed of a few classes, and still others simply use a qualitative measure of resistance and susceptibility (+ or −). Clearly, conclusions on the degree of resistance depend on the assessment of disease; what is considered a resistant reaction is subjective and arbitrary. How plants are grouped to compute segregation ratios is up to the experimenter's discretion, particularly since blue mold reactions do not fall into discrete classes. Therefore, proper resistant and susceptible controls must be included in all experiments, and the experiments should be properly replicated and repeated over time before any conclusions are reached. Ideally, most conditions of growth, inoculation, and evaluation should be standardized as much as possible to minimize nongenetic sources of variability and avoid erroneous conclusions.

157

SUMMARY

To summarize, it appears that at least one major, dominant gene for resistance to blue mold exists in several of the *Nicotiana* species native to Australia. It is possible that the same ancestral gene is present in these species. When resistance is transferred from the nearly immune *Nicotiana* species into *N. tabacum,* the gene (or genes) present in the wild species no longer provides as high a degree of protection against blue mold (Clayton et al, 1967a). Resistance in tobacco does not segregate in neat, Mendelian ratios but appears to be incompletely dominant and/or modified by additional factors in the *N. tabacum* genome. Nevertheless, a relatively high frequency of resistant plants can be recovered from crosses of resistant × susceptible genotypes, suggesting that the mode of inheritance is not highly complex. Moreover, there is no evidence of cytoplasmic inheritance; that is, resistance is believed to be controlled by nuclear genes. Lastly, reactions to this disease are highly influenced by nongenetic factors.

Evaluating Resistance to Blue Mold

Several approaches that breeders have used in developing blue mold-resistant germ plasm have been discussed in previous sections. Selection for resistance has been performed within segregating generations, among inbred lines, or among double-haploid material. Tests have been performed on seedlings in the greenhouse, in the plant bed, or on mature plants under field conditions. Resistant reactions also have been evaluated using the cotyledon test proposed by Schiltz and Izard (1962) (see also Chapter 2). A high correlation is reported between the reaction of the cotyledons in this test and that of mature plants. Attempts to classify genotypes for blue mold resistance in callus culture have not been successful (Reed and Rufty, 1985).

Either artificial inoculations or natural infestations may be used in breeding for blue mold resistance, provided a high degree of uniformity in disease expression can be obtained. The use of spreader rows of susceptible genotypes planted at regular intervals in the field has proved successful in obtaining uniform infestations (Rufty et al, 1985). Experiments by researchers at North Carolina State University indicate that selection for field resistance is most effective if plants are not inoculated until six to eight weeks after transplanting. Plants may be protected from natural infestations before that stage by weekly applications of dithiocarbamate fungicides until a week before inoculation with the fungus (R. C. Rufty, unpublished). Three to four weeks after symptoms are first expressed, selection may be done, based on reduced number of lesions, reduced sporulation, the degree of systemic infection, or a combination of parameters (Schiltz, 1979). Selection in advanced generations may also be performed on the basis of yield under blue mold infestations (Gillham et al, 1977).

Of concern to breeders is the recognition of genetic resistance versus escapes and of acquired or induced resistance (Clayton, 1968; Cruickshank and Mandryk, 1960; Kuć and Tuzun, 1983). Acquired or induced resistance (Kuć and Tuzun, 1983) refers to a reduction in susceptibility to blue mold among tobacco plants previously infected by the fungus. If the initial blue mold attack is light and the weather turns warm and dry, plants may show little or no evidence of blue mold damage, but they are protected against subsequent damage by the fungus.

Breeders must also be concerned with undesirable relationships between blue mold resistance and susceptibility to other diseases and vice versa. For example, the association between resistance to potato virus Y in tobacco and extreme sensitivity to blue mold has been amply documented (Koelle, 1963; Rufty et al, 1984).

A final consideration in breeding for blue mold resistance is the independence or unrelatedness of resistance expressed by the foliage and by the vascular system. Genotypes selected on the basis of reduced percentage of leaf damage have been observed to develop systemic infection, which can cause severe leaf deformation (R. C. Rufty, unpublished). The possibility of independent selection for leaf and stem resistance has been suggested (Vinogradov et al, 1975). Wark et al (1976) reported a correlation value (r) of 0.52 between leaf mold and stem necrosis.

Mechanisms of Resistance

Undoubtedly the mechanisms controlling blue mold resistance are highly complex and are not based on a simple feature. Hypersensitive reactions have been observed in leaf mesophyll cells but not in the epidermis, suggesting that resistant reactions occur after the initiation of infection (Schiltz, 1981). The role of kinetin, the concentration of phenolic compounds such as chlorogenic acid, peroxidase activity, and the activity of other enzymes have been implicated in resistance (Avundzhyan and Shaldzhyan, 1974; Edreva, 1972; Paschenko, 1978; Schiltz, 1981). The presence of duvatrienediols, which are associated with the cuticular wax of tobacco leaves, has also been thought to be involved in blue mold resistance. Some authors believe, however, that such compounds affect germination of conidia and thus play a role in the epidemiology of the disease but not in resistance (Cruickshank et al, 1977).

Whatever its biochemical basis, blue mold resistance is generally manifested in reduced leaf area invaded by the fungus, reduced spore production, and reduced total leaf area destroyed (Clayton, 1968). Rufty and Main (1987) conducted experiments to measure components of partial resistance under highly controlled environmental conditions. Resistant genotypes produced fewer and smaller lesions, had reduced sporulation, and exhibited considerably longer latent periods than susceptible cultivars. These resistance components are expected to reduce the onset and development of blue mold epidemics.

In conclusion, much progress has been made in breeding for blue mold resistance and in understanding the genetics of host-parasite interactions. *P. hyoscyami* is an unpredictable pathogen, however, and research must continue in order to understand its complexity.

LITERATURE CITED

Angell, H. R., and Hill, A. V. 1932. Downy mildew (blue mould) of tobacco in Australia. Counc. Sci. Ind. Res. Aust. Bull. 65. 30 pp.

Anonymous. 1969. Sirogo and Sirone—Mould resistant varieties. Aust. Tob. J. 16:12–13.

Avundzhyan, E. S., and Shaldzhyan, M. M. 1974. Growth-stimulating and inhibiting substances in leaves of tobacco varieties susceptible, resistant, and immune to *Peronosporosis*. Fiziol. Rast. 21:693–698.

Bailov, D., Palakarcheva, M., and Daskalov, S. 1966. Genetic investigations into interspecific hybrids. Pages 656–666 in: Proc. Int. Tob. Sci. Congr. 4th, Athens. National Tobacco Board of Greece, Athens.

Berry, J. W., and McKeen, W. E. 1985. Development of *Peronospora hyoscyami* f. sp. *tabacina* in the resistant host *Nicotiana exigua*. Can. J. Plant Pathol. 7:262–269.

Clayton, E. E. 1945. Resistance of tobacco to blue mold (*Peronospora tabacina*). J. Agric. Res. 70:79–87.

Clayton, E. E. 1967. The transfer of blue mold resistance to tobacco from *Nicotiana debneyi*. Part III. Development of a blue mold resistant cigar wrapper variety. Tob. Sci. 11:107–110.

Clayton, E. E. 1968. The transfer of blue mould resistance to tobacco from *Nicotiana debneyi*. Part IV—Breeding programs 1957–1967. Tob. Sci. 12:112–124.

Clayton, E. E., Heggestad, H. E., Grosso, J. J., and Burk, L. G. 1967a. The transfer of blue mold resistance to tobacco from *Nicotiana debneyi*. Part I. Breeding progress 1937–1954. Tob. Sci. 11:91–97.

Clayton, E. E., Heggestad, H. E., Grosso, J. J., and Burk, L. G. 1967b. The transfer of blue mold resistance to tobacco from *Nicotiana debneyi*. Part II. Chromosome studies. Tob. Sci. 11:102–106.

Corbaz, R. 1962. Research on the control of blue mold of tobacco. CORESTA Inf. Bull. 1962(1):9–19.

Corbaz, R. 1976. Observations made on the blue mold trap collection in 1976. CORESTA Inf. Bull. 1976(3-4):53–56.

Corbaz, R. 1981–1982. Twenty years of blue mold control in Switzerland. Ann. Tab. Sect. 2(17):65–71.

Cruickshank, I. A. M., and Mandryk, M. 1960. The effect of stem infestation of tobacco with *Peronospora tabacina* Adam on foliage reaction to blue mold. J. Aust. Inst. Agric. Sci. 26:369–377.

Cruickshank, I. A. M., Perrin, D. R., and Mandryk, M. 1977. Fungitoxicity of duvatrienediols associated with the cuticular wax of tobacco leaves. Phytopathol. Z. 90:243–249.

Dean, C. E., Heggestad, H. E., and Grosso, J. J. 1968. Transfer of blue mold resistance into F_1 tobacco hybrids. Crop Sci. 8:93–96.

Edreva, A. 1972. A study of the isozyme composition of peroxidase and malate dehydrogenase in *Peronospora tabacina* Adam and its host *Nicotiana tabacum* L. Dokl. Skh. Akad. Sofia 5:121–125.

Gayed, S. K. 1980. Blue mold of tobacco—Past and present. Lighter 50:5–9.

Gayed, S. K. 1985. The 1979 blue mold epidemic of flue-cured tobacco in Ontario and disease occurrence in subsequent years. Can. Plant Dis. Surv. 65:23–28.

Gillham, F. E. M., Wark, D. C., and Harrigan, E. K. S. 1977. Disease resistant flue-cured tobacco breeding lines for north Queensland. I. Resistance to blue mould, *Peronospora tabacina*. Aust. J. Exp. Agric. Anim. Husb. 17:652–658.

Grosso, J. J. 1976. Reaction of diverse *Nicotiana tabacum* germplasm to blue mold. Tob. Sci. 20:154–155.

Hill, A. V. 1963. A strain of *Peronospora tabacina* pathogenic to tobacco lines with resistance derived from *Nicotiana debneyi* and *N. goodspeedii*. Nature (London) 199:396.

Hill, A. V. 1966a. Physiological specialization of *Peronospora tabacina* Adam as a factor in the occurrence of blue mould disease of tobacco. Pages 461–466 in: Proc. Int. Tob. Sci. Congr. 4th, Athens. National Tobacco Board of Greece, Athens.

Hill, A. V. 1966b. Physiologic specialization in *Peronospora tabacina* Adam in Australia. CORESTA Inf. Bull. 1966(1):7–15.

Hill, A. V., and Mandryk, M. 1962. Resistance of seedlings of *Nicotiana* species to *Peronospora tabacina* Adam. Aust. J. Exp. Agric. Anim. Husb. 2:12–15.

Koelle, G. 1963. Observations on the antagonistic tendency between Y-virus and *Peronospora tabacina*. CORESTA Inf. Bull. 1963(1):23.

Kuć, J., and Tuzun, S. 1983. Immunization for disease resistance in tobacco. Recent Adv. Tob. Sci. 9:179–213.

Lea, H. W. 1961. A review of two commercial flue-cured blue mold resistant varieties. CORESTA Inf. Bull. 1961(2):21–27.

Lea, H. W. 1963. The transfer of resistance against blue mold (*Peronospora tabacina* Adam) from *Nicotiana debneyi* to cultivated tobacco. CORESTA Inf. Bull. 1963(3):13–15.

Lea, H. W. 1982. Plant breeding. J. Aust. Inst. Agric. Sci. 48:143–144.

Lucas, G. B. 1980. The war against blue mold. Science 210:147–153.

Manolovi, A. 1978. Use of interspecific hybridization with tobacco for the development of initial material resistant to diseases. Pages 121–125 in: Rep. Natl. Symp. Plant Immunity 1st, Varma, Bulgaria, Vol. 2. Ministry of Agricultural and Food Industry. Institute of Plant Protection, Kostinbrod. (In Bulgarian, summaries in English and Russian)

Marani, A., Fishler, G., and Amirav, A. 1972. The inheritance of resistance to blue mold (*Peronospora tabacina* Adam) in two cultivars of tobacco (*Nicotiana tabacum* L.). Euphytica 21:97–105.

Matthews, P. 1981. Breeding for resistance to downy mildews. Pages 266–286 in: The Downy Mildews. D. M. Spencer, ed. Academic Press, London. 636 pp.

McKeen, W. E. 1981. The 1979 tobacco blue mold disaster in Ontario, Canada. (Letter to the editor) Plant Dis. 65:8–9.

Mihajlova, P., Ivancheva-Gabrovska, M., and Pamoukov, I. 1977. Changes in the pathogenicity of *Peronospora tabacina* Adam under the conditions of Bulgaria. Rastenievud. Nauki 14:123–132.

Nadazdin, M. 1976. The appearance of higher pathogenicity of *Peronospora tabacina* Adam on tobacco test varieties in Herzegovina, Yugoslavia in 1975. Zast. Bilja 27:127–132.

Nesmith, W. C. 1983. The blue mold situation in the U.S. Pages 20–27 in: Blue Mold Symp. 3rd, Tob. Workers Conf. 30th. J. J. Reilly, compiler. Virginia Polytechnic Institute and State University, Williamsburg. 61 pp.

Oczos, A. 1971. Influence of nitrogen nutrition on the course of vegetation, yield quantity, and the degree of susceptibility of tobacco plants belonging to two varieties (resistant and susceptible) to *Peronospora tabacina* Adam. Pamiet. Pulawski 49:167.

Palakarcheva, M., and Dorosiev, L. 1983. The amphidiploids *N. maritima* × *N. tabacum* (4n=80) and *N. noctiflora* × *N. tabacum* (4n=72)—A valuable source of disease resistance. Rastenievud. Nauki (Plant Sci.) 20:68–72.

Palakarcheva, M., Krusteva, D., and Peeva, R. 1983. Promising disease resistant tobacco lines, Djebel Basma type, developed as a result of interspecific hybridization. Rastenievud. Nauki (Plant Sci.) 20:61–67.

Pandeya, R. S., Douglas, G. C., Keller, W. A., Setterfield, G., and Patrick, Z. A. 1986. Somatic hybridization between *Nicotiana rustica* and *N. tabacum:* Development of tobacco breeding strains with disease resistance and elevated nicotine content. Z. Pflanzenzuecht. 96:346–352.

Paschenko, I. N. 1978. Role of phenols in blue mold resistance of tobacco plants. Mikol. Fitopatol. 12:343–346.

Rayner, R. W., and Hopkins, J. C. F. 1962. Blue mold of tobacco. Misc. Publ. 16. Commonwealth Mycological Institute, Kew, Surrey, England. 16 pp.

Reed, S. M., and Rufty, R. C. 1985. Reaction of calli of blue mold resistant and susceptible *Nicotiana* genotypes to infection by *Peronospora tabacina*. Tob. Sci. 29:53–56.

Robinson, R. A. 1983. Pathosystem management. Pages 237–247 in: Durable Resistance in Crops. F. Lamberti, J. M. Waller, and J. A. Van der Graap, eds. NATO Adv. Study Inst. Ser. A., Vol. 55. Plenum Press, New York.

Rufty, R. C., and Main, C. E. 1987. Evaluation of components of partial resistance to tobacco blue mold. (Abstr.) Phytopathology 77:1724.

Rufty, R. C., Gooding, G. V., Jr., and Wernsman, E. A. 1984. Association between resistance to potato virus Y and susceptibility to *Peronospora tabacina* in tobacco. Agron. Abstr. 1984:86.

Rufty, R. C., Wernsman, E. A., and Gooding, G. V., Jr. 1985. Inheritance of resistance to tobacco blue mold. Pages 32–37 in: Tob. Workers Conf. 31st, 7–10 Jan., Pinehurst, NC.

Schiltz, P. 1979. Results of collaborative experiments conducted in 1979 to assess the pathogenicity of *Peronospora tabacina*. CORESTA Inf. Bull. 1979(3):14–19.

Schiltz, P. 1981. Downy mildew of tobacco. Pages 577–599 in: The Downy Mildews. D. M. Spencer, ed. Academic Press, London. 636 pp.

Schiltz, P., and Izard, C. 1962. Susceptibilité cotylédonaire et résistance à *Peronospora tabacina* Adam. C. R. Seances Acad. Agric. Fr. 48:561–565.

Schiltz, P., Coussirat, J. C., and Delon, R. 1977. Resistance of tobacco type *N. debneyi* to blue mold: Probable heredity, appearance of virulent isolates and pest control strategy. Ann. Tab. 14:111–126.

Schweppenhauser, M. A. 1974. Anticipatory resistance breeding to *Peronospora tabacina*. S. Afr. J. Sci. 70:349–351.

Sficas, A. G. 1966. Genetical information obtained in attempts to incorporate blue mold resistance into Oriental tobaccos. Pages 669–676 in: Proc. Int. Tob. Sci. Congr. 4th, Athens. National Tobacco Board of Greece, Athens.

Sficas, A. G., and Ioannidis, N. M. 1980. Performance of Oriental and burley tobacco hybrids in Greece. Tob. Sci. 42:97–101.

Smith-White, S., Macindoe, S. L., and Atkinson, W. T. 1936. Resistance of *Nicotiana* species to blue mould (*Peronospora tabacina* Adam). J. Aust. Inst. Agric. Sci. 2:26–29.

Stover, R. H., and Koch, L. W. 1951. The epidemiology of blue mold of tobacco and its relation to the incidence of disease in Ontario. Sci. Agric. 31:225–252.

Ternovskii, M. F., and Lar'kina, N. L. 1978. Remote hybridization as a method of creating initial material resistant to *Peronospora tabacina* Adam. Sov. Genet. (Engl. Trans.) 14:738–745.

Ternovskii, M. F., Lar'kina, N. L., and Moiseeva, M. E. 1977. Study of the interspecific hybrid immunnyi 580 × *Nicotiana otophora*. Sov. Genet. (Engl. Trans.) 13:666–671.

Todd, F. 1983. The blue mold situation in Central America and Caribbean region. Pages 14–19 in: Blue Mold Symp. 3rd, Tob. Workers Conf. 30th. J. J. Reilly, compiler. Virginia Polytechnic Institute and State University, Williamsburg. 61 pp.

Tuzun, S., and Kuć, J. 1985. Movement of a factor in tobacco infected with *Peronospora tabacina* Adam which systemically protects against blue mold. Physiol. Plant Pathol. 26:321–330.

Vinogradov, V. A., Ternovskii, M. F., Ivanenko, B. G., and Sarychev, Y. F. 1975. Types and genetic sources of blue mold resistance in tobacco. Genetika 12:14–20.

Wark, D. C. 1963. *Nicotiana* species as sources of resistance to blue mould (*Peronospora tabacina* Adam) for cultivated tobacco. Pages 252–259 in: Proc. World Tob. Sci. Congr., 3rd, Salisbury, Southern Rhodesia. Tobacco Research Board, Harare, Zimbabwe. 644 pp.

Wark, D. C. 1970. Development of flue-cured tobacco cultivars resistant to a common strain of blue mould. Tob. Sci. 14:147–150.

Wark, D. C., Wuttke, H. H., and Brouwer, H. M. 1976. Resistance of eight tobacco lines to blue mould in South Queensland, Australia. Tob. Sci. 20:110–113.

Wuttke, H. H. 1969. Different levels of resistance in blue mold resistant tobacco. Aust. J. Agric. Anim. Husb. 9:545–548.

Wuttke, H. H. 1972. Blue mould resistance in tobacco. Aust. Tob. Grow. Bull. 20:6–10.

Chapter 6

Specificity of *Peronospora hyoscyami*

M. L. Menetrez
Plant Pathology Department
North Carolina State University
Raleigh, North Carolina 27695

H. W. Spurr, Jr.
U.S. Department of Agriculture
Agricultural Research Service
Oxford, North Carolina 27565-1555
and
Plant Pathology Department
North Carolina State University
Raleigh, North Carolina 27695

The blue mold pathogen, *Peronospora hyoscyami* de Bary (syn. *P. tabacina* Adam), like all other downy mildews shows a high degree of host specificity (Ingram, 1981). This obligate fungal pathogen infects and causes major economic damage to tobacco only (Lucas, 1980). Although *P. hyoscyami* has been reported to infect tomatoes, peppers, eggplant, and ornamentals such as petunias (Armstrong and Albert, 1933; Mandryk, 1971), all indications are that the fungus can complete its life cycle only when it has infected *Nicotiana*.

Tobacco appears to have something unique that is "recognized" by the pathogen. Leaf surface constituents, amino acids, sugars, and other nutritionally required chemicals have been tested, but without success, to determine the pathogen's specific requirement for tobacco (Crute, 1981; Shepherd, 1962). Biochemical interactions between the tobacco leaf and fungal spores or mycelium may be necessary to the development of a functional relationship between host and pathogen. The molecular events involved in plant-pathogen recognition are unknown (Ralton et al, 1987).

In this chapter, we present a molecular model that may explain the specificity of *P. hyoscyami* with its host. Our definition of specificity of *P. hyoscyami* is related to this proposed model and is supported by cytological observations. We also discuss current and future research on the specificity of *P. hyoscyami.*

Specificity

A DEFINITION

Specificity implies interaction, communication, and recognition between host and microbe. When interactive communication between plant and microbe results in mutual recognition, specificity is the outcome. The recognition event in the pathogen stimulates it to continue development on the host. The recognition event in the plant elicits resistance mechanisms, which, if effective, prevent further development of the pathogen. Plant-pathogen interactions are not random events; they are the result of many years of coevolution (Hogenboom, 1983). Specificity can depend on a simple interaction, such as plant sensitivity to a fungal toxin, or may involve more complex interactions, such as are observed in legume-*Rhizobium* relationships (Lippincott and Lippincott, 1984). How can fungal spores and tobacco leaves interact, communicate, and recognize? Biochemical interactions, communication, and recognition between *P. hyoscyami* and the tobacco plant are possible.

A MODEL

Membrane-bound receptors and their complementary signals have been implicated in animal cell recognition (Halverson and Stacey, 1986). A similar mechanism could determine specificity of *P. hyoscyami* for *Nicotiana*. Because *P. hyoscyami* is an obligate pathogen, it must interact with living hosts to complete its life cycle (Ingram, 1981). Living hosts may produce necessary macromolecules which are not produced by nonliving tissue or are not available to the fungus on culture media. Mutual recognition between *P. hyoscyami* and tobacco could occur when specific signal molecules on the fungal surface bind to specific complementary receptor molecules on the surface of the tobacco leaf. The formation of the fungal-signal/tobacco-receptor complex would cause the fungus to recognize the tobacco plant as a possible host. The signal-receptor complex would also allow the plant to recognize the fungus as a pathogen.

A series of biochemical reactions leading to recognition would begin when the signal molecule interacts with the receptor, resulting in increases in the intracellular concentration of biomolecules called "second messengers" (Sutherland, 1972). Formation of one signal-receptor complex can cause a great increase

166

in the number of second messenger molecules, such as cyclic adenosine monophosphate (AMP) or calcium (Means and Dedham, 1980; Pastan, 1972), which magnify the initial interaction between host and parasite. Second messengers, through their impact on enzyme activity, alter certain processes, including translation and transcription, which eventually results in metabolic and morphological changes in both organisms (Means and Dedham, 1980; Pastan, 1972; Sutherland, 1972). Biological changes in the fungus allow it to successfully penetrate and infect tobacco. Formation of the signal-receptor complex and subsequent intracellular changes in tobacco would lead to metabolic processes directed toward resisting further development of the pathogen.

Plant resistance mechanisms are summoned in all interactions between *P. hyoscyami* and tobacco regardless of whether the tobacco cultivar involved is resistant or susceptible. Susceptible cultivars, however, are unable to adequately limit fungal development. The resistance of susceptible tobacco cultivars against the pathogen may be insufficient because of an inadequate number of receptors on tobacco leaf surfaces or insufficient magnification of the initial signal. Susceptible tobacco is thus unable to effectively stop fungal growth and development.

Thus, the recognition events that are part of the phenomenon of specificity between tobacco and *P. hyoscyami* lead to resistance by tobacco and penetration and development by the fungus. These combined biological changes in the host and parasite are eventually observed as blue mold disease.

The tobacco plant interacts with *P. hyoscyami* during all stages of fungal development: prepenetration, penetration, internal development, and sporulation. We propose that specificity of *P. hyoscyami* is determined during penetration or early internal development of the fungus. A lectin, a tobacco leaf cell wall or cell membrane receptor protein that binds carbohydrates, could be involved. *P. hyoscyami* spores may have carbohydrates on their surfaces that serve as signals and bind to the lectins on tobacco. After germination, *P. hyoscyami* links with the tobacco leaf lectin, forming a carbohydrate-lectin complex. The signal-receptor interaction biochemically communicates to the fungus that a physiological change must occur. Later, chemical and physical changes result in the formation of infection pegs, vesicles, and eventually hyphae and haustoria. Interaction with the fungal sporeling communicates to the tobacco plant that it must call into action all available resistance mechanisms. The plant then undergoes biological changes that help it resist fungal infection.

Most solanaceous plants appear to have specific receptors of *P. hyoscyami*. The severity of blue mold disease depends on the number of receptor molecules on the surface of the plants and on the ability of the various genera to quickly and effectively summon their natural defenses. Some plants, such as petunia, unlike tobacco can quickly and effectively summon resistance mechanisms when first attacked by the blue mold pathogen. Genera related to *Nicotiana,* such as *Petunia hybrida* Vilm., may have receptors or molecules similar to true host receptors. *P. hyoscyami* spores not only germinate on petunia leaf surfaces but also penetrate the leaf surface, indicating that the fungus recognizes the petunia plant as a possible host. Petunias, however, localize and limit fungal development, and the pathogen is unable to develop further and complete its life cycle (Mandryk, 1971). Other solanaceous plants, such as pepper, interact with *P. hyoscyami* in a manner similar to that of petunia (Mandryk, 1971).

Plant characters relevant to host-parasite relationships may evolve from environmental influences (Hogenboom, 1983). These new host characters may be unfavorable, favorable, or neutral to the parasite. Tobacco may have evolved characters favorable to *P. hyoscyami,* whereas other solanaceous plants developed mechanisms that make establishment of the pathogen more difficult. Nonsolanaceous plants such as *Phaseolus* are taxonomically unrelated to true hosts of *P. hyoscyami* and therefore do not contain the necessary receptors. The pathogen may germinate on the surface of the nonhost, but its development within the plant will be aborted. *P. hyoscyami* spores will germinate and form long, slim germ tubes on *Phaseolus* but will not penetrate the bean leaf surface. Because the bean leaf cells do not contain receptors, the *P. hyoscyami* sporelings are unable to form the necessary signal-receptor complex. Consequently, the fungus does not recognize the bean plant as a host, and its metabolic processes continue to be directed toward germ tube elongation. Formation of longer and longer germ tubes depletes energy reserves, and the sporelings eventually starve.

OF *P. HYOSCYAMI*

Few facts are known about the host-pathogen relationships of tobacco with the blue mold pathogen. The plant-microbe relationship of susceptible tobacco with *P. hyoscyami* has been studied cytologically (Henderson, 1937; McKeen and Svircev, 1981; Milholland et al, 1981a; Svircev and McKeen, 1982; Trigiano et al, 1982, 1983a, 1983b, 1985). However, only two cytological comparisons of the interaction of susceptible and resistant tobacco with *P. hyoscyami* have been reported (Kröber and Petzold, 1972; Mandryk, 1971). Unfortunately, Mandryk (1971) began his observations 96 hr after inoculation, and Kröber and Petzold (1972) began their observations 12 hr after infection. Germination, penetration, and internal development of P. hyoscyami occur 4–6 hr (Henderson, 1937) or 0.5–4 hr (McKeen and Svircev, 1981) after inoculation. Therefore, many host-pathogen interactions determining specificity may have occurred by 4 hr after inoculation. Because they give us a time course of infection of the tobacco leaf by the pathogen, cytological studies are a logical beginning for the study of specificity. Our current research on specificity of the blue mold pathogen is based on a time sequence related to the infection process wherein we examine leaf surface phenomena that may be involved in determining recognition between tobacco and P. hyoscyami.

Prepenetration

ARRIVAL AND ADHERENCE

Interactions between tobacco and the blue mold pathogen begin at the prepenetration stage of fungal development, that is, with the arrival, adherence, and germination of fungal spores on leaf surfaces. Windblown P. hyoscyami spores land randomly on a rough and irregular cuticular leaf surface. They encounter other microorganisms, pollen, insects, debris, trichomes, leaf surface chemicals, and exudates. Once the spores land, they bind strongly to the tobacco leaf surface (Menetrez and Spurr, 1987). The ability of fungal spores to adhere to leaf surfaces is a key step in the initiation of disease because surface penetration by the fungus may not be possible without it (Bartnicki-Garcia, 1984).

Spores of the blue mold pathogen bind to surfaces nonspecifically (Menetrez and Spurr, 1987). When we placed wet P. hyoscyami spores on glass and on tobacco, tomato, petunia, and bean leaf disks and tested for adherence, ungerminated and germinated spores adhered strongly to all surfaces. Treating the spores with a protease resulted in a significant decrease in binding only to tobacco leaf surfaces. Adhesion of P. hyoscyami to tobacco appears therefore to be specific.

GERMINATION

Moistened P. hyoscyami spores have the ability to use stored reserves to germinate. Germination occurs on any surface after water-soluble inhibitors of fungal protein synthesis are removed (Hollomon, 1969, 1971, 1973). With many fungi, spore germination ends by the formation of appressoria, the bulbous end of the germ tube that initiates host penetration (Emmett and Parbery, 1975; Littlefield and Bracker, 1972). The presence of appressoria on P.

169

hyoscyami germ tubes, however, is uncertain. Henderson (1937) and Trigiano et al (1983a) describe *P. hyoscyami* appressoria as small and inconspicuous. Other biotrophs, such as the bean rust pathogen (*Uromyces phaseoli* (Reben.) Wint. var. *typica* Arth.), form distinct appressoria and are stimulated to do so by host surface topography (Wynn, 1976). We found, however, that *P. hyoscyami* germ tube morphology was not influenced by isolated tobacco cuticles.

We then considered the possibility that leaf surface chemicals influence spore germination and morphology. A number of the more common leaf surface chemicals, such as α- and β-4,8,13-duvatriene-1,3-diols (DVT-diols), and others not frequently studied, such as α- and β-4,8,13-duvatrienols (DVT-ols), were isolated and tested. The DVT-diols, which are a major component of the leaf cuticle in *N. tabacum* (Cruickshank et al, 1977), were inhibitory to spore germination, as expected. The DVT-ols sucrose esters and hydrocarbon fractions of the isolated chemicals did not inhibit spore germination but also did not influence sporeling morphology (Menetrez et al, 1987). Other compounds that may be important in the specific interaction of *P. hyoscyami* with tobacco leaf surfaces were tested for their effect on spore germination. Spores were incubated with various concentrations of cadaverine, putrescine, spermine, spermidine (Perdrizet and Prevost, 1981), *N*-acetyl glucosamine, glucosamine (Mayama et al, 1975), and dibutryl cyclic monophosphate (Staples and Hoch, 1984). None of the compounds had a significant effect on spore germination. Glucosamine was the only chemical that influenced germ tube morphology; all concentrations of glucosamine caused multiple branching of germ tubes and production of appressoriumlike structures. Appressorium-like structures were also observed at the end of germ tubes when spores germinated on water agar and on tobacco and bean leaf disks. The appressoriumlike structures observed at the ends of *P. hyoscyami* germ tubes are not known to initiate host penetration. Thus we cannot conclude that *P. hyoscyami* germ tubes form appressoria. Nevertheless, it can be concluded that formation of these appressoriumlike structures in *P. hyoscyami* is indiscriminate and unrelated to host recognition.

Penetration and Internal Development

Germinated spores of *P. hyoscyami* penetrate tobacco leaf surfaces directly (Henderson, 1937; McKeen and Svircev, 1981). There are indications that fungal penetration is achieved enzymatically (McKeen and Svircev, 1981). Once the fungus has penetrated, intercellular and intracellular hyphae are formed throughout the leaf tissue (Henderson, 1937; Milholland et al, 1981b;

Trigiano et al, 1983b). Haustoria are initiated as lateral branches of intercellular hyphae (Trigiano et al, 1983b). These intracellular structures penetrate leaf cell walls but only invaginate leaf cell plasma membranes.

There is cytological evidence of resistance to *P. hyoscyami* in susceptible tobacco cultivars during internal development of the fungus (Kröber and Petzold, 1972; Trigiano et al, 1983a). In describing haustorial development of *P. hyoscyami* in infected susceptible tobacco, Trigiano et al (1983b) found papilla formation before haustoria penetrated host cell walls. The formation of papillae is a host resistance mechanism that aids in the exclusion of the pathogen and has been observed, for example, in resistance of barley to powdery mildew infection (Bushnell and Bergquist, 1975). Haustoria, observed by Trigiano et al (1983b) and by Kröber and Petzold (1972) in blue mold-infected tobacco, were always encased by calloselike material. Encasement of haustoria was also associated with resistance and was considered a rare occurrence in compatible interactions (Littlefield and Bracker, 1972). Svircev and McKeen (1982), however, did not observe papillae, nor did they always observe encased haustoria in their cytological studies of *P. hyoscyami*-infected tobacco. Kröber and Petzold (1972) observed resistance to *P. hyoscyami* in susceptible and resistant plants during internal development of the pathogen. The only difference in reaction to infection by the two types of plants was in the speed at which the plants limited the infection process. Infected host cells were rapidly destroyed in resistant plants, and fungal hyphae and haustoria were arrested. The attacked host cells and fungal structures in the susceptible plants become necrotic much later in the disease process.

Histochemical analysis of enzyme activity in tobacco plants also identified host resistance to infection by *P. hyoscyami* (Edreva and Georgieva, 1980). Glucosidases are plant cell wall enzymes that may be involved in plant disease resistance (Halverson and Stacey, 1986). Changes in the activity of α- and β-glucosidases were determined histochemically in resistant and susceptible tobacco cultivars infected with *P. hyoscyami* (Edreva and Georgieva, 1980). Glucosidase activity increased in both cultivars, but the increase in the resistant cultivar was much more rapid than that in the susceptible cultivar.

Detailed comparative histological descriptions of interactions occurring at interfaces of *P. hyoscyami* with nonhosts, resistant and susceptible hosts, and other potential hosts such as petunia and pepper could provide valuable information. They would supply pictorial references from which we might begin to understand the various ways in which different hosts communicate with *P.*

171

hyoscyami. As mentioned above, plant species from genera related to *Nicotiana* have been reportedly infected by the blue mold pathogen (Armstrong and Albert, 1933; Hill, 1966; Mandryk, 1971). All but one of the reported infections were based entirely on macroscopic evaluation of disease severity. The blue mold disease development reported in the various genera by different laboratories varied greatly. According to Armstrong and Albert (1933), sporulation occurred on blue mold-infected tobacco, pepper, tomato, and eggplant, whereas Mandryk (1971) reported only limited disease development when genera besides *Nicotiana* were inoculated with *P. hyoscyami*. When tomato (cultivar Saturn), petunia (cultivar P35), and bush beans (cultivar Blue Lake) were inoculated with *P. hyoscyami* in our laboratory, none of the inoculated plants showed signs of disease either macroscopically or microscopically. Conflicting reports on disease severity from the various laboratories are indicative of incomplete documentation. Precise documentation, including information on age, vigor, and cultivar, is important. Detailed macroscopic data in conjunction with microscopic evidence of disease development are also required for investigations of recognition events.

Concluding Remarks

Specificity is a mutual recognition between interacting organisms; it is an ongoing process of communication. Specificity can be determined at early and late stages of host-pathogen interactions. We have established that specificity of *P. hyoscyami* is not determined during early establishment of the fungus. Arrival, adhesion, and spore germination are nonspecific. Fungal specificity for tobacco appears to be determined during penetration or initial internal development of the pathogen. A specific receptor, possibly a tobacco lectin, could be involved. At present we do not have enough information to determine precisely where specificity of *P. hyoscyami* is actually determined.

A multifaceted research approach to understanding the unique conversation between *P. hyoscyami* and tobacco and additional detailed cytological studies of hosts and nonhosts with *P. hyoscyami* are required. Biochemical studies can determine the identities and involvement of fungal and plant enzymes, lectins, and other possible receptors as well as determine the importance of molecules such as cyclic AMP. Physiological studies during disease development can determine changes in host and pathogen processes such as respiration, protein and nucleic acid metabolism, photosynthesis, growth regulator metabolism, and transpiration. Some progress has already been made toward understanding the host-pathogen relationship of *P. hyoscyami* and tobacco. At present, however, there are more questions than answers concerning specificity of the blue mold pathogen. The study of specificity and plant-pathogen relationships is a challenging, frustrating, and intellectually rewarding endeavor.

Acknowledgment

We thank Clyde Wesley Adcock for technical assistance.

LITERATURE CITED

Armstrong, G. M., and Albert, W. B. 1933. Downy mildew of tobacco on pepper, tomato and eggplant. Plant Dis. Rep. 17:837–839.

Bartnicki-Garcia, S. 1984. Spore germination in fungi: Basic concepts. Pages 111–117 in: Infection Process of Fungi. D. W. Roberts and J. A. Aist, eds. Rockefeller Foundation, New York. 201 pp.

Bushnell, W. R., and Bergquist, S. E. 1975. Aggregation of host cytoplasm and the formation of papillae and haustoria in powdery mildew of barley. Phytopathology 65:310–318.

Cruickshank, I. A. M., Perrin, D. R., and Mandryk, M. 1977. Fungitoxicity of duvatrienediols associated with the cuticular wax of tobacco leaves. Phytopathol. Z. 90:243–249.

Crute, I. R. 1981. The host specificity of peronosporaceous fungi and the genetics of the relationship between host and parasite. Pages 237–253 in: The Downy Mildews. D. M. Spencer, ed. Academic Press, London. 636 pp.

Edreva, A. M., and Georgieva, J. D. 1980. Biochemical and histochemical investigations of α- and β-glucosidase activity in an infectious disease, a physiological disorder and senescence of tobacco leaves. Physiol. Plant Pathol. 17:237–243.

Emmett, R. W., and Parbery, D. G. 1975. Appressoria. Annu. Rev. Phytopathol. 13:147–167.

Halverson, L. J., and Stacey, G. 1986. Signal exchange in plant-microbe interactions. Microbiol. Rev. 50:193–225.

Henderson, R. G. 1937. Studies on tobacco downy mildew in Virginia. Va. Agric. Exp. Stn. Tech. Bull. 62. 20 pp.

Hill, A. V. 1966. Physiologic specialization in *Peronospora tabacina* Adam in Australia. CORESTA Inf. Bull. 1:7–15.

Hogenboom, N. G. 1983. Bridging a gap between related fields of research: Pistil-pollen relationships and the distinction between incompatibility and incongruity in nonfunctioning host-parasite relationships. Phytopathology 73:381–383.

Hollomon, D. W. 1969. Biochemistry of germination in *Peronospora tabacina* (Adam) conidia: Evidence for the existence of stable messenger RNA. J. Gen. Microbiol. 55:267–274.

Hollomon, D. W. 1971. Protein synthesis during germination of *Peronospora tabacina* (Adam) conidia. Arch. Biochem. Biophys. 145:643–649.

Hollomon, D. W. 1973. Protein synthesis during germination of

Peronospora tabacina conidia: An examination of the events involved in the initiation of germination. J. Gen. Microbiol. 78:1–13.

Ingram, D. S. 1981. The biochemistry of host-parasite interactions. Pages 143–163 in: The Downy Mildews. D. M. Spencer, ed. Academic Press, London. 636 pp.

Kröber, H., and Petzold, H. 1972. Licht- und elektronen-mikroskopische untersuchungen über wirt-parasit-beziehungen bei anfälligen und gegen *Peronospora* spp. resisten gezüchteten sorten von Tabac und Spinat. Phytopathol. Z. 74:296–313.

Lippincott, J. A., and Lippincott, B. B. 1984. Concepts and experimental approaches in host-microbe recognition. Pages 195–258 in: Plant-Microbe Interactions: Molecular and Genetic Perspectives. Vol. 1. T. Kosuge and E. W. Nester, eds. Macmillan Publishing, New York. 494 pp.

Littlefield, L. J., and Bracker, C. E. 1972. Ultrastructural specialization at the host-pathogen interface in rust infected flax. Protoplasma 74:271–305.

Lucas, G. B. 1980. The war against blue mold. Science 210:147–153.

Mandryk, M. 1971. Resistance of solanaceous and nonsolanaceous species to *Peronospora tabacina* as shown by necrotrophic reactions. Aust. J. Exp. Agric. Anim. Husb. 11:94–98.

Mayama, S., Rehfeld, D. W., and Daly, J. M. 1975. A comparison of the development of *Puccinia graminis tritici* in resistant and susceptible wheat based on glucosamine content. Physiol. Plant Pathol. 7:243–257.

McKeen, W. E., and Svircev, A. M. 1981. Early development of *Peronospora tabacina* in the *Nicotiana tabacum* leaf. Can. J. Plant Pathol. 3:145–158.

Means, A. R., and Dedham, J. R. 1980. Calmodulin: An intracellular calcium receptor. Nature 285:73–77.

Menetrez, M. L., and Spurr, H. W., Jr. 1987. Non-specific adhesion of *Peronospora tabacina* spores. (Abstr.) Phytopathology 77:1692.

Menetrez, M. L., Spurr, H. W., Jr., Danehower, D. A., and Lawson, D. R. 1987. Toxicity of tobacco leaf surface chemicals to *Peronospora tabacina*. (Abstr.) Page 44 in: Proc. Tob. Chem. Res. Conf., 4–7 Oct., Greensboro, NC.

Milholland, R. D., Lucas, G. B., and Daykin, M. E. 1981a. Histological examination of *Peronospora tabacina* in flue-cured tobacco. Tob. Int. 25:112–113.

Milholland, R. D., Papadopoulou, J., and Daykin, M. 1981b. Histopathology of *Peronospora tabacina* in systemically infected burley tobacco. Phytopathology 71:73–76.

Pastan, I. 1972. Cyclic AMP. Sci. Am. 227:97–105.

Perdrizet, E., and Prevost, J. 1981. Aliphatic and aromatic amines during development of *Nicotiana tabacum*. Phytochemistry 20:2131–2134.

Ralton, J. E., Smart, M. G., and Clarke, A. E. 1987. Recognition and infection processes in plant-pathogen interactions. Pages 217–252 in: Plant-Microbe Interactions: Molecular and Genetic Perspectives. Vol. 2. T. Kosuge and E. W. Nester, eds. Macmillan Publishing, New York. 448 pp.

Shepherd, C. J. 1962. Germination of conidia of *Peronospora tabacina* Adam. Aust. J. Biol. Sci. 15:483–510.

Staples, R. C., and Hoch, H. C. 1984. A sensing mechanism in rust uredospore germlings responsive to host morphology starts the cell cycle.

Pages 126–201 in: Infection Process of Fungi. D. W. Roberts and J. A. Aist, eds. Rockefeller Foundation, New York. 201 pp.

Sutherland, E. W. 1972. Studies on the mechanism of hormone action. Science 177:401–408.

Svircev, A. M., and McKeen, W. E. 1982. The haustorium of *Peronospora hyoscyami* f. sp. *tabacina* in the susceptible tobacco leaf cell. Can. J. Plant Pathol. 4:119–128.

Trigiano, R. N., Van Dyke, C. G., and Spurr, H. W., Jr. 1982. Haustoria of *Peronospora tabacina* in tobacco. (Abstr.) Phytopathology 72:711.

Trigiano, R. N., Van Dyke, C. G., and Spurr, H. W., Jr. 1983a. Blue mold: The development of the pathogen. Pages 6–14 in: Blue Mold Symp. 3rd, Tob. Workers Conf. 30th. J. J. Reilly, compiler. Virginia Polytechnic Institute and State University, Williamsburg. 61 pp.

Trigiano, R. N., Van Dyke, C. G., and Spurr, H. W., Jr. 1983b. Haustorial development of *Peronospora tabacina* infecting *Nicotiana tabacum*. Can. J. Bot. 61:3444–3453.

Trigiano, R. N., Van Dyke, C. G., Spurr, H. W., Jr., and Main, C. E. 1985. Ultrastructure of sporangiophore and sporangium ontogeny of *Peronospora tabacina*. Tob. Sci. 29:116–121.

Wynn, W. K. 1976. Appressorium formation over stomates by the bean rust fungus: Response to a surface contact stimulus. Phytopathology 66:136–146.

Chapter 7

Induced Systemic Resistance to Blue Mold of Tobacco

S. Tuzun
J. Kuć
Department of Plant Pathology
University of Kentucky
Lexington, Kentucky 40546

> *The Wonder of Science*
> "To see what everybody else has seen
> and think what nobody else has thought"
> —Albert Szent-Györgyi

Plants, unlike animals, cannot move to avoid harmful organisms and deleterious environmental effects. Animals survive in a changing environment by locomotion as well as by behavioral and physiological changes, whereas plants do so in the short term by regulating their physiology and in the long term by developmental changes. To survive, a plant must cope with its immediate environment.

Plants not only have survived environmental changes but also have coevolved with potentially harmful organisms, including herbivores, insects, nematodes, fungi, bacteria, and viruses. During this evolution plants acquired multiple mechanisms for defense against harmful organisms. Multiple mechanisms were necessary not only to protect plants from the multitude of hostile organisms, but also to provide adequate defenses against any one organism. A single defense compound with a single site of action would not likely be adequate for survival.

Most organisms do not appreciably damage or cause disease on most plants. The lack of damage may be attributed to preformed chemical or physical factors or to the ability of the plant to respond to the presence of nonself. The lack of obvious macroscopic damage, however, does not necessarily mean a lack of plant response. Microorganisms may cause rapid but restricted damage on plants which is either barely visible macroscopically or requires microscopic examination for detection. Because the microorganism's development is contained, inoculum for further inoculation is restricted and the plant grows and develops without appreciable damage. Plants in or on which organisms develop and reproduce are called hosts; but this coexistence does not always result in disease or have a harmful effect on plant growth and development. To survive, plants must have evolved highly effective defense mechanisms against all organisms in their environment and thus must have transmissible information for activating such mechanisms. Modern agriculture, however, demands high plant yields, quality, and uniformity. These expectations impose an unnatural selection pressure for plant survival, with accompanying risks including loss of genetic diversity and dependence upon chemical pesticides for disease control.

Plants are commonly considered resistant to disease when their economic or aesthetic value is not significantly reduced. Resistance, therefore, is often defined not molecularly or physiologically but economically. However, mechanisms for resistance are commonly observed in susceptible plants (Dean and Kuć, 1985; Deverall, 1977; Kuć, 1981, 1982a, 1982b, 1982c, 1983, 1984, 1985a, 1985b, 1987a, 1987b; Kuć and Rush, 1985; Kuć and Tuzun, 1983; Salt and Kuć, 1985). Different parts of plants may react differently to the same organism, and different types of symptoms can even be seen on the same leaf. As a classic example, the first three to four expanding leaves of apple shoots are often susceptible to apple scab caused by *Venturia inaequalis* (Cke.) Wint., and all others are resistant (Biehn et al, 1966; Grijseels et al, 1964; Nusbaum and Keitt, 1938), even in cultivars considered commercially susceptible. The timing and magnitude of gene expression for resistance mechanisms and the effect of internal and external environment on the activity of gene products are major determinants of resistance. Physiological resistance and "economic" susceptibility can thus be observed on the same cultivar, and "economic" resistance can be induced by environmental factors (Day, 1974; Kuć, 1981, 1982a, 1982b, 1982c, 1983, 1984, 1985a, 1985b, 1987a, 1987b; Kuć and Rush, 1985; Kuć and Tuzun, 1983; Ouchi, 1983). It appears more realistic, therefore, to discuss the timing and magnitude of responses rather than the presence or absence of genes for such responses.

Induction of resistance (immunization) to disease after initial infection has been observed for more than 100 years (Chester, 1933), and many examples of this very interesting phenomenon have been reported in the literature (Dean and Kuć, 1985; Kuć, 1981, 1982a, 1982b, 1982c, 1983, 1985a; Kuć and Tuzun, 1983; Loebenstein, 1972; Sequeira, 1979). In our laboratory we have investigated several aspects of immunization of green bean, tobacco, potato, apple, pear, cucumber, muskmelon, and watermelon (Kuć, 1981, 1982a, 1982b, 1982c, 1983, 1984, 1985a, 1985b, 1987a, 1987b; Kuć and Rush, 1985; Kuć and Tuzun, 1983). In this chapter, we will discuss the immunization of tobacco against viral, bacterial, and fungal pathogens, particularly the blue mold fungus, *Peronospora hyoscyami* de Bary (syn. *P. tabacina* Adam). For additional information, see the recent reviews by Kuć and Tuzun (1983), Salt and Kuć (1985), and Tuzun (1986).

Immunization of Tobacco Against Diseases Caused by Viruses

Ross and co-workers reported localized (Ross, 1959, 1961a) and systemic (Ross, 1961b, 1966; Ross and Bozarth, 1960) resistance against disease caused by tobacco mosaic virus (TMV) following inoculation with this virus on hypersensitive *Nicotiana tabacum* NN. Localized protection was not specific to TMV (Ross, 1961a), and necrotic lesions caused by TMV in three or four lower leaves induced resistance to TMV in up to 16 uninoculated leaves (Ross, 1961b, 1966). Protection lasted for at least 42 days, the longest period tested. Resistance was expressed as a reduction in lesion size and number and appeared stable within a broad range of temperatures, light conditions, inoculum concentrations, and nutrient levels (Ross, 1966). Protection was reported to be transmitted to progeny via seed (Roberts, 1983). Subsequent studies demonstrated that resistance can also be induced in tobacco lacking the *N* gene for hypersensitivity (Fraser, 1979).

Mechanical injury does not induce resistance (Ross, 1966); however, many agents induce resistance to TMV: yeast RNA (Cheo et al, 1968; Gicherman and Loebenstein, 1968), RNA isolated from different plants (Cheo et al, 1968), leaf extracts of several plant species (Verma and Awasthi, 1979, 1980; Verma and Dwivedi, 1984; Verma and Mukerjee, 1977, 1979; Verma et al, 1984), polyinosinic, polycytidylic acid, double-stranded RNA (Stein and Loebenstein, 1970), acetyl salicylic acid (White, 1979), mineral oil (White and Forde, 1985), polyacrylic acid (Gianinazzi and Kassanis, 1974), and a synthetic polyanion (Stein et al, 1979).

The sensitivity of immunization to heat (Ross and Israel, 1970) and protein synthesis inhibitors (Loebenstein et al, 1969; Ota and Taniguchi, 1978; Sela et al, 1969) suggested protein involvement in induced resistance. Antiviral factors (AVFs) or interfering agents were isolated (Sela, 1981; Sela et al, 1966) which appear to be phosphorylated glycoproteins (Mozes et al, 1978; Sela et al, 1966). Interferon prepared from human leukocytes and a synthetic interferon markedly suppressed the multiplication of TMV in tobacco (Orchansky et al, 1982; Rosenberg et al, 1985). Interferon applied before inoculation or within the first hour after inoculation apparently inhibited both TMV-RNA replication and its expression into coat protein (Rosenberg et al, 1985). Further studies indicated that nucleotides with antiviral activity were produced when tobacco tissues were infected with TMV (Reichman et al, 1983). Such nucleotides were not produced when tobacco tissues were treated with human leukocyte interferon or AVF prepared from infected tobacco cells. However, when a polymerase fraction from such tissues was incubated with adenosine triphosphate (ATP) and poly-inosinic, polycytidylic acid, the resultant polymerized ATP markedly inhibited TMV multiplication (Reichman et al, 1983).

Another inhibitor of viral replication (IVR) was isolated from liquid medium containing protoplasts of a local-lesion tobacco infected with TMV (Loebenstein and Gera, 1981) and callus cultures of tobacco (Gat-Edelbaum et al, 1983). The IVR was composed of components with molecular weight 26,000 and 57,000 and appeared to be proteinaceous (Gera and Loebenstein, 1983). The IVR may be indicative of a general stress response in plants that results in the accumulation of a broad spectrum of rather low-molecular-weight proteins. Some of the proteins may directly inhibit the development of infectious agents, whereas others may regulate mechanisms for resistance. Such proteins are frequently referred to as b-proteins, stress proteins, or pathogenesis-related proteins (Gianinazzi et al, 1977; Rohloff and Lerch, 1977). They are also produced in response to bacterial (Ahl et al, 1981) and fungal (Gianinazzi et al, 1980) pathogens of tobacco; however, involvement of such proteins in disease resistance has not been established (Fraser, 1981, 1982).

To elucidate the molecular mechanism of induced resistance to TMV infection, a cDNA clone encoding the nonstructural, 30,000-mol-wt protein of the common strain of TMV was isolated, characterized, and subcloned into SP6 vectors (Oliver et al, 1986). Capped RNAs produced by in vitro transcription reactions, translated in a wheat germ cell-free system, indicated that an intact and functional 30,000-mol-wt protein gene had been cloned (Oliver et al, 1986). Furthermore, a chimeric gene containing a cloned cDNA of the virus coat protein under the control of the cauliflower mosaic virus 35S transcript promoter was introduced into tobacco cells on a tumor-inducing plasmid of *Agrobacterium tumefaciens* (E. F. Smith & Townsend) Conn (Oliver et al, 1986). The transformed plants produced high levels of the virus coat protein and were also protected against TMV (R. N. Beachy, personal communication). These experiments indicated the importance of TMV coat protein in protection and opened new possibilities for crop protection by using plant immunization together with strategies of genetic engineering.

Immunization of Tobacco Against Diseases Caused by Bacteria

Goodman (1978), Goodman et al (1976), Sequeira (1978, 1979, 1983), and Kuć (1983) have reviewed immunization of tobacco against diseases caused by bacteria. Infiltration of heat-killed *Pseudomonas syringae* pv. *tabaci* (Wolf & Foster) Young et al (Lovrekovich and Farkas, 1965) and *Pseudomonas solanacearum* (Smith) Smith (Sequeira et al, 1976) into tobacco leaves induced resistance to the same bacteria. Cells of avirulent and incompatible bacteria were rapidly attached to and enveloped by the host cell wall, whereas virulent strains remained free and multiplied in the intercellular fluid (Sequeira et al, 1977). Attachment of bacteria was suggested to initiate the resistance response. Studies indicated that the lipopolysaccharide portion of bacterial cell walls, especially lipid A section of lipopolysaccharide, was involved in attachment and that lipid A section must be present in a form soluble enough to attach to a receptor, probably a lectin, on the host (Graham et al, 1977). A lectin, with properties identical to those of potato lectin, was extracted from tobacco roots and leaves by infiltration with saline solution and recovery of intercellular fluid by centrifugation (Sequeira, 1978). Such lectins did not function as protectants (Sequeira, 1978); however, they may be involved in recognition. The presence of antibacterial compounds in the intercellular fluid of immunized leaves was reported (Rathmell and Sequeira, 1975; Sequeira and Hill, 1974). Active compounds were heat-stable and had a low molecular weight. One of the compounds appeared to be a terpenoid. It is possible that these compounds, rather than lectins, are involved as inhibitors of bacterial development, and lectins may act as recognition sites for the activation of a defensive reaction(s) that results in the production of such compounds.

Immunization of Tobacco Against Diseases Caused by Fungi

Immunization against blue mold, one of the most devastating diseases of tobacco, is discussed in detail in the following sections. Systemic and localized induced resistance to fungal diseases other than blue mold has been reported. Resistance to black root rot caused by *Thielaviopsis basicola* (Berk. & Br.) Ferr. was induced by prior inoculation with *T. basicola,* tobacco necrosis virus (TNV), TMV (Hecht and Bateman, 1964), or a vesicular-arbuscular mycorrhiza, *Endogone mosseae* (Nicol. & Gerd.) Gerdemann and Trappe (Baltruschat and Schonbeck, 1975). Resistance against another serious fungal disease of tobacco, black shank (caused by *Phytophthora parasitica* Dast. var. *nicotianae* (B. de Haan) Tucker), was induced by a nematode, *Pratylenchus penetrans* (Cobb) Filipjev & Schuurmans-Stekhoven (Inagaki and Powell, 1969; McIntyre and Miller, 1974, 1978); by incompatible races of *Phytophthora parasitica* var. *nicotianae;* by cell-free sonicates of all races of the pathogen (McIntyre and Miller, 1978); and by TMV (McIntyre and Dodds, 1979; McIntyre et al, 1981).

Immunization of Tobacco Against Blue Mold

THE PHENOMENON

A reduction in the severity of blue mold and stunted growth in field-grown tobacco previously infected with the pathogen were reported by Pont in 1959 and confirmed by Cruickshank and Mandryk (1960) and Mandryk (1960) in greenhouse and field experiments. Stem injections with sporangial suspensions of *P. hyoscyami* resulted in the development of high resistance in the foliage to the same fungus about three weeks later (Cohen and Kuć, 1981; Cruickshank and Mandryk, 1960; Mandryk, 1960, 1961). The resistance lasted through flowering and seed set (Cohen and Kuć, 1981; Cruickshank and Mandryk, 1960), but plants were severely stunted. Stunting was partially relieved by high fertilization with nitrogen (Mandryk, 1961). Application of sporangia to the soil surface around stems caused necrosis in the stem and systemically induced resistance but also stunted plant growth (Cohen and Kuć, 1981).

We recently developed a modified technique for stem inoculations (Tuzun, 1986; Tuzun and Kuć, 1985a), which provided protection against blue mold and increased growth of tobacco (Fig. 1). Inoculating tobacco stems outside the xylem induced 90–99% protection against blue mold based on area of necrosis and amount of sporulation relative to controls (Kuć and Tuzun, 1983; Tuzun, 1986; Tuzun and Kuć, 1985a). Protection was about 50% 15 days after stem injection and reached a maximum after 21 days. Unchallenged plants injected with isolate 82 of the fungus were about 40% taller, had about a 30% increase in fresh weight and about a 40% increase in dry weight, had four to six more leaves, and had about 15% more leaf area than control plants at the time the injected plants reached 50% flowering (Tuzun and Kuć, 1985a). Plants injected with isolate 82 reached 50% flowering about two weeks before controls did, but the enhanced growth was evident even when the controls reached 50% flowering (Tuzun and Kuć, 1985a). Increased growth was also observed in field experiments. Plants receiving stem injections had significantly greater height and fresh weight than control plants at normal harvesttimes for controls, unless the injections were done at very early stages of plant growth or if black shank was severe (Tuzun, 1986; Tuzun et al, 1986a). Marketable yield was up to 25% more than that of controls at Kentucky locations. Stem injections decreased the severity of blue mold in six field experiments where the disease developed naturally (Tuzun et al, 1986a), and stem-injected plants were highly protected against metalaxyl-tolerant strains of blue mold in Mexico (Tuzun et al, 1986b). A high degree of protection, without stunting, was also observed on plants with naturally developed stem necrosis in several locations in Mexico (Tuzun et al, 1986b). The cause of this natural stem necrosis at present is not known; however, the necrosis resembled that developed by stem injections with *P. hyoscyami,* and protection was observed only on these plants (Tuzun et al, 1986b).

SPECIFICITY OF INDUCTION AND PROTECTION

Several biological and chemical agents have been tested for their ability to induce systemic resistance to blue mold (Cohen and Kuć, 1981; Kuć and Tuzun, 1983; S. Tuzun and J. Kuć, unpublished). *P. hyoscyami* appears to be the most potent biological inducer of

Figure 1.   Disease symptoms on two tobacco plants that were challenged 21 days after stem inoculation with water (left) and with sporangia of *Peronospora hyoscyami* (right).

183

resistance reported (Cohen and Kuć, 1981; Kuć and Tuzun, 1983). McIntyre et al (1981) reported induced resistance against *P. hyoscyami* by TMV infection of TMV-hypersensitive tobacco; however, Cohen (1978) did not observe the same effect.

Cohen (1978) reported protection against powdery mildew (caused by *Erysiphe cichoracearum* DC.) by prior leaf inoculations with *P. hyoscyami*, but the effect of stem injection with *P. hyoscyami* was not reported. Stem inoculations with *P. hyoscyami* were also reported to induce systemic resistance against TMV (Mandryk, 1963). Heat-killed or sonicated sporangia, as well as three other pathogens and three nonpathogens of tobacco, did not induce resistance to blue mold (Cohen and Kuć, 1981). Nineteen plant-pathogenic fungi belonging to the Peronosporales also failed to induce resistance against blue mold (S. Tuzun and J. Kuć, unpublished), but all of the fungi tested caused necrosis in the stem. However, the necrosis became evident sooner, looked dry, and did not slowly increase in length as did necrosis that developed in stems injected with *P. hyoscyami* (S. Tuzun and J. Kuć, unpublished). Slow development of restricted necrosis may be important in the development of resistance against fungi, bacteria, and viruses in cucumber (Dean and Kuć, 1985; Kuć, 1983).

Of numerous chemicals tested, only β-ionone induced resistance to blue mold (Salt and Kuć, 1985; Salt et al, 1986; Tuzun et al, 1986d). Injection of β-ionone into stems caused increased growth and systemically protected tobacco against blue mold in greenhouse and field tests (Tables 1 and 2). Spraying foliage with β-ionone protected plants in the field but not in the greenhouse (Table 2). As with plants injected with *P. hyoscyami*, early flowering and enhanced suckering accompanied protection and growth increase in plants injected with β-ionone (Salt et al, 1986). β-Ionone also inhibited germination of sporangia ($ED_{50} = 0.15$ ppm) (Leppik et al, 1972). Injections of *P. hyoscyami* sporangia into stem tissue of tobacco plants resulted in a 50- to 600-fold increase in levels of endogenous β-ionone in green, uninjected tissue distant from necrotic lesions but not in the leaves of treated plants (Salt and Kuć, 1985; Salt et al, 1986). The β-ionone did not accumulate in the leaves or nonnecrotic stem tissue of plants injected with β-ionone (Salt et al, 1986).

MOVEMENT OF A PROTECTION FACTOR

Translocation of a factor from the site of inoculation throughout the plant, where it conditions resistance, was implicated in studies with cucurbits inoculated with fungi, bacteria, and viruses (Dean and Kuć, 1985, 1986; Guedes et al, 1980; Kuć, 1982a, 1982b, 1982c, 1983, 1985a, 1985b, 1987a, 1987b). To study the movement of a protection factor produced in the stems of tobacco plants inoculated (immunized) with *P. hyoscyami* sporangia, we girdled plants 10 cm above or below the site of injection at three-day intervals up to 21 days after injection (Tuzun and Kuć, 1985b). Plants girdled above the site of injection on day six or earlier remained susceptible to blue mold (Fig. 2), although enhanced growth was evident with the six-day girdling (Tuzun and Kuć, 1985b). This suggests that protection

Table 1. Effects of injecting stems with sporangia of *Peronospora hyoscyami*, β-ionone, or abscisic acid on growth, morphogenesis, and susceptibility to blue mold of tobacco cultivar Kentucky 14 grown under glasshouse conditions[a]

Treatment[b]	Growth rate[c] (cm/day)	Leaf area with symptoms (%)	Spores[d] (cm⁻²)	Suckering (%)	Flowering index[e]
P. hyoscyami	1.6 a[f]	10 c	325 c	53 a	1.5 a
β-ionone	1.5 a	47 b	2,670 b	69 a	1.6 a
Abscisic acid	0.5 c	57 ab	13,810 a	3 c	0.1 c
Water	1.1 b	61 a	6,980 a	4 c	0.8 b

[a] Reprinted, by permission, from Salt et al (1986).
[b] The experiment was repeated 12 times. The total numbers of plants examined were *P. hyoscyami*, 130; β-ionone, 70; abscisic acid, 35; and water, 137.
[c] From initial treatment of tobacco plant until challenge.
[d] Number of *P. hyoscyami* sporangia harvested per square centimeter of total leaf area.
[e] 0 = No apparent flower primordium; 0.5 = barely detectable primordium, flagging of apical leaves; 1 = mature flower primordium; 2 = initiation of flower opening; 3 = full flowering; 4 = senescent flowers. Plants were rated at the time of challenge.
[f] Numbers followed by different letters indicate significantly different means ($P = 0.01$) as determined by Student's t-test.

Table 2. Effects of stem injection with *Peronospora hyoscyami* and β-ionone treatments on growth and resistance to blue mold of field-grown Kentucky 14 tobacco plants[a]

Treatment	Mean increase in height (cm)	Mean number of infected leaves per plant	Mean number of lesions per plant
Induced resistance (*P. hyoscyami*)	92.6 a	1.75 c	8.59 d
Stem injected with β-ionone	83.6 b	2.90 b	29.46 c
Sprayed with β-ionone	73.5 c	4.93 a	62.98 b
Control	9.7 c	5.23 a	78.20 a

[a] Reprinted, by permission, from Salt et al (1986). Letters designate means significantly different by Duncan-Waller K-ratio t-test ($P = 0.05$). Means represent 80 plants per treatment.

and increase in growth are not related to each other. Girdling below the site of injection decreased neither enhanced growth nor protection. Plants were protected when girdled above the site of injection on day nine or later and challenged 21 days after stem injection (Fig. 2). Protection was significantly reduced when plants were challenged at the time of girdling, nine days after stem injections, compared to protection of plants challenged 21 days after stem injections and girdled nine days after stem injections (Tuzun and Kuć, 1985b). This may indicate that the protection factor may act as a signal for conditioning the cells at the site of challenge and that a lag period is necessary for the signal to take effect. The protection factor was transmitted through grafting from rootstock to scion (Tuzun and Kuć, 1985b). The possibility that β-ionone is a

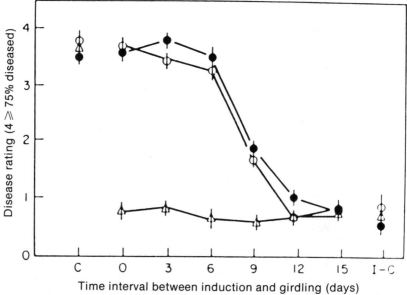

Figure 2. Effect of the time of girdling above or below the site of inoculation with *Peronospora hyoscyami* on the severity of blue mold in foliage of tobacco challenged with the fungus 21 days after stem inoculation. Data for girdling above the site of stem inoculation are from two different experiments (o,•), three plants per treatment per experiment, as representative of six experiments performed. Data for girdling below the site (Δ) are from one experiment with three plants per treatment. Vertical bars indicate standard deviations. Disease ratings were determined seven days after challenge (0 = no evidence of disease; 1 = 1–10%, 2 = 11–39%, 3 = 40–74%, and 4 = 75% or more of leaf area with lesions). C (control) indicates that stem was injected with water and girdled on day 0; I-C (inoculated control) indicates that stem was inoculated but not girdled. (Reprinted, by permission, from Tuzun and Kuć, 1985b)

186

signal was investigated in our laboratory. Gas chromatographic analyses of steam distillates from leaves of tobacco stems injected with β-ionone indicated that β-ionone has little mobility in the plant itself (Salt et al, 1986); it may act as an inducer of a signal, or a metabolite of β-ionone may act as a signal.

PHYSIOLOGICAL CHANGES IN TOBACCO PLANTS INFECTED WITH P. HYOSCYAMI

Inhibitors of Germination

Leppik et al (1972) extracted quiesone, a potent inhibitor of germination of sporangia of P. hyoscyami, in low quantities from tobacco leaves infected with P. hyoscyami. The biological activity of the compound for spore germination is very high ($ED_{50} = 0.0001$ ppm), but it does not inhibit elongation of germ tubes (Leppik et al, 1972). Quiesone was synthesized as a racemic mixture and was shown to be biologically active (Mori, 1973); however, its biological activity was 100-fold less than that of the original compound. Washing spores treated with quiesone diminished the activity, suggesting that the compound does not have an effect on protein synthesis (Leppik et al, 1972). A compound with similar R_f values was extracted from sporangia with acetone. Because the fungus is an obligate parasite, whether quiesone is produced by the host or the fungus is not known.

Shepherd and Mandryk (1962) reported the presence of substances inhibitory to sporangium germination in extracts of N. tabacum stems injected with P. hyoscyami sporangia. These substances were not detected in healthy plants or in N. debneyi plants injected with P. hyoscyami. The very high resistance of N. debneyi to P. hyoscyami may have restricted the development of the fungus and the production of extractable inhibitors. The relation of these compounds to quiesone is not known. It is unlikely, however, that germination inhibitors could be the sole determinant of systemically induced resistance because they are active only as inhibitors of sporangium germination. Immunization is not confined to the epidermis of tobacco (Cohen and Kuć, 1981), and germination of sporangia on immunized plants does not appear to be reduced (Y. Cohen, personal communication). In addition, small, chlorotic, often sterile lesions are formed on the leaves of immunized plants (Tuzun, 1986). The infiltration of germinated and ungerminated sporangia into immunized leaves of tobacco did not overcome resistance (Cohen and Kuć, 1981).

Cruickshank et al (1977) reported that α- and β-4,8,13-duvatriene-1,3-diols (DVTs), associated with cuticular waxes of tobacco, inhibited germination of P. hyoscyami sporangia ($ED_{100} = 25$ ppm).

187

Further studies indicated that DVTs may be involved in age-related resistance of tobacco to blue mold (Reuveni et al, 1986, 1987). Dipping tobacco leaf strips in acetone for 1 sec removed DVTs and part of the resistance of tobacco plants nine weeks old or older; however, older leaves dipped in acetone were less susceptible than undipped leaves of younger tobacco plants (Reuveni et al, 1987). DVT was the only leaf component active against *P. hyoscyami* that was removed by dipping for 1 sec in acetone (Reuveni et al, 1987). Adding leaf extract back to the same tissue from which it was removed by an acetone dip restored resistance (Reuveni et al, 1987), and adding DVT to young, very susceptible leaves to levels found in 15-week-old plants made the young leaves highly resistant (S. Tuzun and J. Kuć, unpublished). Increased levels of DVT, relative to DVT in Kentucky 14, were associated with immunization and in some cases with genetic resistance (Tuzun et al, 1986c). However, some genetically resistant cultivars were resistant without increased levels of DVT, and removal of DVT did not diminish the full resistance of an immunized or genetically resistant plant (Tuzun et al, 1986c). Plants stem-injected with *P. hyoscyami* were resistant under low light conditions without an increase in DVT content (S. Tuzun and J. Kuć, unpublished). These results suggest that DVT may be a part of the general defense mechanism in some genetically resistant cultivars, in susceptible cultivars as a function of aging (Reuveni et al, 1987), and as a result of high light intensity and other stress (Court, 1982; Tuzun et al, 1986c). The content of DVT is not the only determinant of resistance in immunized and nonimmunized plants.

Changes in Soluble Carbohydrate

Soluble carbohydrate increased systemically in tissues of tobacco plants stem-injected with sporangia of *P. hyoscyami* (Table 3). Increases ranged from 1.2-fold to eightfold by three weeks postinoculation (Salt et al, 1988). Most of the increase was in free glucose; lesser increases in fructose and a variable increase in sucrose were found. The increase is not due to blockage of vascular transport from leaves to roots, elevated amylase or invertase activities, or hydrolysis of starch reserves. Administration of exogenous sugars to tobacco plants by various means did not consistently affect susceptibility to blue mold; neither glucose nor fructose inhibited germination of *P. hyoscyami* sporangia. Increased amounts of sugars may be due to enhanced photosynthesis and may be responsible in part for the increased growth noted in immunized plants.

Changes in Enzymes and Fungitoxic Secondary Metabolites

Increases in peroxidase, polyphenoloxidase, and lipoxygenase activities were associated with immunization of tobacco (S. D. Salt, personal communication). Six sesquiterpenoid phytoalexins— capsidiol, reshitin, lubimin, solavativone, phytotuberin, and phytuberol—were detected in tobacco leaves infected with *P. hyoscyami* (K. Stolle, personal communication; S. Tuzun and J. Kuć, unpublished); however, production of these compounds apparently was not associated with immunization (K. Stolle, personal communication).

Persistence of Immunization in Tobacco

Immunization against blue mold initiated by a single injection of a sporangial suspension of *P. hyoscyami* lasted throughout the life of the plant (Tuzun, 1986; Tuzun and Kuć, 1985a). Grafting experiments indicated that full-size plants developed from 10-cm-long immunized scions grafted on nonimmunized rootstocks were also immunized (Table 4). Furthermore, plants derived via tissue culture from leaves and midribs of parents injected with *P. hyoscyami* were also systemically protected against disease (Tables 5 and 6). Protection was expressed as a reduction in sporulation on younger plants and as a reduction in symptom severity as well as in sporulation on older plants (Table 5). Plants derived from leaves of immunized plants were also systemically protected against blue mold under high natural disease pressure in three field tests conducted in 1985 and 1986 in Kentucky (Tables 6 and 7).

Table 3. Effects of stem infection by *Peronospora hyoscyami* on total soluble carbohydrates in tobacco tissue[a]

Tissue	Carbohydrates, as glucose equivalent (μmol/g of dry wt.)
Leaves	
Controls	230
Stem-infected	598*
Stems	
Green tissue	
Controls	160
Stem-infected	530**
Necrotic tissue	
Stem-infected	258*

[a]Reprinted, by permission, from Salt et al (1988). Data represent the means of 14 independent experiments performed over two years, with six to 16 plants per treatment per experiment. One asterisk indicates data are significantly different from the respective controls at $P = 0.05$ by Student's t-test; two asterisks indicate significance at $P = 0.01$.

189

Lucas et al (1985) also observed protection with callus-derived plants challenged by spraying; however, their interpretation was negative because plants were not protected in young stages of development or when they were challenged using different techniques or with a very high concentration of sporangia. Even genetically resistant plants, bred through conventional techniques, are susceptible at very young stages of development (R. C. Rufty, personal communication; S. Tuzun and J. Kuć, unpublished), and resistance of younger plants may be overcome with high inoculum concentration applied to a single site by the drop-inoculation technique.

Development of resistance was also evident in plants derived via tissue culture from nonimmunized plants in two of the field tests (Table 6), but resistance was consistently and considerably higher in plants developed via tissue culture from immunized plants. This may indicate that stress caused by development in tissue culture may induce resistance in plants, and this effect might be markedly enhanced in plants derived via tissue culture from immunized plants.

Protection was not transmitted via seed collected from plants injected with *P. hyoscyami* or seed from plants derived from tissue culture of *P. hyoscyami*-injected plants (Tuzun and Kuć, 1987). This may indicate that the effect of immunization was carried over to the regenerants epigenetically or that changes in the genome of stem-injected tobacco were carried over only in vegetative tissue.

Immunization is indeed very stable in tobacco plants stem-

Table 4. Severity of blue mold on induced and noninduced tobacco scions grafted on induced or noninduced tobacco rootstocks[a]

Rootstock	Scion	Disease severity[b] (Mean ± SD)	Sporulation (Mean ± SD)
Control	Induced	1.90 ± 0.09	$2.1 \times 10^5 \pm 7.2 \times 10^4$
Induced	Control	0.99 ± 0.19	$9.8 \times 10^4 \pm 6.5 \times 10^4$
Induced	Induced	0.48 ± 0.30	$9.8 \times 10^4 \pm 5.3 \times 10^4$
Control	Control	4.03 ± 0.46	$11.6 \times 10^5 \pm 4.9 \times 10^5$

[a]Reprinted, by permission, from Tuzun and Kuć (1985b). Data are for three experiments with four plants per treatment. Induced scions about 10 cm long were cut from the growing tips of plants whose stems had been injected with sporangia of *Peronospora hyoscyami* or water three weeks earlier. The scions were grafted on tobacco rootstocks whose stems had been injected with sporangia or water three weeks before grafting. Scions were challenged with sporangia of *P. hyoscyami* (5×10^4/ml) five weeks after grafting.
[b]Disease ratings were determined seven days after challenge: 0 = no evidence of disease; 1 = 1–10% of leaf area with lesions; 2 = 11–39%; 3 = 40–75%; 5 = >75% of leaf area covered by lesions, with severe necrosis. SD = standard deviation.

Table 5. Symptoms of blue mold on tobacco plants grown from seed or derived via tissue culture from parents stem-injected with sporangia of *Peronospora hyoscyami* or water in greenhouse tests[a]

	Leaf stage of challenged plants[b]							
	Two-leaf stage		Three- to four-leaf stage			Seven- to eight-leaf stage		
Source of plants	Disease rating[c]	Sporulation per plant	Disease rating[c]	Sporulation per plant		Disease rating[c]	Sporulation[d]	
Leaves from parents stem-injected with *Peronospora hyoscyami*	1.6 A	2×10^5 B[e]	2.0 B	0.7×10^5 C		0.8 B	0.6×10^5 B	
Leaves from parents stem-injected with water	2.1 A	8×10^5 A	2.9 A	34×10^5 B		2.8 A	25.4×10^5 A	
Seed	1.7 A	14×10^5 A	3.2 A	59×10^5 A		—	—	

[a] Reprinted, by permission, from Tuzun and Kuć (1987).

[b] Plants were challenged by spraying them with a suspension of 10^4 sporangia per milliliter.

[c] 0 = No evidence of disease; 1 = 1–10% of leaf area with lesions; 2 = 11–40%; 3 = 41–75%; 4 = 76–100%. Both leaves were rated on plants in the two-leaf stage, and the three most severely diseased leaves were rated on plants in the three- to four- and seven- to eight-leaf stages.

[d] Sporulation on the two most infected leaves per plant.

[e] Different letters indicate that data are significantly different ($P < 0.05$) by Duncan-Waller K-ratio t-tests.

191

injected with *P. hyoscyami*. It is possible that stem injection releases compounds that cause permanent changes in transmissible information or the expression of such information as related to blue mold resistance. The changes are carried over during differentiation in tissue culture, but not via seed, and become fully expressed as plants age. Instability of plant genomes is well established (Marks, 1984; Walbot and Cullis, 1985), and modifications in the genome are possible during stress. In this case, a specific and persistent low

Table 6. Symptoms of blue mold on tobacco plants grown from seed or derived via tissue culture from parents stem-injected with sporangia of *Peronospora hyoscyami* or water in field tests[a]

Source of plants	Lesions/ plant[b]	Sporulation/ lesion[c]	Sporulation potential/ plant[d]
Leaves from parents stem-injected with *Peronospora hyoscyami*	0.7 (0.3) C[e]	5.7×10^4 B	4.2×10^4 B
Leaves from parents stem-injected with water	15.5 (9.1) B	78.0×10^4 A	1.2×10^7 A
Seed	23.1 (18.4) A	119.0×10^4 A	2.7×10^7 A

[a] Reprinted, by permission, from Tuzan and Kuć (1987). Challenge inoculum was obtained from plants with sporulating lesions that were transplanted to the field.
[b] Data in parentheses are for plants that were transplanted to the field on 8/2/85. All other field data are for plants transplanted to the field on 8/21/85. Data for sporulation of plants transplanted on 8/2/85 were not collected.
[c] Twenty-five lesions were excised per treatment and were allowed to sporulate in the laboratory.
[d] Lesions/plant $\times$ sporulation/lesion.
[e] Different letters indicate that data are significantly different ($P<0.05$) by Duncan-Waller K-ratio t-tests.

Table 7. Protection of tissue culture regenerants from immunized and nonimmunized burley (Kentucky 14) tobacco and seed-grown plants against blue mold (1986)[a]

Block no.	Seed control	Control tissue culture	Injected three times	Injected once
Block I	3.72 ± 0.23	3.12 ± 0.60	0.80 ± 0.35	0.83 ± 0.28
Block II	3.85 ± 0.14	3.42 ± 0.40	0.72 ± 0.29	0.76 ± 0.30
Block III	3.94 ± 0.14	3.18 ± 0.79	0.66 ± 0.22	0.85 ± 0.33
Mean	3.85 ± 0.12	3.24 ± 0.16	0.73 ± 0.07	0.81 ± 0.05

[a] Seed control refers to plants derived from seed. Control tissue culture refers to regenerants from plants stem-injected with water. Test regenerants were from plants stem-injected with sporangia of *Peronospora hyoscyami* either once or three times. Seventy-five plants were included per treatment. Twenty-five plants were included per block. Data are shown ± standard error. Disease was rated on a scale from 0 to 4, where 4 = >75% of leaf area with lesions.

level of stress caused by injecting stems with *P. hyoscyami* might induce change. Experiments on the molecular level are in progress to elucidate the mechanism by which induced resistance is transferred to regenerants.

Discussion

The phenomenon of induced systemic resistance is widely distributed in the plant kingdom. Immunization is nonspecific and in many cases is very effective and persistent. Immunization against blue mold has been studied for many years in our laboratory. It is always fascinating for us to see plants of the same genetic background, grown under the same conditions, respond differently to a very devastating disease. Plants injected with sporangia of *P. hyoscyami* have a specific necrosis in the stem and are highly resistant to blue mold, whereas plants injected with water lack the necrosis and are susceptible. It also is fascinating to see the plants injected with *P. hyoscyami* grow larger than those injected with water.

Over the years of study, it has been very important for us to test the effectiveness of immunization under field conditions. Thus, plant immunization is not only an interesting laboratory project but is also a possible method of controlling disease in the field. This method will be especially pertinent if strains of *P. hyoscyami* tolerant to metalaxyl become established in the United States. The effectiveness of immunization against blue mold and the accompanying yield increase have been tested under several field conditions in the United States. The protection was also evident in Mexico, where metalaxyl-tolerant strains of the fungus have developed. Natural development of protection against metalaxyl-tolerant strains of the fungus in naturally stem-infected plants was observed in Mexico at several farms. The protection was highly correlated with the presence of necrosis in the stem, which was very similar to necrosis resulting from stem injection with *P. hyoscyami*. Naturally immunized plants were not only resistant to blue mold but also looked more vigorous than other plants in the field. We are investigating this intriguing phenomenon further.

Injections of β-ionone into stem tissue of tobacco mimicked injections with sporangia of *P. hyoscyami*. Further investigation in this area may result in the discovery of compounds more active than β-ionone. This could reduce dependence on injections with living sporangia for the control of blue mold and may result in a technology (spraying or seed treatment) more easily applicable to field control of disease.

Stem injections resulted in many changes in the plant tissue,

193

which may or may not be directly involved in immunization against blue mold. An overall increase in metabolism of such plants is evident. Investigations of the mechanism of this increase may not only increase our understanding of normal plant metabolism but may also provide further insight into the response of plants to stress. Is it possible to develop plants with varying levels of carbohydrates, proteins, lipids, and secondary metabolites by the timely application of biological or chemical agents?

Induced resistance was transferred to regenerants via tissue culture. This may indicate an involvement of transmissible information that conditions cells to rapidly respond to a pathogen. One of our major research objectives is to find the molecular basis of this transfer on the level of gene expression, mRNA, and translation products. Immunization of plants may provide a technology for the protection of plants against disease that would minimize our dependence on numerous other control tactics for plant protection and would permit multiplication of disease-resistant plants from existing high-quality, high-yielding cultivars.

Acknowledgments

Our research reported in this chapter was supported in part by grants from the Ciba-Geigy Corporation and R. J. Reynolds Corporation, by U.S. Department of Agriculture cooperative agreement 43YK-5-0030, and by the Scientific and Technical Research Council of Turkey.

LITERATURE CITED

Ahl, P., Benjama, A., Sumson, R., and Gianinazzi, S. 1981. New host proteins (b-proteins) induced together with resistance to a secondary infection in tobacco. Phytopathol. Z. 192:201–212.

Baltruschat, H., and Schonbeck, F. 1975. Untersuchungen über den Einfluss der endotropen Mycorrhiza auf den Befall von Tabak mit *Thielaviopsis basicola*. Phytopathol. Z. 84:172–188.

Biehn, W. L., Williams, E. B., and Kuć, J. 1966. Resistance of mature leaves of *Malus atrosanguinea* 804 to *Venturia inaequalis* and *Helminthosporium carbonum*. Phytopathology 56:588–589.

Cheo, P. C., Linder, R. C., and McRitchie, J. J. 1968. Effect of foreign RNA on tobacco mosaic virus lesion formation. Virology 35:82–86.

Chester, K. S. 1933. The problem of acquired physiological immunity in plants. Q. Rev. Biol. 8:129–154, 275–324.

Cohen, Y. 1978. Protection of tobacco against *Erysiphe cichoracearum* by *Peronospora tabacina*. Ann. Appl. Biol. 89:317–321.

Cohen, Y., and Kuć, J. 1981. Evaluation of systemic resistance to blue mold induced in tobacco leaves by prior stem inoculation with *Peronospora hyoscyami* f. sp. *tabacina*. Phytopathology 71:783–787.

Court, W. A. 1982. Factors affecting the concentration of the duvatrienediols of flue cured tobacco. Tob. Sci. 41:94–97.

Cruickshank, I. A. M., and Mandryk, M. 1960. The effect of stem infection of tobacco with *Peronospora tabacina* on foliage reaction to blue mold. J. Aust. Inst. Agric. Res. 26:369–372.

Cruickshank, I. A. M., Perrin, D. R., and Mandryk, M. 1977. Fungitoxicity of duvatrienediols associated with the cuticular wax of tobacco leaves. Phytopathol. Z. 90:133–146.

Day, P. R. 1974. Genetics of Host-Parasite Interaction. Freeman, San Francisco. 238 pp.

Dean, R. A., and Kuć, J. 1985. Induced systemic protection in plants. Trends Biotechnol. 5:125–129.

Dean, R. A., and Kuć, J. 1986. Induced systemic protection in cucumbers. The source of the "signal." Physiol. Mol. Plant Pathol. 28:227–233.

Deverall, B. J. 1977. Defence Mechanisms of Plants. Cambridge University Press, Cambridge. 110 pp.

Fraser, R. S. S. 1979. Systemic consequences of the local lesion reaction to tobacco mosaic virus in a tobacco variety lacking the *N* gene for hypersensitivity. Physiol. Plant Pathol. 14:383–394.

Fraser, R. S. S. 1981. Evidence for the occurrence of the "pathogenesis-related" proteins in leaves of healthy tobacco plants during flowering. Physiol. Plant Pathol. 19:69–76.

Fraser, R. S. S. 1982. Are "pathogenesis-related" proteins involved in acquired systemic resistance of tobacco plants to tobacco mosaic virus? J. Gen. Virol. 58:305–313.

Gat-Edelbaum, O., Altman, A., and Sela, I. 1983. Polyinosinic-polycytidylic acid in association with cyclic nucleotides activates the antiviral factor (AVF) in plant tissues. J. Gen. Virol. 64:211–214.

Gera, A., and Loebenstein, G. 1983. Further studies of an inhibitor of virus replication from tobacco mosaic virus-infected protoplasts of a local lesion-responding tobacco cultivar. Phytopathology 73:111–115.

Gianinazzi, S., and Kassanis, B. 1974. Virus resistance induced in plants by polyacrylic acid. J. Gen. Virol. 23:1–9.

Gianinazzi, S., Pratt, H. M., Shewry, P. R., and Miflin, B. J. 1977. Partial purification and preliminary characterization of soluble leaf protein specific to virus infected tobacco plants. J. Gen. Virol. 34:345–351.

Gianinazzi, S., Ahl, P., Cornu, A., and Scalla, R. 1980. First report of host b-protein appearance in response to a fungal infection in tobacco. Physiol. Plant Pathol. 16:337–342.

Gicherman, G., and Loebenstein, G. 1968. Competitive inhibition by foreign nucleic acids and induced interference by yeast-RNA with the infection of tobacco mosaic virus. Phytopathology 58:405–409.

Goodman, R. N. 1978. Inducible resistance responses in plants to pathogenic bacteria. Mycopathologia 65:107–113.

Goodman, R. N., Huang, P. Y., Huang, J. S., and Taipanich, V. 1976. Induced resistance to bacterial infection. Pages 35–42 in: Biochemistry and Cytology of Plant-Parasite Interaction. K. Tomiyami, J. M. Daly, I. Uritani, H. Oku, and S. Ouchi, eds. Kodahansha Ltd. Elsevier, Tokyo. 236 pp.

Graham, T. L., Sequeira, L., and Huang, T. S. R. 1977. Bacterial lipopolysaccharides as inducers of disease resistance in tobacco. Appl. Environ. Microbiol. 34:424–432.

Grijseels, A. J., Williams, E. B., and Kuć, J. 1964. Hypersensitive response in selections of *Malus* to fungi nonpathogenic to apple. Phytopathology 54:1152–1154.

Guedes, M., Richmond, S., and Kuć, J. 1980. Induced systemic resistance to anthracnose in cucumber as influenced by the location of the inducer inoculation with *Colletotrichum lagenarium* and the onset of flowering and fruiting. Physiol. Plant Pathol. 17:229–233.

Hecht, E. I., and Bateman, D. F. 1964. Nonspecific acquired resistance to pathogens resulting from localized infections by *Thielaviopsis basicola* or viruses in tobacco leaves. Phytopathology 54:523–530.

Inagaki, H., and Powell, N. T. 1969. Influence of the root-lesion nematode on black shank symptom development in flue-cured tobacco. Phytopathology 59:1350–1355.

Kuć, J. 1981. Multiple mechanisms, reaction rates and induced resistance in plants. Pages 259–272 in: Plant Disease Control. R. C. Staples and G. Toenniessen, eds. John Wiley & Sons, New York. 339 pp.

Kuć, J. 1982a. Induced immunity to plant disease. Bioscience 32:854–860.

Kuć, J. 1982b. The immunization of cucurbits against fungal, bacterial and viral disease. Pages 137–153 in: The Physiological and Biochemical Basis of Plant Infection. Y. Asada, W. Bushnell, S. Ouchi, and C. P. Vance, eds. Japan Scientific Society Press, Tokyo, and Springer-Verlag, Berlin. 362 pp.

Kuć, J. 1982c. Plant immunization—Mechanisms and practical implications. Pages 157–178 in: Active Defense Mechanisms in Plants. R. K. S. Wood and E. Tjamos, eds. Plenum Press, New York. 381 pp.

Kuć, J. 1983. Induced systemic resistance in plants to diseases caused by bacteria and fungi. Pages 191–220 in: Dynamics of Host Defence. J. Bailey, ed. Academic Press, Sydney. 233 pp.

Kuć, J. 1984. Phytoalexins and disease resistance mechanisms from a perspective of evolution and adaptation. Pages 100–118 in: Origins and Development of Adaptation. Ciba Foundation Symposium 102. Pitman, London. 273 pp.

Kuć, J. 1985a. Expression of latent genetic information for disease resistance in plants. Pages 302–318 in: Cellular and Molecular Biology of Plant Stress. J. Key and T. Kosuge, eds. Alan R. Liss Inc., New York. 494 pp.

Kuć, J. 1985b. Induced systemic resistance to plant disease and phytointerferons—Are they compatible? Fitopatol. Bras. 10:9–33.

Kuć, J. 1987a. Plant immunization and its applicability for disease control. Pages 255–274 in: Non-conventional Approaches to Disease Control. I. Chet, ed. John Wiley & Sons, New York. 373 pp.

Kuć, J. 1987b. Translocated signals for plant immunization. Ann. N.Y. Acad. Sci. 494:221–223.

Kuć, J., and Rush, J. 1985. Phytoalexins. Arch. Biochem. Biophys. 236:455–472.

Kuć, J., and Tuzun, S. 1983. Immunization for disease resistance in tobacco. Recent Adv. Tob. Sci. 9:179–213.

Leppik, R. A., Hollomon, D. W., and Bottomley, W. 1972. Quiesone: An inhibitor of germination of *Peronospora tabacina* conidia. Phytochemistry 11:2055–2063.

Loebenstein, G. 1972. Inhibition, interference and acquired resistance during infection. Pages 32–61 in: Principles and Techniques in Plant Virology. I. Kado and H. O. Agrawal, eds. Van Nostrand Reinhold, New York. 345 pp.

Loebenstein, G., and Gera, A. 1981. Inhibitor of virus replication released from TMV-infected protoplasts of a local lesion-responding tobacco cultivar. Virology 116:132–139.

Loebenstein, G., Sela, B., and van Praagh, T. 1969. Increase of TMV local lesion size and virus multiplication in hypersensitive host in the presence of actinomycin D. Virology 37:42–48.

Lovrekovich, L., and Farkas, G. L. 1965. Induced reaction against wildfire disease in tobacco leaves treated with heat-killed bacteria. Nature 205:823–824.

Lucas, J. A., Dolan, T. E., and Coffey, M. D. 1985. Nontransmissibility to regenerants from protected tobacco explants of induced resistance to *Peronospora hyoscyami*. Phytopathology 75:1222–1225.

Mandryk, M. 1960. Host pathogen relationship in tobacco plants which were stem injected with *Peronospora tabacina*. Aust. J. Agric. Res. 11:16–26.

Mandryk, M. 1961. The relationship between acquired resistance to *Peronospora tabacina* in *Nicotiana tabacum* and soil nitrogen levels. Aust. J. Agric. Res. 13:10–16.

Mandryk, M. 1963. Acquired systemic resistance to TMV in *Nicotiana tabacum* evoked by stem inoculations with *Peronospora tabacina*. Aust. J. Agric. Res. 14:316–318.

Marks, J. L. 1984. Instability in plants and the ghost of Lamarck. Science 224:1415–1416.

McIntyre, J. L., and Dodds, J. A. 1979. Induction of localized and systemic protection against *Phytophthora parasitica* var. *nicotianae* by tobacco mosaic virus infection on tobacco hypersensitive to the virus. Physiol. Plant Pathol. 15:321–330.

McIntyre, J. L., and Miller, P. M. 1974. Decrease in the incidence of tobacco black shank by root infestations of *Pratylenchus penetrans*. (Abstr.) Proc. Am. Phytopathol. Soc. 1:140–141.

McIntyre, J. L., and Miller, P. M. 1978. Protection of tobacco against *Phytophthora parasitica* var. *nicotianae* by cultivar-nonpathogenic races, cell-free sonicates, and *Pratylenchus penetrans*. Phytopathology 68:235–239.

McIntyre, J. L., Dodds, J. A., and Hare, J. D. 1981. Effects of localized infections of *Nicotiana tabacum* by tobacco mosaic virus on systemic resistance against diverse pathogens and an insect. Phytopathology 71:297–301.

Mori, K. 1973. Synthesis of dl-3-isobutyroxy-β-ionone and dl-dehydrovomifoliol. Agric. Biol. Chem. 37:2899–2905.

Mozes, R., Antignus, Y., Sela, I., and Harpaz, I. 1978. The chemical nature of an antiviral factor (AVF) from virus-infected plants. J. Gen. Virol. 38:241–249.

197

Nusbaum, C., and Keitt, G. 1938. A cytological study of host-parasite relations with *Venturia inaequalis* on apple leaves. J. Agric. Res. 56:595–618.

Oliver, M. J., Dean, C. M., De, B. K., and Beachy, R. N. 1986. In vitro transcription and translation of cloned cDNAs encoding the 30-kDa protein gene of TMV. Virology 155:277–283.

Orchansky, P., Rubenstein, M., and Sela, I. 1982. Human interferons protect plants from virus infection. Proc. Natl. Acad. Sci. USA 79:2278–2280.

Ota, N., and Taniguchi, T. 1978. Effects of chemicals on systemic acquired resistance in tobacco var. Samsun NN. Ann. Phytopathol. Soc. Jpn. 44:47–51.

Ouchi, S. 1983. Induction of resistance or susceptibility. Annu. Rev. Phytopathol. 21:289–315.

Pont, M. 1959. Blue mold *Peronospora tabacina* Adam of tobacco in north Queensland. Some aspects of chemical control. Queensl. J. Agric. Sci. 16:299–327.

Rathmell, W. G., and Sequeira, L. 1975. Induced resistance in tobacco leaves: The role of inhibitors of bacterial growth in the intercellular fluid. Physiol. Plant Pathol. 5:65–73.

Reichman, M., Devash, Y., Suhadolnik, R. J., and Sela, I. 1983. Human leukocyte interferon and antiviral factor AVF from virus-infected plants stimulate plant tissues to produce nucleotides with antiviral activity. Virology 128:240–244.

Reuveni, M., Tuzun, S., Cole, J. S., Siegel, M. R., and Kuć, J. 1986. The effects of plant age and leaf position on the susceptibility of tobacco to blue mold caused by *Peronospora tabacina*. Phytopathology 76:455–458.

Reuveni, M., Tuzun, S., Cole, J. S., Siegel, M. R., Nesmith, W. C., and Kuć, J. 1987. Removal of duvatrienediols from the surfaces of tobacco leaves increases the susceptibility to blue mold. Physiol. Mol. Plant Pathol. 30:441–451.

Roberts, D. A. 1983. Acquired resistance to tobacco mosaic virus transmitted to the progeny of hypersensitive tobacco. Virology 124:161–163.

Rohloff, H., and Lerch, B. 1977. Soluble leaf proteins in virus infected plants and acquired resistance: Investigation on *Nicotiana tabacum* cv. Xanthinc. and Samsun. Phytopathol. Z. 89:306–316.

Rosenberg, N., Reichman, M., Gera, A., and Sela, I. 1985. Antiviral activity of natural and recombinant human leukocyte interferons in tobacco protoplasts. Virology 140:173–178.

Ross, A. F. 1959. Local immunity induced by tobacco mosaic virus in hypersensitive tobacco and its modification by potato virus X. (Abstr.) Phytopathology 49:549.

Ross, A. F. 1961a. Localized acquired resistance to plant virus infection in hypersensitive host. Virology 14:329–339.

Ross, A. F. 1961b. Systemic acquired resistance induced by localized virus infections in plants. Virology 14:340–358.

Ross, A. F. 1966. Systemic effects of local lesion formation. Pages 127–150 in: Viruses of Plants. A. B. R. Beemster and S. Dijkstra, eds. North Holland Publishing Co., Amsterdam. 342 pp.

Ross, A. F., and Bozarth, R. F. 1960. Resistance induced in one plant part as a result of virus infection in another part. (Abstr.) Phytopathology 50:652.

Ross, A. F., and Israel, H. W. 1970. Use of heat treatments in the study of acquired resistance to tobacco mosaic virus in hypersensitive tobacco. Phytopathology 60:755–770.

Salt, S. D., and Kuć, J. 1985. Elicitation of disease resistance in plants by the expression of latent genetic information. Pages 47–68 in: Bioregulators for Pest Control. Paul A. Hedin, ed. American Chemical Society, Washington, DC. 540 pp.

Salt, S. D., Tuzun, S., and Kuć, J. 1986. Effects of ionone-related compounds on the growth of tobacco and resistance to blue mold. Physiol. Mol. Plant Pathol. 28:287–297.

Salt, S. D., Pan, S. Q., and Kuć, J. 1988. Carbohydrate changes in tobacco systemically protected against blue mold by stem injection with *Peronospora tabacina*. Phytopathology 78:733–738.

Sela, B., Loebenstein, G., and van Praagh, T. 1969. Increase of tobacco mosaic virus multiplication and lesion size in hypersensitive host in presence of chloramphenicol. Virology 39:260–264.

Sela, I. 1981. Antiviral factors from virus infected plants. Trends Biochem. Sci. 6:31–33.

Sela, I., Harpaz, I., and Birk, Y. 1966. Identification of the active component of an antiviral factor isolated from virus infected plants. Virology 28:71–78.

Sequeira, L. 1978. Lectins and their role in host-pathogen specificity. Annu. Rev. Phytopathol. 16:453–481.

Sequeira, L. 1979. Recognition between plant host and parasites. Pages 71–84 in: Host-Parasite Interfaces. B. Nicoll, ed. Academic Press, New York. 144 pp.

Sequeira, L. 1983. Mechanism of induced resistance in plants. Annu. Rev. Microbiol. 37:51–79.

Sequeira, L., and Hill, L. M. 1974. Induced resistance in tobacco leaves: The growth of *Pseudomonas solanacearum* in protected tissues. Physiol. Plant Pathol. 4:447–455.

Sequeira, L., Gaard, G., and de Zoeten, G. A. 1976. Attachment of bacteria to host cell walls: Its relation to mechanisms of induced resistance. Proc. Am. Phytopathol. Soc. 3:233.

Sequeira, L., Gaard, G., and de Zoeten, G. A. 1977. Interaction of bacteria and host cell walls: Its relation to mechanisms of induced resistance. Physiol. Plant Pathol. 10:43–50.

Shepherd, C. J., and Mandryk, M. 1962. Auto inhibitors of germination and sporulation in *Peronospora tabacina*. Trans. Br. Mycol. Soc. 45:233–244.

Stein, A., and Loebenstein, G. 1970. Induction of resistance to tobacco mosaic virus by Poly I, Poly C in plants. Nature (London) 226:363–364.

Stein, A., Loebenstein, G., and Spiegel, S. 1979. Further studies of induced interference by a synthetic polyanion of infection by tobacco mosaic virus. Physiol. Plant Pathol. 15:241–245.

Tuzun, S. 1986. Immunization of tobacco against blue mold. Dissertation, University of Kentucky, Lexington.

Tuzun, S., and Kuć, J. 1985a. A modified technique for inducing systemic resistance to blue mold and increasing growth in tobacco. Phytopathology 75:1127–1129.

Tuzun, S., and Kuć, J. 1985b. Movement of a factor in tobacco infected with *Peronospora tabacina* Adam which systemically protects against blue mold. Physiol. Plant Pathol. 26:321–330.

Tuzun, S., and Kuć, J. 1987. Persistence of induced systemic resistance to blue mold in tobacco plants derived via tissue culture. Phytopathology 77:1032–1035.

Tuzun, S., Nesmith, W., Ferriss, R. S., and Kuć, J. 1986a. Effects of stem injections with *Peronospora tabacina* on growth of tobacco and protection against blue mold in the field. Phytopathology 76:938–941.

Tuzun, S., Nesmith, W., Wiglesworth, M., Kuć, J., and Juárez, J. 1986b. Protection of tobacco against blue mold caused by metalaxyl-tolerant strains of *Peronospora tabacina* by stem injection with the fungus. (Abstr.) Phytopathology 76:1092.

Tuzun, S., Reuveni, M., Siegel, M. R., and Kuć, J. 1986c. Removal of antifungal factors from leaves of tobacco with acetone and its effect on genetic resistance and induced systemic resistance to blue mold. (Abstr.) Phytopathology 76:1092.

Tuzun, S., Salt, S. D., Nesmith, W., and Kuć, J. 1986d. Effects of stem injections with *Peronospora tabacina* and β-ionone treatments on blue mold control and growth of burley tobacco. Biol. Cult. Tests Control Plant Dis. 1:55.

Verma, H. N., and Awasthi, L. P. 1979. Antiviral activity of *Boerhaavia diffusa* root extract and physical properties of the virus inhibitor. Can. J. Bot. 57:926–939.

Verma, H. N., and Awasthi, L. P. 1980. Occurrence of a highly antiviral agent in plants treated with *Boerhaavia diffusa* inhibitor. Can. J. Bot. 58:2141–2144.

Verma, H. N., and Dwivedi, S. D. 1984. Properties of a virus inhibiting agent, isolated from plants which have been treated with leaf extracts from *Bougainvillea spectabilis*. Physiol. Plant Pathol. 25:93–101.

Verma, H. N., and Mukerjee, K. 1977. Properties of the interfering agent from brinjal leaves inducing resistance against TMV. New Bot. 4:137–143.

Verma, H. N., and Mukerjee, K. 1979. Induction of antiviral resistance in host plants by *Datura* leaf extracts. Indian Phytopathol. 32:95–97.

Verma, H. N., Chowdhury, B., and Rostogi, P. 1984. Antiviral activity in leaf extracts of different *Clerodendrum* species. Z. Pflanzenkr. Pflanzenschutz 91:34–41.

Walbot, V., and Cullis, C. A. 1985. Rapid genomic change in higher plants. Annu. Rev. Plant Physiol. 36:367–396.

White, R. F. 1979. Acetyl salicylic acid (aspirin) induces resistance to tobacco mosaic virus in tobacco. Virology 99:410–412.

White, R. F., and Forde, S. M. D. 1985. The effect of postinoculation with mineral oil on TMV multiplication in tobacco leaves and protoplasts. Phytopathol. Z. 113:171–177.

Chapter 8

Epidemiology and Biometeorology of Tobacco Blue Mold

C. E. Main
J. M. Davis[1]
Department of Plant Pathology
North Carolina State University
Raleigh, North Carolina 27695-7616

Downy mildew of tobacco, caused by *Peronospora hyoscyami* de Bary f. sp. *tabacina* (Adam) Skalický (syn. *P. tabacina* Adam), is a classical compound-interest disease that develops into local as well as macroscale epidemics. The fungus is highly weather-sensitive. During periods of cool, wet, and overcast weather, the disease develops and spreads rapidly because of the polycyclic multiplication of the pathogen. When the weather becomes clear, hot, and dry, the epidemic usually becomes quiescent.

The Problem

Blue mold is a wary enemy of tobacco growers and is an interesting subject for scientific inquiry, largely because of its unpredictable occurrence and the resulting uncertainties of crop loss. Blue mold is a high-risk disease. Some years it does not appear at all. In 1979 and 1980, blue mold spread unabated northward across the United States to Canada at the rate of 10–32 km per day (Aylor, 1986). The rate slowed above 35° latitude in both years. This displacement of the epidemic front (Gayed, 1983; Nesmith, 1984) was several times faster than that calculated for the 1958–1962 epidemics in Europe (1.0 km/day) and the slow northward spread in the United States between 1931 and 1947 (0.5 km/day), as calculated by Zadoks and Kampmeijer (1977).

[1]Professor Davis is also a member of the Department of Marine, Earth and Atmospheric Sciences.

In epidemiological parlance, blue mold is classed as a "polycyclic r strategist" type of disease. Its fast development is determined by such qualities as potentially high levels of initial inoculum, short latent period, and large numbers of effective dispersal units or spores. *P. hyoscyami* is a primary consumer in the ecological sense. Tobacco-*P. hyoscyami* represents a "pathosystem" (sensu Zadoks and Schein [1979]) within the larger hierarchical agroecosystem related to tobacco production. The pathosystem has certain characteristics of its own while responding to components of the larger ecosystem such as climate and human activities.

Tobacco is produced commercially in 95 countries around the world on 4 million hectares. Tobacco and *P. hyoscyami* coexist year-round in the warm, wet agroclimatic farming conditions (Duckham and Masefield, 1970) characteristic of the Mediterranean and Caribbean basins. In these "source" regions, the disease is endemic, although its intensity changes from year to year. The continuity of the *P. hyoscyami* species suggests that Van der Plank's (1963) threshold theorem, $iR_c > 1$, applies, where i = infectious period and R_c = basic infection rate; that is, each lesion should produce at least one effective daughter spore per appropriate time unit.

Tobacco is a seasonal crop in the temperate, warm and cool, humid farming zones bordering the above-mentioned basins. Following a crop-free period (winter) each year, the tobacco is exposed to asexual, windborne sporangiospores originating from inoculum sources in the tropical zones. The fungus is not known to overwinter in the temperate zones, so inoculum is introduced anew each year. Blue mold epidemics have both a spatial and a temporal discontinuity between these source regions and temperate target zones. In the temperate zones, the epidemics are usually cyclic (yearly) and progressive; that is, once established, they advance as a more or less definable front (Weltzien, 1981). In some years and areas, however, a discontinuity in space occurs when new outbreaks occur hundreds of kilometers beyond the perceptible front or appear as totally isolated, local epidemics. In these cases long-distance transport of inoculum is suspected. It is common to have no disease in a given year or to have local geographic areas that periodically escape the disease. The difference between continuous and discontinuous epidemic fronts is related to inoculum dispersal patterns, localized weather, spatial aggregation of tobacco fields within production regions, and planting schedules. Of course, humans mediate the occurrence and intensity of blue mold and greatly affect the epidemic pattern through their efforts to manage the disease with chemical fungicides and resistant host cultivars.

The blue mold-tobacco pathosystem apparently operates independently on four continents, namely, Australia, North and

South America, and Europe. History records that humans introduced *P. hyoscyami* into the United States in 1921 and into Europe in 1958 from Australia (Schiltz, 1981). Explosive epidemics resulted. With time, plant pathologists were able to lessen the damage brought about by these cyclic epidemics. Zadoks and Schein (1979) called this situation "managed endemicity." However, plant pathologists have had little control over the extensiveness of the epidemics, that is, the reintroduction of new inoculum each year due to long-distance transport of sporangiospores of the pathogen.

The tobacco-*P. hyoscyami* pathosystem provides a unique conceptual framework for studying all components of the blue mold disease. Certain questions arise. Does the pathosystem function similarly on all four continents? Do inocula move from source to target area each year? Why is there a discontinuity in blue mold occurrence in some years? How can we predict or forecast blue mold occurrence early enough for growers to take appropriate action? And lastly, how can we best evaluate the results of new disease management strategies?

Temperature Tolerance

In the United States before 1979, blue mold was chiefly a plant bed disease. Hot summer temperatures prevented field development (Rider et al, 1961). Blue mold prevalence and intensity changed dramatically in 1979 and 1980. Some 319,000 ha of tobacco, grown in 600 counties in 17 states largely adjacent to the East Coast, were subjected to an intracontinental epidemic of macroscale proportions. Losses in the United States and Canada were estimated at $252 million in 1979 and $94 million in 1980 (Todd, 1981). Estimates for Cuba and Latin America are not available, but heavy losses occurred there also.

Field blue mold occurred and persisted and viable spores were produced as late as the last week in July during the hot summer months in North Carolina (Main et al, 1985; Moss and Main, 1985). Wuest and Schmitt (1965) had reported that isolates of the pathogen from the United States and from Europe responded similarly to temperature. Moss and Main (1988) conducted controlled-environment studies in North Carolina on *P. hyoscyami* isolates collected in 1964, 1979, 1980, and 1983. The four isolates survived and sporulated at daytime temperatures up to 38°C. Computer mapping (SYMAP) of disease occurrence and temperature provided additional evidence for the existence of thermophilic ecotypes within the *P. hyoscyami* population (Moss and Main, 1984). No major shifts in weather (compared to 30-year normals) or tobacco germ plasms (commercial cultivar development) could be related to the widespread field epidemics of 1979 and 1980 (Davis and Main, 1984; Davis and Sabones, 1979).

Davis et al (1981) used principal components analysis to describe the spatial and temporal features of meteorological conditions in 1980. They identified three main components related to blue mold development and spread: seasonal precipitation, early-season temperatures, and late-season temperatures. However, because the analysis was based on monthly meteorological data at widely separated locations, it could not have detected small-scale temporal or spatial variation in the meteorological field which may have been important in localized, sporadic outbreaks.

Biometeorology

The effect of environmental factors on sporulation, germination, survival, and dispersal of sporangiospores of *P. hyoscyami* is discussed in Chapter 9, and aspects of the subject have been reviewed recently by Aylor (1986), Davis and Main (1984), and Populer (1981). However, a brief description is necessary here to fully understand the dynamics of inoculum movement and disease spread. Some of the following paragraphs have been largely excerpted from our earlier publication on blue mold (Davis and Main, 1984; copyright ©1984 by D. Reidel Publishing Company, Dordrecht, Holland; used by permission).

Although the time frame varies some, a typical sequence of events for infection and disease development is as follows. Once the sporangiospores arrive at the leaf surface, infection can occur in as little as 2–4 hr. A five- to seven-day symptom-free incubation period then occurs, during which the pathogen grows inside the leaf tissue. The appearance of visible symptoms (yellow lesions) signals the end of the incubation period. The disease is first detectable by surveillance teams at this point. Under controlled environmental conditions, the incubation period can be as short as three days. This period increases under less than ideal conditions and with the age of the tobacco plants.

Maximum sporulation occurs at 15–23° C, although some sporulation can occur at temperatures as low as 1–2° C and as high as 30°C (Cruickshank, 1961). However, longer exposures to high temperatures (30–40° C), superimposed on a 20° C incubation period, delayed and eventually suppressed lesion appearance and sporulation (Rotem and Cohen, 1970). Rider et al (1961) reported that day temperatures above 30°C for more than 6 hr inhibited sporulation the following night.

Sporulation can occur on the day that symptoms first appear but occurs with greater frequency on the following day. For sporangiospores to appear in the early morning hours, the relative humidity must have exceeded 95% for at least 3 hr, and darkness must have lasted at least 1.5 hr (Cruickshank, 1963). Uozumi and Kröber (1967) found that at 20°C, after a 13-hr dry photoperiod, a moist, dark period lasting at least 2 hr was required to induce sporulation, and maximum sporulation was induced after 5 hr of darkness.

Spore liberation requires a rise in temperature, a decrease in relative humidity (which for a constant vapor pressure must, by definition, occur with a rise in temperature), and an increase in insolation (Cohen, 1976; Hill, 1961). Sporangiophores of *P. hyoscyami* react to dry air by desiccating and twisting counterclockwise (Pinckard, 1942). As the entangled sporangiophore branches disengage, the resulting spring action mechanically ejects spores. Forcible discharge from unentangled sporangiophores has also been observed. With renewed exposure to high humidities, sporangiophore twisting has been observed to reverse itself (Hill, 1960). According to Hill (1961), radiation is equally important in spore release. The loss of sporangiophore turgidity and the associated spore release do not occur, according to Hill, in reaction to a decrease in ambient humidity; rather, they can be a reaction to a decrease in leaf water potential brought about by elevated levels of evapotranspiration, the energy for which is solar in origin.

On days characterized by many hours of sunshine or only scattered clouds, the spore concentration in the air increases rapidly and reaches a maximum in the second to the fourth hour of release. Aylor and Taylor (1983) found that spores are usually released between 0800 and 1500 hr eastern standard time (EST), with peak release between 1000 and 1300 hr EST. They estimated that $0.14-1.4 \times 10^{11}$ spores can be released into the air during a 2-hr period from 100 ha of severely infected tobacco. Spore concentration in the air decreases more slowly than it increases; the decrease may take 4-8 hr, after which a few spores may still remain in the atmosphere until late evening. A series of peaks for spore release is associated with sunny periods when clear and overcast periods alternate (Hill, 1961; Populer, 1981).

Hill (1961) observed that with the onset of rain, a short period of spore liberation occurs regardless of the wind. If a steady rain continues for several hours, the air is effectively cleansed of sporangiospores after the initial peak. The number of rain-liberated sporangiospores is usually higher during the day than at night (Populer, 1981), since spores are produced during the night and are available for release during the day.

Kucharek (1987) suggested that water from overhead irrigation and rainfall are associated with first occurrences of tobacco blue mold. Plant beds and fields receiving regular irrigation had a higher incidence of blue mold than unirrigated fields. Kucharek considered moisture to be a more important variable than temperature for blue mold occurrences in northern Florida.

Rotem and Aylor (1984) studied the development of *P. hyoscyami* epidemics at season's end in Connecticut during periods of suboptimal to marginal weather conditions. Nighttime infections were less frequent but not eliminated by low temperatures in September and October. Inoculum disappeared by mid-November, and no sporangiospores remained for overwintering.

The effect of host plants, such as *Nicotiana* species and resistant cultivars of *N. tabacum,* on sporulation rates is considerable and should be taken into account in modeling studies. *P. hyoscyami* is capable of sporulating on commercial tobacco for several successive nights on the same lesion. Rufty has shown in Chapter 5 that the incubation and latent periods are longer, while lesion area and sporulation rates are greatly reduced, on some recently released tobacco breeding lines (Rufty and Main, 1987). When this resistant germ plasm becomes available in commercial cultivars, the use of these cultivars could reduce disease intensity and inocula.

Populations of the pathogen on *N. repanda* in south-central Texas have been implicated as inocula for burley tobacco in Kentucky (Davis et al, 1987). In *N. repanda* the incubation period is seven to 14 days, and the fungus develops systemically without killing the plant (Reuveni et al, 1986a). Both local and systemic lesions are capable of sporulating for 60 days. When environmental conditions are favorable, sporulation occurs over all plant parts and surfaces, resulting in great quantities of sporangiospores. *N. repanda* appears to be an ideal host for survival of *P. hyoscyami,* thereby providing significant quantities of inoculum from a long-term source. Periods of temperatures above 38° C have been observed to reduce but not eliminate this Texas source of spores.

Long-Range Inoculum Transport

For cyclic epidemics of blue mold to develop and spread in the commercial tobacco region of the United States, there must be adequate populations of susceptible host plants and a source of inoculum. The obligate parasite *P. hyoscyami* is restricted to tobacco species and is not known to overwinter within the production areas. Windblown, asexual sporangiospores are considered to be the agents of dispersal. The spores may originate on winter-grown tobacco in the tropical zones where the disease is endemic.

Meteorological trajectory analysis has been used to investigate the hypothesis of long-range inoculum transport. The first published attempt to apply hand-calculated trajectory analysis to the dispersal of *P. hyoscyami* spores indicated that the inoculum that initiated the 1979 epidemic in the United States and Canada came from source areas in the Caribbean (Lucas, 1980). Computer-assisted trajectory analysis has been used since 1981 to trace the probable pathways of inoculum-laden air parcels and to identify potential inoculum source regions.

A trajectory represents a curve in space that traces the positions successively occupied by a moving air parcel—in the case of blue mold, the spore cloud. Computer models can systematically generate hundreds of forward and backward trajectories in support of short- or long-range spore transport studies, over any time period. Forward, source-oriented trajectories are useful in determining the tobacco regions over which sporangiospores travel from a given source. Backward, receptor-oriented trajectories from documented outbreaks aid in locating new or well-known inoculum source areas.

Davis and Main (1984) suggested a set of "blue mold trajectory guidelines" to account for both meteorological and biological components of inoculum movement. Only trajectories satisfying the following guidelines are considered probable: active sporulation at the point of origin of the forward trajectory has been confirmed or is highly probable; weather conditions along the transport route are conducive to maintaining spore viability, and the chances of precipitation scavenging are not limiting; the target area has a substantial population of susceptible host plants; weather conditions at the target area are favorable for spore deposition, germination, infection, and continued development of disease; and trajectory parcels arrive over the target area at least one to two latent periods (seven to 14 days) before the first reported occurrence of blue mold in the target area.

Several atmospheric air pollution trajectory models have proved to be very useful. The atmospheric transport and dispersion (ATAD) model (Heffter, 1980) has been used to identify source regions of *P. hyoscyami* for epidemics of blue mold of tobacco in Connecticut in 1979 and 1980 (Aylor et al, 1982), in North Carolina in 1980 (Davis and Main, 1984, 1986), and in Kentucky in 1981 and 1982 (Davis and Main, 1986; Davis et al, 1985). An improved version of the ATAD model, known as the branching atmospheric trajectory (BAT) model (Heffter, 1983), has been used to investigate epidemics in North Carolina and Kentucky (Davis and Main, 1986; Davis et al, 1987).

Davis and Main (1984) hypothesized that once active sporulation had begun in northern Florida and southern Georgia in early April of 1980, atmospheric circulation systems transported inoculum

207

northward over the eastern United States. In regions where susceptible host plants were growing in the field and conditions were generally favorable for infection, the disease appeared after suitable latent periods. Inoculum leaving the northern Florida-southern Georgia source region could have been transported over both short and long distances. Spores transported to tobacco fields in South Carolina would have fallen on susceptible host plants. Spores carried greater distances (to the mid-Atlantic states) would have arrived when few host plants were in the field. Large-scale infection in these regions had to await further field transplanting, even though the inoculum was available earlier in the growing season. Once blue mold occurred in southern North Carolina, as a result of short-range (across the South Carolina border) or long-range (from the border between northern Florida and southern Georgia) inoculum transport, or both, there was a high probability that southern North Carolina served as one of the inoculum source regions for outbreaks in states farther north.

At present it is not possible to assess fully the value of atmospheric trajectory analysis in epidemiological investigations. First, the models themselves require further evaluation. Davis (1987) discusses some of the work that has been done to evaluate models. For example, the ATAD model simulations of Clarke et al (1983) were found to be most accurate for well-defined flow patterns, especially on the trailing side of high-pressure systems. Transport studies of *P. hyoscyami* spores in North Carolina were done under just such synoptic circumstances; thus, we have a high level of confidence that air parcels originating in the northern Florida-southern Georgia source region in 1980 passed over North Carolina, as the trajectory model indicated.

A second problem in relating trajectory analysis to the spread of blue mold is the lack of direct evidence that sporangiospores are actually present and viable in the air parcels being traced. Although the assumption is enticing, and probably true, the evidence is largely circumstantial. Aylor (1986) has taken a modeling approach in an attempt to better document the nature of the evidence. He proposed a framework for estimating the interregional spread of pathogens like *P. hyoscyami* by combining existing data and logical assumptions on biometeorological components of sporulation rate, escape, transport and dilution, survival, and deposition into a physical model of inoculum production and transport, then adding air parcel trajectories and weather records to the model. The model has important heuristic value in focusing biometeorological research. Aylor cautioned, however, that the calculations are subject to large uncertainties, especially in sporulation rate, survival, and wet deposition. To test his model, he provided a hypothetical example of spore transport to a tobacco field in Connecticut from a source 700 km distant. Skeptics, however, may not be convinced that inoculum can be transported over long distances until the spores are somehow tagged with genetic or other markers at the source region and subsequently trapped and identified at the disease outbreak location. This degree of verification may be costly and will involve both ground-based and atmospheric-based sampling.

Typical Synoptic Weather Scenario

Almost every year in the eastern United States, meteorological conditions during the spring months are highly favorable for the northward transport of spores from southern source regions. A typical series of meteorological events associated with a transport case might center around a synoptic situation that has a high-pressure center located near the East Coast, with an approaching frontal system located in the central United States. The clockwise flow around the high would bring warm, moist maritime tropical air northward from the Gulf of Mexico into the southeastern United States. Because the air motion associated with a high-pressure area is divergent in the lower atmosphere, there would be a general subsidence of air over the region. This subsidence would tend to inhibit the development of showers in the warm, moist air. The release of *P. hyoscyami* spores into the lower atmosphere coincides with the morning establishment of the daytime atmospheric boundary layer. The efficient mixing characteristic of the daytime boundary layer would result in the spores being mixed throughout the lower atmosphere. Spores liberated and entrained into the lower atmosphere at this time would travel northward under generally partly cloudy conditions, with little chance of being removed by precipitation scavenging. However, the viability of these spores could be drastically reduced under these circumstances because of the prolonged exposure to ultraviolet radiation.

As the high moves farther off the East Coast and the frontal system approaches from the west, the air mass over the Southeast would become increasingly unstable. The approach of the front would tend to enhance the upward motion. At this point in the life cycle of such a synoptic system, conditions are most favorable for spore transport. The general ascending air motion, together with the turbulence in the boundary layer, could fill the air mass with spores. Increased cloud cover would be expected, which would provide some protection from the ultraviolet radiation. Shower activity would be increasing; however, precipitation scavenging would not yet be a problem.

Continued eastward movement of the front would increase shower activity to the point that precipitation scavenging could be a factor. Conditions for spore transport in this weather system would be ideal for only a few days.

This scenario is usually repeated many times (though usually not in the idealized sequence discussed here) during the spring. It is highly probable that over a period of weeks, significant numbers of spores could be transported to the tobacco regions of the Southeast.

Future Research

Several avenues of research related to biometeorology and aerobiology of blue mold are presently being pursued. Both source- and receptor-oriented trajectory climatologies are needed. Based on the source-oriented trajectory climatology, the probability that a spore-laden air parcel that leaves a region of diseased plants would arrive at a particular target location during a given period of the year could be assessed. On the other hand, if the pathogen should become established in a certain region, the receptor-oriented trajectory climatology would allow us to assess the probability that the inoculum originated from a particular source region.

Additional research is needed on virtually all aspects of the transport process: spore production rate, escape of the spores from the canopy, actual transport of the spores in the lower atmosphere, survivability of the spores during transport, and both dry and wet deposition of spores. In addition, because meteorological factors at the potential outbreak site, particularly temperature and moisture, are important to the initiation and continued development of a disease, the spatial and temporal behavior of these parameters in critical combinations—cool temperatures coupled with adequate moisture—should also be expressed in probabilistic terms.

Davis (1987) proposed another avenue of research, which involves the 48-hr atmospheric boundary layer wind forecasts derived from the Nested-Grid Numerical Weather Prediction Model in conjunction with a transport model (ATAD or BAT) to predict the movement of a spore cloud over the next two days. Other output parameters from the numerical prediction model could be used to assess the viability of spores and to predict the impact of precipitation scavenging during the transport process.

Summary

The blue mold epidemics of 1979 and 1980 in the Western Hemisphere drew attention to and focused research on epidemiological and biometeorological aspects of the tobacco-*P. hyoscyami* pathosystem. Plant pathologists, meteorologists, and climatologists, working with computer-assisted atmospheric transport models and applying their experience with aerial dispersion phenomena, have opened new doors in the investigation of macroscale epiphytotics. Although the research during the 1980s has been concentrated on the Caribbean-United States system, the results, technology, and interpretations are certainly transferable to other laboratories around the world.

Documented case studies of blue mold epidemics between 1979 and 1986 have been used to propose three likely pathways of disease spread and inoculum movement in the eastern United States. In some years the disease spread progressively northward from Florida and Georgia. In other years it occurred first in Kentucky and the adjoining mountains of North Carolina without first occurring in the southeastern United States. In these cases the inoculum is thought to have originated in south-central Texas on *N. repanda* or from cultivated tobacco in Mexico. However, we cannot rule out a third possibility, namely that sporangiospores are entrained from unknown sources at some point along the calculated "highway." Because of the rather specific weather requirements of the blue mold pathogen, climatic scenarios have been developed that may be able to relate long-range sporangiospore transport to outbreaks of disease far in advance of the front edge of the general epidemic.

Blue mold epidemics in the Caribbean-United States system appear to follow no long-term, biologically based periodicity. The extensive spread of temperature-tolerant *P. hyoscyami* through Latin America, however, may change this situation in the future, if for no other reason than that there is increased inoculum potential. Sporangiospores are apparently produced frequently and abundantly in areas where blue mold is endemic and are carried northward, and perhaps southward, from the warm, humid overwintering zones. Long-distance transport of inoculum is the connecting link in the regional pathosystem. To the best of our knowledge, this dispersal is one-way; no evidence is available to indicate that inoculum is cycled southward from temperate to tropical zones. However, the type (pathogenicity) of inoculum, not the quantity of inoculum, may determine the possibility of an epidemic.

At present, all commercial tobacco cultivars in the United States are susceptible to blue mold. The widespread use of systemic fungicides is the chief deterrent to future epidemics. Already the wily pathogen has developed resistance to some of these chemical barriers in Latin America and Texas (Reuveni et al, 1986b; Wiglesworth et al, 1986). Adaptation and evolution continue in the tobacco-*P. hyoscyami* pathosystem. Resistance in *P. hyoscyami* to systemic acylalanine fungicides, combined with temperature-tolerance in the pathogen population, poses a dangerous situation. Judging from the speed at which the 1979 and 1980 epidemics spread in the United States, the tobacco crop is at serious risk of a major catastrophic epidemic should high-temperature strains of *P. hyoscyami* be introduced via long-distance, airborne transport.

When blue mold occurs first in Florida and Georgia and the disease front moves northward, agricultural extension workers and tobacco farmers soon become aware of the potential risk. However, after several years of low or no blue mold incidence, farmers tend to become complacent. Assuming low risk, they may cease to use the systemic fungicides that are available. When blue mold does break out and spread, relating the pattern of disease occurrence to spore transport is difficult if spatial patterns of fungicide deployment cannot easily be documented. Tobacco farmers do not generally understand that viable *P. hyoscyami* sporangiospores can be transported great distances before causing disease on isolated fields within production regions. This is why blue mold is so treacherous and different from other endemic tobacco diseases. Each year each untreated field is a possible site for pathogen development and multiplication.

Forecasting approaches suggested by Aylor (1986) and Davis (1987) based on trajectory analysis, transport models, and weather analysis may provide plant pathologists, extension personnel, and tobacco farmers the necessary time to employ existing and yet-to-be-identified management strategies to avoid serious losses from blue mold.

Acknowledgments

We thank W. C. Nesmith, extension plant pathologist at the University of Kentucky, for data and interpretation pertaining to blue mold occurrences in Kentucky during 1981–1986. We also thank J. F. Clarke, meteorologist with the Environmental Protection Agency at Research Triangle Park, North Carolina, for initial assistance and suggestions in using the ATAD model. Support for these studies was provided by the North Carolina Tobacco Foundation, R. J. Reynolds Tobacco Company, and the National Crop Loss Design Committee, U.S. Department of Agriculture–Cooperative States Research Service.

LITERATURE CITED

Aylor, D. E. 1986. A framework for examining inter-regional aerial transport of fungal spores. Agric. For. Meteorol. 38:263–288.

Aylor, D. E., and Taylor, G. S. 1983. Escape of *Peronospora tabacina* spores from a field of diseased tobacco plants. Phytopathology 73:525–529.

212

Aylor, D. E., Taylor, G. S., and Raynor, G. S. 1982. Long-range transport of tobacco blue mold spores. Agric. Meteorol. 27:217–232.

Clarke, J. F., Clark, T. L., Ching, J. K. S., Haagenson, P. L., Husar, R. B., and Patterson, D. E. 1983. Assessment of model simulation of long-distance transport. Atmos. Environ. 17:2449–2462.

Cohen, Y. 1976. Interacting effects of light and temperature on sporulation of *Peronospora tabacina* on tobacco leaves. Aust. J. Biol. Sci. 29:281–289.

Cruickshank, I. A. M. 1961. Environment and sporulation in phytopathogenic fungi. II. Conidia formation in *Peronospora tabacina* Adam as a function of temperature. Aust. J. Biol. Sci. 14:198–207.

Cruickshank, I. A. M. 1963. Environment and sporulation in phytopathogenic fungi. IV. The effect of light on the formation of conidia of *Peronospora tabacina* Adam. Aust. J. Biol. Sci. 16:88–98.

Davis, J. M. 1987. Modeling the long-range transport of plant pathogens in the atmosphere. Annu. Rev. Phytopathol. 25:169–188.

Davis, J. M., and Main, C. E. 1984. A regional analysis of the meteorological aspects of the spread and development of blue mold on tobacco. Boundary-Layer Meteorol. 28:271–304.

Davis, J. M., and Main, C. E. 1986. Applying atmospheric trajectory analysis to problems in epidemiology. Plant Dis. 70:490–497.

Davis, J. M., and Sabones, M. E. 1979. Meteorology and blue mold: June, 1979. Pages 29–43 in: Report: Blue Mold Symposium I. North Carolina State University, Raleigh. F. A. Todd, compiler.

Davis, J. M., Main, C. E., and Bruck, R. I. 1981. Analysis of weather and the 1980 blue mold epidemic in the United States and Canada. Plant Dis. 65:508–512.

Davis, J. M., Main, C. E., and Nesmith, W. C. 1985. The biometeorology of blue mold on tobacco. Part II: The evidence for long-range sporangiospore transport. Pages 473–498 in: Movement and Dispersal of Agriculturally Important Biotic Agents. D. R. MacKenzie, C. S. Barfield, G. G. Kennedy, and R. D. Berger, eds. Claitors Publishing Co., Baton Rouge, LA. 611 pp.

Davis, J. M., Main, C. E., and Nesmith, W. C. 1987. The meteorological aspects of the 1985 occurrence of blue mold in Kentucky. (Abstr.) Phytopathology 77:1729.

Duckham, A. N., and Masefield, G. B. 1970. Farming Systems of the World. Chatto and Windus, London. 542 pp.

Gayed, S. K. 1983. Blue mold incidence, spread and severity in the United States and Canada, 1981. Lighter 53:27–30.

Heffter, J. L. 1980. Air Resources Laboratories atmospheric transport and dispersion model (ARL-ATAD). NOAA Tech. Memo ERL-ARL-81. National Oceanic and Atmospheric Administration, Silver Spring, MD. 17 pp.

Heffter, J. L. 1983. Branching atmospheric trajectory (BAT) model. NOAA Tech. Memo ERL-ARL-121. National Oceanic and Atmospheric Administration, Silver Spring, MD. 16 pp.

Hill, A. V. 1960. Spore release in *Peronospora tabacina* Adam. Nature (London) 185:940.

Hill, A. V. 1961. Dissemination of conidia of *Peronospora tabacina* Adam. Aust. J. Biol. Sci. 14:208–222.

213

Kucharek, T. A. 1987. Rainfall, irrigation water, and temperatures associated with first occurrences of tobacco blue mold in leaf production area of north Florida from 1979 to 1984. Plant Dis. 71:336–339.

Lucas, G. B. 1980. The war against blue mold. Science 210:147–153.

Main, C. E., Davis, J. M., and Moss, M. A. 1985. The biometeorology of blue mold of tobacco. Part I: A case study in the epidemiology of the disease. Pages 453–471 in: Movement and Dispersal of Agriculturally Important Biotic Agents. D. R. MacKenzie, C. S. Barfield, G. G. Kennedy, and R. D. Berger, eds. Claitors Publishing Co., Baton Rouge, LA. 611 pp.

Moss, M. A., and Main, C. E. 1984. Application of computer cartography to estimate the impact of temperature tolerance in *Peronospora tabacina* on tobacco production in the Southeast. (Abstr.) Phytopathology 74:630.

Moss, M. A., and Main, C. E. 1985. Temperature tolerance of *Peronospora tabacina* in the U.S. (Abstr.) Phytopathology 75:1341.

Moss, M. A., and Main, C. E. 1988. The effect of temperature on sporulation and viability of isolates of *Peronospora tabacina* collected in the United States. Phytopathology 78:110–114.

Nesmith, W. C. 1984. The North American blue mold warning system. Plant Dis. 68:933–936.

Pinckard, J. A. 1942. The mechanism of spore dispersal in *Peronospora tabacina* and certain other downy mildew fungi. Phytopathology 32:505–511.

Populer, C. 1981. Epidemiology of downy mildews. Pages 57–105 in: The Downy Mildews. D. M. Spencer, ed. Academic Press, New York. 636 pp.

Reuveni, M., Nesmith, W. C., and Siegel, M. R. 1986a. Symptom development and disease severity in *Nicotiana tabacum* and *N. repanda* caused by *Peronospora tabacina*. Plant Dis. 70:727–729.

Reuveni, M., Nesmith, W. C., Wiglesworth, M. D., and Siegel, M. R. 1986b. Detection of metalaxyl resistance in *Peronospora tabacina* on wild tobacco (*Nicotiana repanda*) in Texas. (Abstr.) Phytopathology 76:1116.

Rider, N. E., Cruickshank, I. A. M., and Bradley, E. F. 1961. Environment and sporulation of phytopathogenic fungi. III. *Peronospora tabacina* Adam: Field environment, sporulation and forecasting. Aust. J. Agric. Res. 12:1119–1125.

Rotem, J., and Aylor, D. E. 1984. Development and inoculum potential of *Peronospora tabacina* in the fall season. Phytopathology 74:309–313.

Rotem, J., and Cohen, Y. 1970. The effect of temperature on the pathogen and on the development of blue mold disease in tobacco inoculated with *Peronospora tabacina*. Phytopathology 60:54–57.

Rufty, R. C., and Main, C. E. 1987. Evaluation of components of partial resistance to tobacco blue mold. (Abstr.) Phytopathology 77:1724.

Schiltz, P. 1981. Downy mildew of tobacco. Pages 577–599 in: The Downy Mildews. D. M. Spencer, ed. Academic Press, New York. 636 pp.

Todd, F. A. 1981. The blue mold story. Pages 9–25 in: Report: 29th Tobacco Workers Conference. F. A. Todd, compiler. Lexington, KY. 109 pp.

Uozumi, T., and Kröber, H. 1967. Der Einfluss des Lichtes auf die Konidienbildung von *Peronospora tabacina* Adam an Tabakblättern. Phytopathol. Z. 59:372–384.

Van der Plank, J. E. 1963. Plant Diseases: Epidemics and Control.

Academic Press, New York. 349 pp.

Weltzien, H. C. 1981. Geographic distribution of downy mildews. Pages 31–43 in: The Downy Mildews. D. M. Spencer, ed. Academic Press, New York. 636 pp.

Wiglesworth, M., Nesmith, W., Reuveni, M., Tuzun, S., Siegel, M., Kuć, J., and Juárez, J. 1986. Metalaxyl resistance of *Peronospora tabacina* on tobacco in Mexico. (Abstr.) Phytopathology 76:1116.

Wuest, P. J., and Schmitt, C. G. 1965. Greenhouse tests to compare European and Beltsville isolates of *Peronospora tabacina*. Plant Dis. Rep. 49:367–370.

Zadoks, J. C., and Kampmeijer, P. 1977. The role of crop populations and their deployment, illustrated by means of a simulator, EPIMUL 76. Pages 164–190 in: The Genetic Basis of Epidemics in Agriculture. P. R. Day, ed. New York Academy of Science, New York. 400 pp.

Zadoks, J. C., and Schein, R. D. 1979. Epidemiology and Plant Disease Management. Oxford University Press, New York. 427 pp.

Chapter 9

Effect of Environment on Sporulation, Dispersal, Longevity, and Germination of Conidia of *Peronospora hyoscyami*

I. A. M. Cruickshank
Division of Plant Industry
Commonwealth Scientific and Industrial
  Research Organization (CSIRO)
Canberra, Australia

Conidia are of primary importance in the spread and development of blue mold of tobacco (*Nicotiana tabacum*). During the tobacco growing season, the following asexual life cycle is characteristic of the development of *Peronospora hyoscyami* de Bary f. sp. *tabacina* (Adam) Skalický (syn. *P. tabacina* Adam): Conidia are produced on conidiophores, which emerge from stomata predominantly on the abaxial or lower surfaces of disease lesions on tobacco leaves. Conidia are released from these fruiting structures and are dispersed by air currents to neighboring plants, which may be within the same crop or at some distance in neighboring crops. Upon arriving on healthy tobacco leaf surfaces, conidia germinate and infection may follow. Infection in turn leads to vegetative growth of the fungus within the leaf tissues. The asexual life cycle normally is completed in four to seven days by the emergence of new conidiophores and their production of conidia. A sexual phase, oospore formation followed by zoospore formation, also occurs in the life cycle of this pathogen under some climatic conditions. This phase may contribute to the overwintering of blue mold. The life cycle of *P. hyoscyami* is summarized in Figure 1.

The environment affects many aspects of the life cycle of *P. hyoscyami* which are important to the epidemiology of blue mold. Early reports (see reviews by Hill [1957] and Rayner and Hopkins

[1962]) concerned mainly field observations of the disease and its spread in plant seedling beds and field crops in relation to meteorological conditions measured above the plants following natural infection. Although this approach led to many results of great importance for the control of blue mold, it tended to limit the advancement of basic knowledge essential for further progress (Hill, 1957).

This chapter emphasizes results obtained from controlled experiments in the laboratory, glasshouse, and field plots, especially experiments designed to explore the limits and the optimum values of variables such as moisture, temperature, light, and nutrition and their interactions. Because much of the research on the biology of *P. hyoscyami* was done between 1955 and 1975, this chapter is in part historical. The results discussed, however, are still

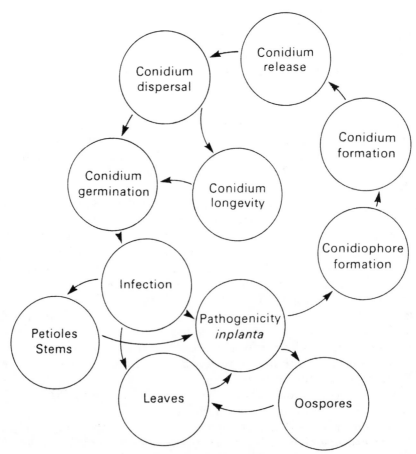

Figure 1.   Stages in the life cycle of *Peronospora hyoscyami*.

valid and will always be important to the epidemiology of blue mold of tobacco.

Formation of Conidia

WATER RELATIONS AND SPORULATION

Blue mold is a downy mildew. As in other downy mildews, water relations play a major role in the formation of conidia. In early studies in this area (Armstrong and Sumner, 1935; Clayton and Gaines, 1933; Dixon et al, 1936), sporulation was reported to be limited to the range of humidity from saturation to slightly below dew point. It was reported to be most abundant when these conditions occurred at night or over prolonged periods of overcast weather.

In an attempt to investigate quantitatively how water relations affect sporulation under controlled conditions, Cruickshank and Müller (1957) developed a leaf disk technique (Fig. 2). The relative humidity over the leaf surface was controlled by glycerol-water solutions, while the diffusion pressure deficit of the leaf tissues was controlled by floating them on aqueous mannitol solutions. With this simple methodology, the effect of small differences in vapor pressure in the so-called boundary layer or phyllosphere of the leaf could be studied independently of the hydrostatic pressures inside the leaf, while maintaining other conditions constant.

Relative Humidity

Using the above methodology, Cruickshank (1958) reported that 97–100% relative humidity was necessary in the leaf boundary layer for maximum sporulation (Fig. 3). Sporulation dropped significantly between 97 and 96% relative humidity. Further decreases in relative humidity resulted in progressive reductions in sporulation intensity until at 90% relative humidity, sporulation was almost completely inhibited. These results demonstrated the critical sensitivity of sporulation of *P. hyoscyami* to relative humidity in the close vicinity

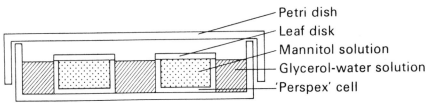

Figure 2. Microenvironment chamber. (Reprinted, by permission, from *Nature,* Vol. 180, pp. 44–45 [Cruickshank and Müller, 1957]. Copyright 1957 Macmillan Journals Limited)

219

of the leaf surface where conidiophores emerge from the leaf and conidia are formed. Many workers have reported that above the crop, relative humidities below 97% may be accompanied by heavy sporulation. This is probably because of differences between relative humidity at the boundary layer and in the ambient atmosphere (Burrage, 1971), which may be affected by radiation, air movement, and other conditions. Collins (1964) proposed the term "critical relative humidity," which encompasses wind speed, air temperature, and heat loss from the crop, as a more serviceable term than ambient relative humidity. In the field the relative humidity is obviously affected by many factors.

Diffusion Pressure Deficit

In experiments in which diffusion pressure deficits in the plant tissue were adjusted from 2.6 to 20.6 atm (Cruickshank, 1958), maximum sporulation occurred at 2.6 atm. Small increases in diffusion pressure deficit were accompanied by very significant reductions in sporulation (Fig. 4). These results clearly showed that sporulation is also critically sensitive to diffusion pressure deficit in infected leaf tissue.

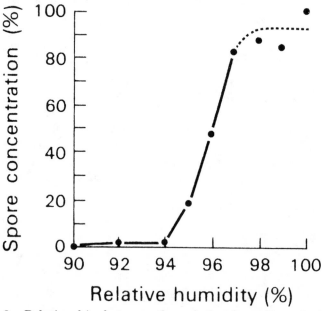

Figure 3. Relationship between the relative humidity of air in the boundary layer and sporulation of *Peronospora hyoscyami*. (Reprinted, by permission, from Cruickshank, 1958)

Relative humidity follows a diurnal cycle in nature, being highest at night and lowest during the daylight hours. Wolf and McLean (1940) reported that under natural conditions, conidia were produced at daybreak each morning if moisture relationships were favorable. In a more detailed quantitative analysis of the process of fructification under optimum relative humidity and diffusion pressure deficit conditions, Cruickshank (1958) found that conidiophores and immature conidia were first observed at 0300 hr but that mature conidia were first produced at 0600 hr and peak production was reached at 0900 hr.

In experiments manipulating the relationships between relative humidity and time, it was shown that the times of maximum or near maximum sporulation intensity could be influenced to some extent by the time of onset of optimum relative humidity. It was also shown that in addition to the requirement for a minimum period of optimum relative humidity at a specific time of day for sporulation, there was a critical stage in conidiophore development that was completely dependent on optimum humidity conditions. A drop in relative humidity to 90% or less before this critical stage of conidiophore development had passed inhibited fructification. If

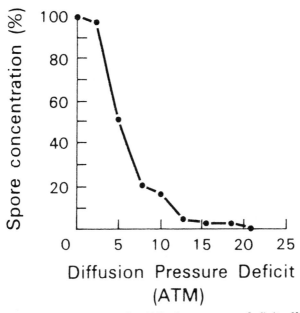

Figure 4. Relationship between the diffusion pressure deficit of host tissue and sporulation of *Peronospora hyoscyami*. (Reprinted, by permission, from Cruickshank, 1958)

221

conidiophores had developed beyond the critical stage, however, conidial formation continued irrespective of changes in relative humidity. Subminimum periods of optimum relative humidity were not cumulative and had no effect on sporulation.

In summary, the collective results on water relations and sporulation demonstrate the great importance of water relations and show that even minor deviations from the optimum relative humidity-time balance will either lengthen the incubation period of disease development in planta or significantly decrease the intensity of sporulation. Either or both results could greatly affect the epidemiology of blue mold.

SPORULATION AS A FUNCTION OF TEMPERATURE

Clayton and Gaines (1933, 1945), Armstrong and Sumner (1935), and Dixon et al (1936) reported observations on the effect of temperature on sporulation. Their values for the minimum, optimum, and maximum temperatures varied with the locality, the conditions under which the observations were made, and the isolate of *P. hyoscyami*. They did not attempt to put their observations on a quantitative basis.

Length of Incubation Phase of Infection and Sporulation Intensity

By growing tobacco plants under several temperature regimes both before and after inoculation and by progressive daily sampling of infected leaf disks from these plants, Cruickshank (1961b) found that the sporulation ability of *P. hyoscyami* rose from zero on day 3 to a maximum on days 7 and 8 under the temperature regime 28°C day, 14°C night (Fig. 5). For the temperature regime 20°C day, 15°C night, the period from inoculation to initial appearance of conidia was one or two days longer, but the time to maximum conidial production did not change significantly (eight days). Some sporulation occurred even after 17 days. Sporulation intensity was correlated with the temperature regimes of plant growth.

Effect of Infected Leaf Temperature

The cardinal temperatures for sporulation of *P. hyoscyami* under optimum humidity conditions have been identified (Cruickshank, 1961b) as 1–2°C (minimum), 15–23°C (optimum range), and about 30°C (maximum). These temperatures were independent of the plant growth temperature regime and the isolate of *P. hyoscyami* studied. However, sporulation intensity, especially over the optimum temperature range, appeared to be causally related to the physiological state of the tobacco plant, the length of the incubation period before sporulation occurs, and the isolate of the pathogen.

222

Temperature-Time Interactions

Incubation of infected leaf disks for various time-temperature combinations (Cruickshank, 1961b) has shown that over the optimum temperature range for sporulation, variation in length of treatment had little or no effect. At less favorable temperatures, however, duration of exposure was important. Incubation of leaf disks at day temperatures of 7.8 or 34.5°C significantly depressed the sporulation response over the whole time range; the effect of the high temperature was much greater than that of the low temperature. In the reciprocal case, where the effect of decreasing time periods was studied, short exposures to low or high temperatures had little effect on sporulation intensity, as they occurred after sporulation had been initiated. However, when the low or high temperature was initiated earlier in the diurnal cycle, the sporulation response was progressively reduced. The effect was again greatest at the higher temperatures. Moss and Main (1985) cast doubt on the inhibitory effect of high temperatures on sporulation in a report on an isolate of *P. hyoscyami* in the United

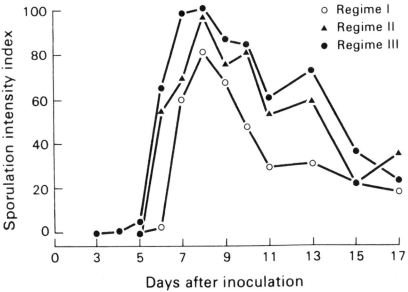

Figure 5. Time course of sporulation intensity of *Peronospora hyoscyami* in relation to temperature regime. Groups of six tobacco plants were conditioned for two weeks to each of the following environmental regimes (day temperature [0830–1630 hr], night temperature [1630–0830 hr], day relative humidity, night relative humidity): regime I, 20°C, 15°C, 48%, 50–70%; regime II, 25°C, 18°C, 35%, 35–50%; regime III, 28°C, 24°C, 40%, 42–50%. (Reprinted, by permission, from Cruickshank, 1961b)

States that sporulated after exposure to 36 and 25°C day-night temperatures.

The laboratory situations discussed above are oversimplified compared to the ever-fluctuating conditions in the field. They emphasize, however, that duration of exposure to a given temperature, and not just temperature alone, determines inter alia the final sporulation intensity. In general, hot days followed by hot or cold nights should be least favorable for sporulation unless races tolerant to high temperatures become widespread. Cold days and cold nights should favor maximum sporulation under optimum water relations. If thermophilic races of *P. hyoscyami* become widespread, high summer temperatures, which traditionally have been associated with restricted development of blue mold, may no longer exercise this ecological restraint (Moss and Main, 1985).

Temperature has also been reported to affect the size of conidia (Smith, 1970). Infected plants grown at relatively low temperatures (15°C day, 10°C night) exhibited significantly larger conidia (20.6 μm long by 17.4 μm wide) than plants grown at high temperatures (30°C day, 25°C night) (namely, 18.2 μm long by 14.9 μm wide).

LIGHT AND SPORULATION

A diurnal cycle of sporulation is characteristic of downy mildews in nature. Yarwood (1937) suggested that this was because of the alternation of light and darkness in the normal day.

Light Intensity

Several investigators have studied the effect of exposing infected leaves to continuous light and continuous darkness on sporulation intensity under favorable moisture and temperature conditions (Cruickshank, 1963; Jardot, 1966a; Uozumi and Kröber, 1967). They generally agreed on the effect of light on sporulation, although there were some quantitative differences in their data. Cruickshank's (1963) studies concerned single cycles of sporulation only. He used a light tower with an incandescent light source. Incident light was measured at the leaf disk surfaces. Leaf disk samples were cut at 1600 hr from infected leaves of seedlings growing under natural photoperiod conditions and were irradiated overnight until 0900 hr. Under these conditions the ED_{50} for inhibition of sporulation was 16 μW·cm^{-2}. Inhibition was almost complete at about 320 μW·cm^{-2}, and the effect occurred irrespective of the leaf surface irradiated. When whole plants were irradiated (about 800 μW·cm^{-2}), however, sporulation was very significantly depressed, but some sporulation did occur (about 9% with reference to the continuous-darkness controls).

Under somewhat different experimental conditions in which leaf disks were inoculated and subsequently exposed to continuous irradiation over the several-day infection period, Jardot (1966a) reported the appearance of more or less normal conidiophores either with or without conidia or bearing conidia of aberrant shape. Uozumi and Kröber (1967) confirmed that in continuous light, mass sporulation was absent; however, if the light period was extended for 36–48 hr, a small number of conidia were produced.

Light-Temperature Interactions

Cohen (1976) observed that when infected leaf disks were placed in growth cabinets at 100% relative humidity, calibrated to air temperatures of 6–23°C, and covered with various neutral filters to vary light intensity, light intensity of about 500 μW·cm^{-2} caused 45, 99.6, and 100% inhibition of sporulation at temperatures of 15.6, 19.4, and 24°C, respectively, relative to the dark controls at the same temperatures. Raising the light intensity to about 800 μW·cm^{-2} prevented conidial formation at 20.2°C but suppressed it by only 57% at 15.7°C. When leaf temperature was lowered to 8 and 10°C, however, light had the opposite effect; it stimulated conidial production above the dark controls. Maximum stimulation occurred at about 800 μW·cm^{-2} at both temperatures. Thus, Cohen (1976) showed that the inhibitory effect of continuous irradiation was temperature-dependent.

Photoperiod

Continuous light and continuous darkness represent contrived situations. It is more relevant to consider the interaction of light and darkness on sporulation per se and on sporulation intensity. It is also important to determine whether the effects of light and darkness on infected leaves act directly on the pathogen or are expressed through metabolic changes in the plant tissue reacting to the exposure to light and dark treatments, and whether moisture is also involved.

When infected leaf disks were exposed to progressively longer periods of darkness at 20°C and 98–100% relative humidity, Cruickshank (1963) observed that at least 7 hr of darkness was necessary for maximum sporulation. In experiments under European conditions, Uozumi and Kröber (1967) observed that only 5 hr of darkness was necessary. These authors suggested that light conditions may control the time at which sporulation occurs and the quality as well as the quantity of conidia formed. They stated that darkness was required to initiate sporulation but that sporulation as a process was governed essentially by the duration of the periods of both light and darkness that preceded it.

When multiple short exposures of infected leaf disks to darkness collectively equaled 6 hr and were interspersed with light radiation, Cruickshank (1963) observed that the effects of the dark periods were additive but that, with the exception of the 3-hr treatments, the effects were significantly less than those of the continuous-darkness controls. Cohen et al (1978) reported the effect of alternating light and dark periods in cycles of 1–4 hr. Exposing infected leaf disks in moist chambers to incandescent irradiation for 1–15 min/hr during a 24-hr period reduced conidial yield by 0–85%. When the treatments were given every 2 hr, conidial yield was reduced by 0–42%, and exposures every 3 hr had no effect on conidial production. When leaf disks were exposed to irradiation for 1 min, alternating with 14–59 min of darkness in repeating cycles for 24 hr, conidial production was reduced from 80 to 21%. Thus, under each of these conditions, sporulation was significantly and progressively inhibited as the length of the light period increased.

The time of day at which infected leaf disks received dark treatments, in addition to affecting sporulation intensity, also influenced to some extent the time of day at which sporulation occurred within a 24-hr sporulation cycle (Cruickshank, 1963). Cruickshank (1963) observed that, provided infected leaves had been exposed to darkness, subsequent exposure to light had no significant effect on conidiophore emergence or sporulation intensity. This was further evidence for the notion that the effect of light on the reproduction process of *P. hyoscyami* is not a direct one.

Relationship of Sporulation to Photosynthesis

Cohen and Rotem (1970) cited and used the information that dichlorophenyl-dimethylurea (DCMU) blocks the Hill reaction in photosynthesis without interfering with other biological processes. They sprayed infected tobacco plants with DCMU either before or after exposure to a 12-hr light period and compared the sporulation response obtained with that of infected plants maintained either in light or in darkness. Infected plants sprayed with DCMU before exposure to light produced few or no conidia. On the other hand, plants sprayed with DCMU after exposure to light and just before exposure to darkness produced normal quantities of conidia. Thus, DCMU did not change the normal patterns of sporulation or that resulting from the inhibitory effect of light. In later studies, Cohen (1976) floated leaf disks on DCMU solutions (10^{-4}–10^{-6}) at 100% relative humidity and 20°C under blue light or in darkness. Floating infected leaf disks on sucrose solutions also did not enable *P. hyoscyami* to sporulate under continuous light. The negative results of these experiments confirmed the earlier results and by implication confirmed that inhibition of photosynthesis during the sporulation period does not reduce the yield of conidia in darkness nor does it enable the pathogen to sporulate under continuous light.

Action Spectrum of Conidial Formation

Cruickshank (1963) studied the action spectrum of white light with regard to sporulation of *P. hyoscyami* in infected leaf disks using filtered light from 402 to 760 nm under conditions of equal energy ($1.5 \, \mu\text{W}\cdot\text{cm}^{-2}$ at the leaf surface). The light source was a 500-W tungsten lamp combined with monochromatic Zeiss-Jena interference filters. Under these conditions, sporulation was not inhibited at 402 nm or in the spectral region 715–760 nm. Maximum

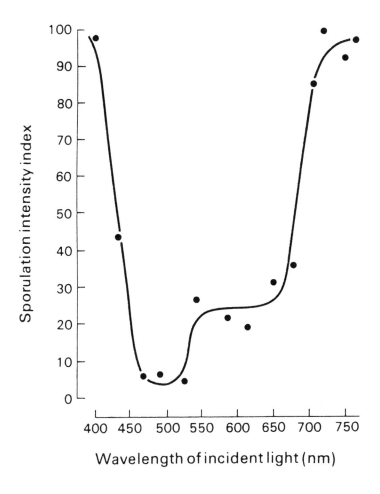

Figure 6. Action spectrum of sporulation of *Peronospora hyoscyami* in infected tobacco leaf disks. Energy level was held constant at $1.5 \, \mu\text{W}\cdot\text{cm}^{-2}$ of leaf area. (Reprinted, by permission, from Cruickshank, 1963)

227

inhibition occurred at 469–524 nm, with a shoulder at around 600–625 nm (Fig. 6). Thus, within the visible spectrum, the blue-green region was primarily responsible for sporulation inhibition. For the narrow spectral region represented by the monochromatic light source (469 nm), the ED_{50} value for inhibition in terms of energy required for the reaction was 0.58 $\mu W \cdot cm^{-2}$ of leaf surface (Fig. 7). Cohen (1976) confirmed and extended these results.

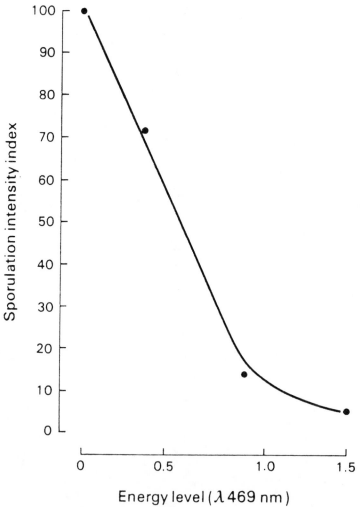

Figure 7. Relationship between energy level of monochromatic light (469 nm) at the surface of infected leaf disks and intensity of sporulation of *Peronospora hyoscyami*. (Reprinted, by permission, from Cruickshank, 1963)

Metabolic Implications

As discussed by Cruickshank (1963) and confirmed by Cohen (1976), the major point that emerges from the light-dark irradiation experiments is that sporulation inhibition by light involves a very low-energy reaction. Cruickshank postulated that sporulation was a dark-induction phenomenon in which major metabolic cycles were probably not involved. He speculated that it might be linked with hormonal changes that are inhibited by a photosensitive mechanism. Cohen (1976) argued on the basis of evidence presented in his paper that an enzymatic buildup of a postulated antisporulant during a wet light period and its enzymatic decay over a dry dark period may explain the inhibitory effect of light on sporulation and its reversal by darkness. Some indirect evidence was obtained for the diffusion of an inhibitory compound from irradiated to nonirradiated areas of detached leaves. However, no evidence was presented to suggest whether the postulated antisporulant compound was produced by the host, by the pathogen, or by the host-pathogen interaction, nor is it known which of the three responds to the light signal. The precise nature of the chemistry and biochemistry of the light inhibitory effect remains an interesting problem and a challenge to physiological plant pathologists. Clarification could lead to the development of new methods of blue mold control.

Conidial Release

The mechanistic aspects of the release of conidia by *P. hyoscyami* were first described in some detail by Pinckard (1942), who believed release was brought about by the twisting movements of conidiophores exposed to rapidly changing and decreasing humidity. In studies on a related downy mildew, *P. destructor* (Berk.) Casp., Yarwood (1943) confirmed that conidia were released following changes in relative humidity. He also demonstrated that mechanical movements of the leaf could release conidia.

Cruickshank (1958) reexamined this phenomenon and attempted to put it on a quantitative basis by using a modification of the leaf disk technique of Cruickshank and Müller (1957). Leaf disks in which *P. hyoscyami* had sporulated heavily were carefully and rapidly transferred from the very high-humidity conditions (98–100% relative humidity) required for sporulation to conditions of lower relative humidity. The intensity of conidial release was measured by counting after 1 hr the number of conidia trapped on glycerol-treated slides positioned immediately under the sporulating lesions. The effect on conidial release of a single mechanical shock of increasing magnitude, with relative humidity maintained at about 100%, was also studied. Both changes in relative humidity of the air layer close to the leaf surface and mechanical shocks under high relative humidity conditions were important contributory factors in conidial release. They were independent of each other, and their effect increased with their magnitude. The response was progressive and not simultaneous or all-or-none.

The above observations using leaf disks have been confirmed under seedbed conditions (Jenkins and Valli, 1966; Valli, 1966; Waggoner and Taylor, 1958). Waggoner and Taylor (1958), however, emphasized that the diurnal cycle of release indicated that conidia were released as the conidiophore shrivels in the morning but not while it is shriveled or as it is taking up moisture in the evening. They concluded that the absence of release at midday meant that forcible discharge was necessary or that conidia on conidiophores on the leaf surface were protected from the turbulent air. The absence of conidial release in the evening was claimed to indicate that the forcible discharge mechanism does not work when conidiophores are rewetted and are becoming turgid. The release of conidia appears to be associated with a rapid process, while the uptake of moisture by conidiophores is a relatively slow process.

Cruickshank's experiments on conidial release involved sudden changes in relative humidity. Jardot (1966c), on the other hand, arranged his experiments so that relative humidity was reduced slowly and progressively. In his studies small numbers of conidia were collected between 100 and 90% relative humidity, but high concentrations were not collected until the relative humidity had fallen below 90%, which corresponded to the optimum conditions for conidial release.

Hill (1960, 1961), while agreeing in general with the importance of water relations to conidial release, suggested that diffusion pressure deficit rather than relative humidity was paramount. He pointed out that in field experiments, the number of conidia trapped each hour of the day rose to a maximum between 0930 and 1100 hr for periods of 12–16 consecutive days and that this daily cycle was not interrupted by overnight relative humidity too low for sporulation. Thus, he believed that conidial release was not conditional on decreasing relative humidity preceded by overnight saturation. Hill (1961) also reported that at any relative humidity, relatively few conidia were trapped in a calm atmosphere compared with those trapped in a turbulent atmosphere with varying humidity and temperature.

Because diurnal periodicity for the release of conidia was maintained under a wide range of environmental conditions, Hill (1961) argued that there must be some mechanism for ensuring that conidia were dispersed in this way and were not all released on the day of production. He argued that because transpiration from diseased leaf tissue was greater than from healthy tissue (Cruickshank and Rider, 1961), it could be a factor in the collapse of conidiophores commencing at the basal end adjacent to the leaf stoma, as described by Pinckard (1942). To further support his diffusion pressure deficit hypothesis, Hill cited experiments in which sporulating leaves were dried and stored for several months before being placed in a saturated atmosphere overnight, in which the leaves absorbed water and the conidiophores became turgid. When the leaves were redried, conidia were discharged in the same manner as for fresh green leaves. Conidiophores placed on moist glass slides also became turgid. Hill argued that because water was absorbed through the stalk end of the conidiophore, rather than directly from the atmosphere as in the latter case, turgidity of conidiophores depended on water supply from the leaf and not on the ambient humidity. Hill argued that conidiophores on green leaves become turgid each night and release conidia each morning in phase with the diurnal diffusion pressure deficit cycle of the infected leaf. Water relations relating to the plant-pathogen association are clearly very important in the release of conidia, just as they are to their formation. Hill's arguments are forceful but still require direct experimental proof.

Conidial Dissemination and Dispersal

In the previous section, the effect of environment on conidial release per se was discussed. This section will be more concerned with the numbers of conidia in the atmosphere in the vicinity of sporulating lesions on leaves of tobacco plants growing in the glasshouse or in field plots. In most cases, Hirst spore traps were used to estimate the mean density of conidia per cubic centimeter over time.

DIURNAL PERIODICITY

Continuous light in the field and in the glasshouse (Hill, 1961) showed a well-defined daily periodicity in the content of conidia in the atmosphere (Fig. 8). The mean time at which the numbers of conidia trapped began to increase was between 0530 and 0839 hr. In Hill's experiments, the greatest numbers occurred between about 1000 and about 1400 hr. They then decreased to a few by about 1500–1930 hr or occasionally later. The number of conidia increased over periods of 3–7 hr, and the total time that relatively high numbers were present varied from 7.3 to 18.5 hr. Maximum numbers of conidia were recorded at approximately the same time each day despite wide variations in weather conditions. The number of hours from sunrise before maximum numbers of conidia were recorded was independent of field locality and glasshouse conditions. Rain and wind also dispersed conidia (Fig. 8).

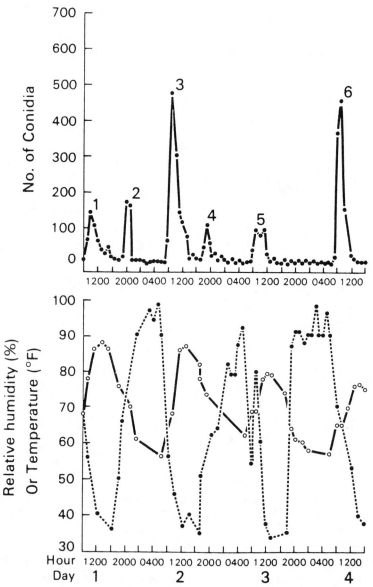

Figure 8. Dissemination of *Peronospora hyoscyami* conidia in the field, showing peaks of diurnal dissemination at 1, 3, 5, and 6; the effect of 0.25 mm of rain at 2; and the effect of wind at 4. (Reprinted, by permission, from Hill, 1961)

Hill (1961) reported that under glasshouse conditions where the temperature rose 3.2–7.2° C during a period of 3–7 hr, the most conidia were trapped at temperatures near the maximum. In the field the increase in conidia began at 13.3–14.9° C, and maximum numbers were recorded at 18.7–21.3° C. In this case, the number of conidia trapped reached a maximum 3–4 hr before the time of the maximum temperature, 24.5–25.9° C. Thus, in this situation, a temperature rise of 5.4–6.4° C during a period of 3–4 hr was associated with an increase in the number of conidia disseminated. In both field and glasshouse, dissemination was associated with increasing temperature during the morning.

Hill (1961) found with continuous trapping under field conditions that conidia were present in the atmosphere every hour for up to 11 days. However, very few were present at humidities near saturation, a result confirmed by Jardot (1966c). An increase in the number of conidia trapped in the field was associated with a decrease in the relative humidity after sunrise, but dissemination ceased before the relative humidity reached its lowest point. In the field, maximum numbers of conidia were trapped within the relative humidity range 55–76%. In the glasshouse, a drop in relative humidity was not always associated with an increase in conidia. Similarly, at levels of humidity near saturation, an increase in temperature did not cause dissemination. Few conidia were trapped during periods of slow change in temperature and humidity (compare with Jardot, 1966c), whereas rapid changes promoted dissemination. In summary, Hill concluded that dissemination was associated with a rapid increase in temperature, even though changes in humidity may be very small, and that the daily pattern of dissemination occurred over a wide range of humidity. Populer (1962) confirmed Hill's (1961) observation that dissemination intensity appeared to have little connection with the amount of rainfall.

LIGHT

Diurnal periodicity of dissemination did not occur in darkness or continuous light, but it could be induced by alternation of light and dark (Hill, 1961). The daily pattern in the numbers of conidia trapped was characterized by few to none during darkness, followed by an increase beginning soon after sunrise. Light periods of 5–30 min caused small increases in numbers of conidia trapped, and this increase was progressive for longer light periods up to 8–12 hr. When the effects of light and temperature treatments were compared, Hill (1961) found that increases in conidia due to higher temperatures occurred for a short time at the beginning of the treatments, then were followed by a rapid decline, whereas with light, increased numbers of conidia were present for a minimum of about 9 hr.

By trapping conidia in the field, Populer (1966) confirmed that liberation of conidia of *P. hyoscyami* mainly followed a periodical daily pattern. He observed that dissemination of conidia started as solar radiation increased to $0.5 \; cal \cdot min^{-1} \cdot cm^{-2}$, temperature increased, relative humidity fell below 80%, and leaf wetness dropped to zero. Dissemination followed the variations in irradiation, temperature, and humidity, and the dissemination curves were reported to fit particularly well with the radiation curves in excess of $0.5 \; cal \cdot min^{-1} \cdot cm^{-2}$. Thus, according to Populer, radiation energy appeared to play an all-important part in the process of conidial dissemination.

LEAF MOVEMENT

As discussed above, Hill (1961) observed that in the field light rain showers accompanied by gusts of wind caused the number of conidia trapped per hour to increase significantly. Hill simulated these conditions in the glasshouse and confirmed that conidia became airborne as a result of violent leaf movement and that the number of conidia could rise and fall sharply within a few minutes. In these experiments, however, few conidia were disseminated as a result of leaf movement in a nearly saturated atmosphere (compare with Cruickshank, 1958). The most conidia were trapped within the first few minutes after air movement was increased. Thereafter only a low number of conidia were released during the period of constant wind speed. Fewer conidia were trapped, however, during periods of increasing leaf movement than during the regular daily dispersal period. Populer (1966) confirmed that conidia were released as a result of change in wind speed but could find no constant relationship between conidial dispersal and wind speed.

Note that the traditional practice in the growing of shade tobacco of raising the tent walls to control blue mold in fact has the reverse effect (Aylor and Taylor, 1982). The practice had no effect on reducing leaf wetness but increased the wind speed within the tent. The net result of raising the walls may actually be to spread blue mold, according to these authors.

LONG-RANGE TRANSPORT OF CONIDIA

Many researchers and tobacco pathologists have reported on the broad hectare aspects of the epidemiology of blue mold. Other chapters in this book discuss in detail various aspects of two major blue mold epidemics in the last 30 years that have spelled disaster for tobacco crops and major losses for tobacco growers in Europe and North America. I will discuss here only three papers that bear on this topic, as they serve to highlight the main principles involved.

Waggoner and Taylor (1955) studied the spread of conidia in shade tobacco and in open-field tobacco by mapping the appearance of blue mold lesions. They concluded that conidia of *P. hyoscyami* from blue mold lesions lead to primary infections for a distance of only several meters downwind and very little upwind. Based on their observations, they believed that sources of infection within a grower's own tobacco crop were more dangerous than infections in a distant or even a neighboring crop.

More recently, Aylor et al (1982) examined long-range transport of conidia of *P. hyoscyami* over several hundred kilometers. They pointed out that the probability of a conidium reaching a given crop from afar depends on airflow from the source region, the size of the source and the number of conidia released into the air at the source, the dilution caused by atmospheric turbulence, and the numbers of spores lost by deposition on vegetation and on the ground during their flight. A further factor that should be considered in such a statistical analysis of probability is the size of the target cropping area in a collective sense. To this list of variables directly affecting the survival of conidia could be added factors that affect longevity (e.g., ultraviolet light), which will be discussed later in this chapter. Aylor et al (1982) acknowledged the many uncertainties involved in computing conidial transport over long distances. The probability of success for any individual conidium is extremely low. However, the fact that epidemics occur in some cases in very isolated localities is circumstantial evidence that some conidia do survive in spite of the overwhelming odds. Backward trajectories have been used to infer the origin of conidia (Aylor et al, 1982; see also Chapter 8). As better and more complete information becomes available on the various parameters involved, it should be possible to compute forward trajectories. Such information would assist in the construction of predictive models useful in disease forecasting and crop loss assessment.

Aylor and Taylor (1983) also studied the escape of *P. hyoscyami* conidia from small fields of tobacco severely infected with blue mold. They measured the vertical profiles of conidial concentration and wind speed above the crops on several days during the hours of peak release of conidia. The rate of conidial escape derived from these measurements ranged from one to seven per square meter per second. Aylor and Taylor used their results in a mathematical model to estimate conidial escape from more extensive plantings.

Longevity and Viability of Conidia

LONGEVITY ASSESSED IN TERMS OF IN VITRO GERMINATION

Angell and Hill (1932), in one of the earliest reports in this area, observed that longevity of conidia of *P. hyoscyami* was affected by changes in humidity and storage temperature. Hill (1961) confirmed this result but also observed that maximum longevity at all temperatures did not occur at the same relative humidity.

In a more detailed study, Hill (1969a) examined the viability of conidia stored in water at various temperatures, on agar blocks, and on leaf surfaces. In each case, viability tests based on germination in vitro were performed at 15°C. Conidia stored in water had short survival times at 15 and 20°C and longer survival at 25°C. However, at very high temperatures (35 and 37.5°C), the survival times were very short (1 hr and 30 min, respectively). Conidia stored on agar blocks at 30°C for 96 hr, 35°C for 24 hr, or 37.5°C for 5 hr did not germinate. In studies of the longevity of conidia stored in situ on leaf disks, the disks were cut from the leaves in the presporulation stage of infection and were allowed to sporulate under optimum conditions. The leaf disks were then transferred to the in situ storage conditions described below, and samples of conidia were taken over time for viability tests. Germination of conidia stored at 5°C was low (5–25%) throughout a period of 17 days. At 10–15°C, germination was about 55% from the second to the fifth day, while at 20, 25, and 30°C, the peak of the viability curve (70%) occurred after storage for 1–2 days. Thereafter there was rapid loss in viability at these temperatures. Conidia survived in situ under these conditions for a much shorter time than conidia from leaf disks stored in desiccators at 43% relative humidity and 20°C. Under the latter conditions, viability remained fairly high over the first three days and declined to zero after 23 days.

Kröber (1965) examined the viability of conidia stored in air-dried soil and dust similar to that found in tobacco drying sheds. Under such conditions during the winter (in Germany), conidia were reported to survive for as long as four to five and a half months.

LONGEVITY ASSESSED IN TERMS OF INFECTIVITY

Most viability studies have used conidial germination as a proxy for viability. Hill (1969b) recognized that germination may tell only part of the story. He complemented germination tests with tests for lesion production using very low inoculum concentrations. Infectivity was 98–100% for fresh conidia but decreased to less than 3% for conidia stored for 24 hr at 20°C. The percentage of inoculum drops that produced lesions decreased from 73% before conidia were stored in water to 0.8% after storage for 24 hr. The number of conidia required for lesion production rose from 1.4 for fresh conidia to 90 for conidia stored for 24 hr in water at temperatures of 5–25°C. This corresponded to a drop in percentage germination at all temperatures tested from 98.5 to 3%.

236

In comparisons similar to those described above, Hill (1969b) stored conidia in a desiccator (43% relative humidity, 20°C) and sampled them over time for viability and infectivity. At zero time mean infectivity was about 30% lower than mean germinability in vitro. This difference decreased with storage time (Fig. 9). The calculated ED_{50} value occurred after two days' storage. In general, the decline in the percentage of infective conidia was matched by the decline in the percentage of conidial germination.

Jankowski (1966) stored conidia at 0–5°C and 40–50% relative humidity. Infectivity under these conditions was high (72%) for 117 days but fell sharply thereafter. Only 1.1% of conidia were infective after 143 days. Cohen and Eyal (1984) agreed with earlier reports that conidia of *P. hyoscyami* showed prolonged longevity and infectivity when kept attached to conidiophores on leaves and stored at low relative humidity.

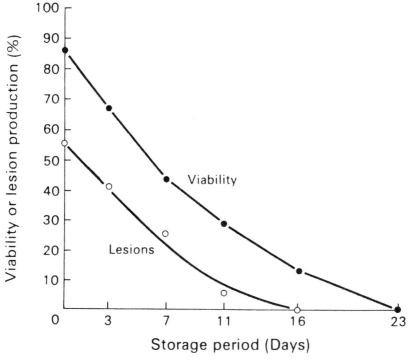

Figure 9. Viability (expressed as germination percentage) and lesion production (expressed as percentage of effective inoculum drops) of *Peronospora hyoscyami* conidia stored at 20°C and 43% relative humidity (means of five observations plotted in all cases). (Reprinted, by permission, from Hill, 1969b)

TEMPERATURE-HUMIDITY INTERACTIONS

Hill (1962a) showed that as temperature increased, maximum longevity occurred at lower relative humidities. However, Kröber (1965) showed that conidia survived longer under cool, dry conditions, with moisture having a more pronounced effect than temperature. Conidia were shown to lose or gain weight according to the ambient humidity (Shepherd et al, 1971). At 94% relative humidity, all conidia were swollen, whereas at 88% relative humidity, all were shrunken. Even at 91.4% relative humidity, however, where 50% of the conidia were swollen, no germination was observed. Conidial viability, as determined by Kröber (1965), was adversely affected by storage both at high temperatures and at high humidities, and the effect was progressive over time. Shepherd et al (1971) reported that conidia suspended in water were more readily killed by high temperatures than were conidia heat-treated at 0 or 43% relative humidity.

EFFECT OF ULTRAVIOLET LIGHT

Angell and Hill (1931), Shepherd (1962), and Peresȳpkin and Zrazhevskaya (1967) demonstrated that conidia of *P. hyoscyami* were rapidly killed by exposure to sunlight. Under conditions of partial dehydration (54% relative humidity) and under dry conditions (0% relative humidity), however, conidia were more resistant to ultraviolet light than in water suspensions (Shepherd et al, 1971) (Fig. 10).

Bashi and Aylor (1983) and Rotem et al (1985) recently reexamined the role of solar radiation in conidial viability and reported that it was a dominant factor in the survival of conidia. Only about 3% of detached conidia and 47% of attached conidia survived a 3-hr exposure to solar radiation (8.6 $MJ \cdot m^{-2}$ at about 32°C) (Rotem et al, 1985). These authors also reported that the long-wave (>290 nm) ultraviolet radiation needed to kill conidia in the open was about 10^3 times greater than the dosage of short-wave (254 nm) ultraviolet radiation required to kill them in the laboratory. They speculated that the much lower efficiency of long-wavelength ultraviolet light out of doors may be, in part, due to the processes of photoreactivation.

Rotem et al (1985) also reported that an increase in temperature from 32.1°C in solar radiation treatments to 37.3°C in ultraviolet filter-treated samples resulted in a decrease in relative humidity of about 20%. They argued that because *P. hyoscyami* is relatively sensitive to relative humidity, conidia might be affected not only by increased temperature but also by decreased humidity. The fact that conidia survived better following the drier treatments than

238

following the more humid treatments indicated to them that the fungicidal effect of solar radiation exceeded the effect of dryness.

Cryogenic Storage of Conidia

An effective technique for long-term cryogenic storage of conidia of *P. hyoscyami* was first reported by Bromfield and Schmitt (1967). The conidia were first suspended in 15% dimethylsulfoxide and cooled to −20°C. They were then transferred to liquid nitrogen for long-term storage at −180°C. Conidia under these conditions were reported to remain viable and infective for at least 25 months.

In other studies directed more toward understanding cryogenic storage as a possible factor in the overwintering of this fungus,

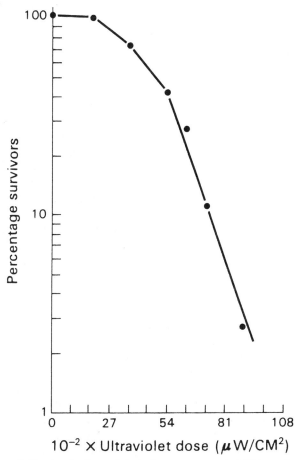

Figure 10. Effect of ultraviolet dosage on viability of conidia of *Peronospora hyoscyami*. (Reprinted, by permission, from Shepherd, 1962)

239

Cohen and Kuć (1980) and Gayed and Brown (1984) observed that conidia could survive at $-20°$ C for at least three months and that they could survive several cycles of repeated freezing $(-20°$ C) and thawing (25° C). As in the high-temperature and solar radiation treatments described above, survival was better for conidia attached to conidiophores on leaves than for conidia suspended in water. In the latter case, the rate of thawing was also important to conidial viability. In epidemiological terms, the possibility of a winter survival role for conidia of *P. hyoscyami* in countries that experience very severe winters cannot be overlooked.

Conidial Germination and Infectivity

Germination may be studied in vitro or in vivo. Germination, however, in no way guarantees infection, because often preinfection defense mechanisms must be overcome before infection is assured. There are also postinfection defense mechanisms, but these will not be discussed in this chapter.

GERMINATION IN VITRO

Angell and Hill (1931) reported that conidia of *P. hyoscyami* would germinate in water droplets on glass slides but noted that the viability of freshly collected conidia varied greatly. These results were confirmed by Wolf et al (1934), Armstrong and Sumner (1935), and Clayton and Gaines (1945). In retrospect, the variability was probably the result of the presence of autoinhibitors of germination (Shepherd and Mandryk, 1962), which have been shown to be present especially in high concentrations of conidia. Autoinhibitors were observed to be nonvolatile, relatively stable, and readily removed by washing conidia with water. Shepherd and Mandryk (1962) claimed that biologically and chromatographically similar substances were present in infected leaves before sporulation occurred, and it was suggested that they may enter conidia from the infected leaf tissue when conidia are formed. One compound believed to be involved in inhibition of germination of *P. hyoscyami* in situ has been isolated and tentatively identified as 5-isobutyroxy-β-ionone (quiesone, $ED_{50} = 0.0001$ μg/ml) (Leppik et al, 1971).

Cruickshank (1961a) obtained uniformly high rates of germination by seeding Difco Bacto prune agar with washed conidia. In an equally satisfactory alternative technique (Shepherd, 1962), washed conidia were suspended in water or chemical solutions, and drops of the suspension were placed on Difco Bacto agar blocks. Shepherd (1962) also obtained high germination rates by seeding chemically defined liquid media with washed conidia, provided aeration was adequate.

240

Effect of Temperature

Wolf et al (1934) demonstrated that some germination occurred over the range 7.2–15.5°C within 2 hr and that 50–59% germination occurred at 21°C after 5 hr. Conidia incubated at 26°C for 22 hr did not germinate. Armstrong and Sumner (1935) reported the optimum temperature range for germination to be 15–23°C using incubation periods of 22–48 hr. No germination was reported at temperatures above 29°C.

Clayton and Gaines (1945) found that the germination responses of their isolates fell into two distinct classes, with optimum temperature ranges of 1.5–10°C and 17.7–26.1°C. This was probably the first evidence for the presence of physiological strains of *P. hyoscyami* (see Chapter 1).

In studies on the effect of temperature on the germination response (Fig. 11), Cruickshank (1961a) confirmed that germination was time- and temperature-dependent. Time was very important in determining the cardinal temperature response curves (Cruickshank, 1961b). Initially, germination occurred most rapidly at 27.2°C. After 6 hr, however, there was no difference in germination over the range 15.2–27.2°C; after 12 hr, the range had widened still further to 8.6–27.2°C. Initially, germ tubes grew fastest at the higher temperatures in the range studied; after 12 hr, however, the optimum temperature range for growth was 15.2–17.8°C.

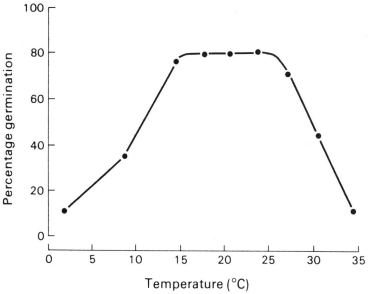

Figure 11.   Effect of temperature on germination of conidia of *Peronospora hyoscyami*. (Reprinted, by permission, from Cruickshank, 1961a)

241

Effect of Organic Substrates

Shepherd (1962) examined the effects on *P. hyoscyami* of added vitamins, a wide range of sugars, amino acids, purines and pyrimidines, and their analogues. In general, the presence of available sources of carbon and nitrogen enhanced germination and germ tube growth. More specifically, germination was stimulated by riboflavin (Fig. 12), sorbitol, magnesium sulfate, calcium chloride, potassium nitrate, and sodium phosphate. The omission of any one of these compounds reduced the rate of germination.

Effects of pH of Medium, Light, and Age of Conidia

Shepherd (1962) reported a broad optimum pH range (5.5–8.0) on agar. In liquid medium, the optimum pH was 6.5–8.0. Shepherd observed that visible light did not affect germination; however, ultraviolet light (<400 nm) reduced germination to 2.7%. In studies on conidial age, Shepherd (1962) reported that washed conidia showed no loss in germination capacity after being stored at normal temperatures for up to 6.5 hr; after 18 hr, however, germination was

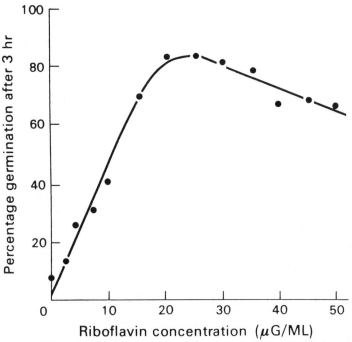

Figure 12.   Effect of riboflavin concentration on germination of conidia of *Peronospora hyoscyami* in liquid suspension. (Reprinted, by permission, from Shepherd, 1962)

negligible. It is clear from other reports on the longevity of conidia discussed above that conditions of storage are very important in studies of the effect of the age of conidia on germination.

GERMINATION IN VIVO AND INFECTIVITY

In early studies (Darnell-Smith, 1929; Henderson, 1937), *P. hyoscyami* conidia were reported to germinate in water droplets on leaves within 3–24 hr at 10–15°C, but no quantitative data were supplied. Shepherd and Mandryk (1963) reexamined this topic. They found that germination of washed conidia (5×10^4/ml) on unwashed attached and detached leaves and detached flower parts was very low, averaging 1.7% (range 1–22%). When the leaves were washed before inoculation and riboflavin was added to the inoculum suspension, germination rates rose to 95%. Addition of riboflavin without the leaf prewashing step resulted in intermediate germination levels. Examination of the leaf washings led to the detection of inhibitory fractions.

Subsequently, Cruickshank et al (1977) isolated and identified two diterpenoid isomers with fungitoxic properties from the surface of healthy tobacco leaves. These compounds, α- and β-isomers of 4,8,13-duvatriene-1,3-diol, were shown to account for greater than 0.1% by weight of the fresh tobacco leaf. Their ED_{50} values toward germination in vitro of *P. hyoscyami* were about 20 μg/ml. Keene and Wagner (1985) recently reported that these compounds are synthesized in the glandular heads of tobacco trichomes. It is of interest that duvatrienediols are not present on leaves of *N. debneyi*, a blue mold-resistant *Nicotiana* species. Germination of conidia on leaves of this species has been reported to be relatively high (65%) (Shepherd and Mandryk, 1963). These chemical and biological data support the suggestion (Shepherd and Mandryk, 1963) that fungitoxic compounds associated with the cuticular waxes of tobacco leaves may play a role in the epidemiology of blue mold but not in the resistance per se of tobacco to this disease. These results emphasize the overriding importance of in vivo studies relative to in vitro studies in this area.

Several authors (Angell and Hill, 1932; Dixon et al, 1936; Hill, 1957; Wolf et al, 1934) have reported that infection requires moisture on the leaf surface. In studies on the duration of leaf wetting necessary for infection, Kröber (1967) observed that no infection occurred where leaves incubated at 10 and 20°C were wet for only 1 hr. With longer wetting times, however, infection increased progressively. This result emphasized the importance of overnight dew formation on leaves in relation to the epidemiology of blue mold. Inoculum concentration, temperature, cultivar of tobacco, and age of the tobacco plant also influenced infectivity in conidia.

243

The interaction between inoculum concentration and the duration of the leaf wetness period in relation to disease development is discussed in the next section.

Disease Development in Planta

Once infection has occurred, pathogens are to some extent protected from the effects of environment. Several factors that affect lesion size and disease severity are discussed in this section.

EFFECT OF TEMPERATURE

Clayton and Gaines (1945) concluded from their observations that the area of leaf tissue that shows disease symptoms is a function of temperature. Hill and Green (1965) in more detailed studies in this area reported that when both day and night temperatures were between about 16 and 24°C, conditions were most suitable for early symptom appearance. Over the temperature ranges studied (12–32°C day, 4–32°C night), decreases in night temperature and decreases in both day and night temperatures below 16–24°C delayed symptom appearance more than increases above the 16–24°C range. Extension of the day temperature periods from 8 to 12 hr usually lengthened the incubation period at day temperatures of 12–32°C by one or more days. At day temperatures of 16–28°C, the incubation period was usually shorter for plants at night temperatures below 12°C. Where the number of dead leaves was used as a measure of disease development, it was observed that leaves were destroyed most rapidly when the day temperature was 20–28°C and the night temperature was 20–24°C.

Jardot (1966b), in studies on the effect of preinoculation temperatures (5–30°C), observed no significant difference in the length of the incubation period from inoculation to initiation of sporulation where the leaves were incubated after inoculation at 20°C. However, when plants were incubated at 20°C for 24 hr before inoculation and were then transferred to temperatures ranging from 5 to 30°C, the incubation period was significantly longer at temperatures below 20°C. At 10°C the incubation period was nine days, as opposed to four to five days at 20°C.

Rotem and Cohen (1970) studied the effect of more extreme temperatures than those studied by the previous authors. When temperature was held constant, the optimum temperature for disease development was 25°C. The optimum temperature, however, was nearer 20–25°C under 12-hr thermoperiods of 20°C at night and 20–40°C during the day. Shortening the high-temperature periods during the day to 2 hr resulted in a shift of the optimum temperature for disease development to 30–35°C. Exposure of infected but still symptomless plants to temperatures lethal to the fungus (45°C) induced development of sterile lesions within 24 hr; 35°C led to the most accentuated lesions. Rotem and Cohen concluded that maximum expression of symptoms occurs at temperatures much higher than those that permit growth of *P. hyoscyami*. They stated, however, that for the high temperatures to exert their effect required a certain degree of previous colonization at a favorable temperature. They reported that, under these conditions, symptoms develop whether the pathogen remains alive or dies.

EFFECT OF SOIL

Smith et al (1979) applied three rates of nitrogen (84, 168, and 252 kg/ha) in one, two, three, four, and five side-dressings on the cultivar Speight G-28 in the field on sandy soil in Florida. Incidence of blue mold increased as the nitrogen level was increased.

Plants of susceptible tobacco cultivars grown in soils that have been used for pasture production for some years are characteristically succulent and highly susceptible to blue mold. This has been presumed to be the result of high soil nitrogen. To evaluate this hypothesis, Hill (1962b) grew plants of flue-cured tobacco cultivar Virginia Gold on several soil types under controlled conditions. He found that where the soils were high in organic matter, tobacco leaves were soft and succulent and retained their juvenile phase of susceptibility to blue mold. On the other hand, when nitrogen was added to soils low in organic matter, leaves did not have these characteristics and the tissues were relatively resistant. The form in which nitrogen is applied, organic or inorganic, appears to be more important than nitrogen per se.

EFFECT OF INOCULUM CONCENTRATION
AND LENGTH OF LEAF WETNESS PERIOD

Plants are commonly inoculated under experimental conditions with concentrations of conidial suspensions of about 5×10^4 conidia per milliliter. In nature, except under severe epiphytotic conditions, conidia are distributed in much lower numbers. In view of this, Hill (1966) and later Kröber (1969b) studied the effect of spore load and the length of the leaf wetness period on disease development.

Hill (1966) reported that the shortest interval between inoculation and appearance of symptoms and production of conidia was three to four days and that the major requirements for this were very high numbers of conidia in the inoculum, a leaf wetness or infection period of 4 hr or longer, a day temperature of 20–28°C, and a night temperature of about 20°C. Under less favorable conditions, according to Hill, the length of the incubation period could be increased by up to 100%. Symptoms took longest to appear when inoculum concentrations were very low (five conidia per milliliter). No significant difference in the incubation period was observed for leaf wetness periods of 8 and 16 hr, but in both cases, the incubation periods were significantly shorter than for a leaf wetness period of 4 hr if the inoculum concentrations were low. However, with low conidial concentrations and short leaf wetness periods (4 hr), the number of lesions was not necessarily directly related to conidial concentration, and extending the leaf wetness periods to 8 hr did not necessarily result in an increased number of lesions. At all conidial concentrations, the incubation period was shortest at night temperatures of about 20°C.

Kröber (1969b) reported that increasing the concentration of conidia in the inoculation droplet increased the frequency of infection over that obtained with the lower concentrations (10–100 conidia per inoculation drop). Over the higher concentration range (100–500 conidia per inoculation drop), the effect was much less. The effect of inoculum concentration was very great in seedlings, less in young plants, and barely significant in adult plants. It is apparent that inoculum concentration is extremely important in relation to the development of disease in the early weeks or months of a growing season and to projections of the course of disease development. These results also emphasize the importance of using control measures in the early stages of blue mold development in a crop.

Oospores

The significance of oospores in the life cycle of *P. hyoscyami* under field conditions is open to debate. Wolf et al (1936) claimed to have evidence for the survival of oospores after storage for four years. Person et al (1955), on the other hand, failed to obtain germination. They believed this was because of attack by microorganisms. Irrespective of the importance of oospores, there are many records of their occurrence in Canada, central Europe, the Soviet Union, and the United States (Borovskaya, 1968; Florczak, 1965; Kröber and Massfeller, 1962; Lucas, 1975; Markhaseva, 1963; Pawlik, 1961; Peresÿpkin and Markhaseva, 1966; Svircev, 1983).

Kröber and Weinmann (1964) conducted the most extensive experimental studies in this area. They obtained oospores from infected leaves and stored them for several months under various conditions: at uniform temperatures around 15°C in closed containers; at temperatures alternating between 15°C and slight frost in the open in either dry or saturated atmospheres (in some cases, oospores were kept in distilled water for the last 14 days of their storage); and in leaf compost prepared from severely infected

246

leaves and a peat-loam-sand mixture in the open. Infectivity tests were positive for oospores stored under these conditions. However, the incubation period was 15–43 days, and the percentage infectivity was very low. Infectivity could not be increased by special treatments such as washing.

In subsequent experiments, Kröber (1969a) reported infectivity among oospores stored for eight to 50 months in natural soils, indicating that dormancy may extend for considerable lengths of time. Oospores stored not in natural soil but in artificial substrates such as quartz sand or perlite, however, lost their infectivity. Kröber (1969a) concluded that oospores probably play only a minor role, if any, in the epidemiology of blue mold.

Concluding Remarks

In the pre-1950 era of blue mold research, studies were mainly descriptive in nature and were, for the most part, based on field observations. More recently, research on this disease has become more analytical. Experiments have been conducted under controlled conditions, and the results have been expressed in quantitative terms. The analytical approach has complemented the descriptive approach and in general has confirmed the primary observations of the earlier researchers in this field. Both approaches have contributed to the building up of our knowledge of the factors plant pathologists are faced with in analyzing epiphytotics and in the longer term in devising integrated programs for disease control.

The asexual cycle of blue mold appears to far outweigh the sexual cycle in importance. The asexual cycle is associated with a short incubation period and thus many generations of conidia throughout the tobacco growing season. Prolific production of conidia, combined with their airborne spread, also adds to the high disease-causing potential of the blue mold pathogen. The role of oospores in the life cycle of *P. hyoscyami* in Australia and North America is dubious at best. In Europe and the Soviet Union, they could be somewhat more relevant, although the data are far from convincing.

Relative humidity of the leaf boundary layer, diffusion pressure deficit of the leaf tissue, temperature, and light all clearly play a role in affecting sporulation intensity of *P. hyoscyami*. Relative humidity, leaf movement, and diffusion pressure deficit are important in conidial release. Temperature appears to be of critical importance to the length of the incubation period between infection and sporulation, assuming other conditions are optimal for sporulation. Conidial infection depends on temperature and how long the leaf is wet. Germination appears to be almost an Achilles' heel for the fungus. In the first place, conidia in situ contain compounds that inhibit germination where high numbers of conidia are concerned. In the second place, the glandular hairs of tobacco leaves secrete inhibitory compounds that appear to greatly reduce the germination in vivo of conidia relative to their germination potential in vitro. Postinfection plant responses, which are discussed elsewhere in this book, also may reduce the number of successful infections. It is perhaps not surprising that *P. hyoscyami* produces very large numbers of conidia as a matter of survival.

Relative humidity, diffusion pressure deficit, and temperature may be recorded, and the information obtained may be of value in disease forecasting, but they cannot be manipulated in relation to controlling blue mold in the field. (In seedling beds and in shade-grown tobacco, there may be possibilities in this direction of which I am unaware.) Although light cannot be controlled or its effects exploited in the field, knowledge of the metabolic processes associated with the dark-induction phenomenon discussed above may be subject to economic exploitation. The work of Cohen and Rotem (1970) makes this appear to be a promising area for further investigation.

Looking back 20 years since my direct involvement in blue mold research began, it is clear that for the most part, laboratory studies have provided details of the effect of environment, especially the interaction of one environmental factor with another, on blue mold development. The laboratory studies have placed the descriptive approach of earlier workers on a sounder basis and have provided insights into some of the environmental effects, which may lend themselves to integration into either disease forecasting or disease control strategies.

LITERATURE CITED

Angell, H. R., and Hill, A. V. 1931. Blue mould of tobacco: Longevity of conidia. J. Counc. Sci. Ind. Res. (Aust.) 4:181–184.
Angell, H. R., and Hill, A. V. 1932. Downy mildew (blue mould) of tobacco in Australia. Counc. Sci. Ind. Res. Aust. Bull. 65. 30 pp.
Armstrong, G. M., and Sumner, C. B. 1935. Investigations on downy mildew of tobacco. S.C. Agric. Exp. Stn. Bull. 303. 23 pp.
Aylor, D. E., and Taylor, G. S. 1982. Aerial dispersal and drying of *Peronospora tabacina* conidia in tobacco shade tents. Proc. Natl. Acad. Sci. USA 79:697–700.
Aylor, D. E., and Taylor, G. S. 1983. Escape of *Peronospora tabacina* spores from a field of diseased tobacco plants. Phytopathology 73:525–529.
Aylor, D. E., Taylor, G. S., and Raynor, G. S. 1982. Long-range transport of tobacco blue mold spores. Agric. Meteorol. 27:217–232.
Bashi, E., and Aylor, D. E. 1983. Survival of detached sporangia of *Peronospora destructor* and *Peronospora tabacina*. Phytopathology

73:1135–1139.

Borovskaya, M. F. 1968. Oospory̅-istochnik vozobnovleniya peronosporoza tabaka (*Peronospora tabacina* Adam). Mikol. Fitopatol. 2:311–315.

Bromfield, K. R., and Schmitt, C. G. 1967. Cryogenic storage of conidia of *Peronospora tabacina*. Phytopathology 57:1133.

Burrage, S. W. 1971. The microclimate at the leaf surface. Pages 91–101 in: Ecology of Leaf Surface Microorganisms. T. F. Preece and C. H. Dickinson, eds. Academic Press, London. 640 pp.

Clayton, E. E., and Gaines, J. G. 1933. Control of downy mildew disease of tobacco through temperature regulation. Science 78:609–610.

Clayton, E. E., and Gaines, J. G. 1945. Temperature in relation to development and control of blue mold (*Peronospora tabacina*) of tobacco. J. Agric. Res. 71:171–182.

Cohen, Y. 1976. Interacting effects of light and temperature on sporulation of *Peronospora tabacina* on tobacco leaves. Aust. J. Biol. Sci. 29:281–289.

Cohen, Y., and Eyal, H. 1984. Infectivity of conidia of *Peronospora hyoscyami* after storage on tobacco leaves. Plant Dis. 68:688–690.

Cohen, Y., and Kuć, J. 1980. Infectivity of conidia of *Peronospora tabacina* after freezing and thawing. Plant Dis. 64:549–550.

Cohen, Y., and Rotem, J. 1970. The relationship of sporulation to photo-synthesis in some obligatory and facultative parasites. Phytopathology 60:1600–1604.

Cohen, Y., Levi, Y., and Eyal, H. 1978. Sporogenesis of some fungal plant pathogens under intermittent light conditions. Can. J. Bot. 56:2538–2543.

Collins, B. G. 1964. The atmospheric conditions affecting sporulation of blue mould in tobacco. Aust. J. Exp. Agric. Anim. Husb. 4:178–184.

Cruickshank, I. A. M. 1958. Environment and sporulation in phytopatho-genic fungi. I. Moisture in relation to the production and discharge of conidia of *Peronospora tabacina* Adam. Aust. J. Biol. Sci. 11:162–170.

Cruickshank, I. A. M. 1961a. Germination of *Peronospora tabacina*: Effect of temperature. Aust. J. Biol. Sci. 14:58–65.

Cruickshank, I. A. M. 1961b. Environment and sporulation in phytopatho-genic fungi. II. Conidia formation in *Peronospora tabacina* Adam as a function of temperature. Aust. J. Biol. Sci. 14:198–207.

Cruickshank, I. A. M. 1963. Environment and sporulation in phytopatho-genic fungi. IV. The effect of light on the formation of conidia of *Peronospora tabacina*. Aust. J. Biol. Sci. 16:88–98.

Cruickshank, I. A. M., and Müller, K. O. 1957. Water-relations and sporulation of *Peronospora tabacina* Adam. Nature (London) 180:44–45.

Cruickshank, I. A. M., and Rider, N. E. 1961. *Peronospora tabacina* in tobacco: Transpiration, growth and related energy considerations. Aust. J. Biol. Sci. 14:45–57.

Cruickshank, I. A. M., Perrin, D. R., and Mandryk, M. 1977. Fungitoxicity of duvatrienediols associated with the cuticular wax of tobacco leaves. Phytopathol. Z. 90:243–249.

Darnell-Smith, G. P. 1929. Infection experiments with spores of the blue mould disease of tobacco. Agric. Gaz. N.S.W. 40:407–408.

Dixon, L. F., McLean, R. A., and Wolf, F. A. 1936. Relationship of climatological conditions to the tobacco downy mildew. Phytopathology

26:735-759.

Florczak, K. 1965. Warunki tworzenia sie oospor *Peronospora tabacina* Adam i zakażenia przez oospory. Biul. Cent. Lab. Przem. Tyton. 1965(1-2):17-28.

Gayed, S. K., and Brown, D. A. 1984. The effect of successive cycles of freezing and thawing on the germination of *Peronospora tabacina* conidia. Lighter 54:22-23.

Henderson, R. G. 1937. Studies on tobacco downy mildew in Virginia. Va. Polytech. Inst. Tech. Bull. 62.

Hill, A. V. 1957. Blue mould of tobacco. CSIRO (Aust.) Div. Plant Ind. Tech. Pap. 9. 16 pp.

Hill, A. V. 1960. Spore release in *Peronospora tabacina*. Nature (London) 185:940.

Hill, A. V. 1961. Dissemination of conidia of *Peronospora tabacina* Adam. Aust. J. Biol. Sci. 14:208-222.

Hill, A. V. 1962a. Longevity of conidia of *Peronospora tabacina* Adam. Nature (London) 195:827-828.

Hill, A. V. 1962b. Soil as a factor in the incidence of *Peronospora tabacina* Adam on tobacco. Aust. J. Agric. Res. 13:650-661.

Hill, A. V. 1966. Effect of inoculum spore load, length of infection period, and leaf washing on occurrence of *Peronospora tabacina* Adam (blue mould) of tobacco. Aust. J. Agric. Res. 17:133-146.

Hill, A. V. 1969a. Factors affecting viability of spore inoculum in *Peronospora tabacina* Adam and lesion production in tobacco plants. I. The inoculum. Aust. J. Biol. Sci. 22:393-398.

Hill, A. V. 1969b. Factors affecting viability of spore inoculum in *Peronospora tabacina* Adam and lesion production in tobacco plants. II. Lesion production. Aust. J. Biol. Sci. 22:399-411.

Hill, A. V., and Green, S. 1965. The role of temperature in the development of blue mould (*Peronospora tabacina* Adam) disease in tobacco seedlings. I. In leaves. Aust. J. Agric. Res. 16:597-607.

Jankowski, F. 1966. Badania in vivo nad czasokresem zachowania zdolności infekcyjnej przez konidia *Peronospora tabacina* Adam. Biul. Cent. Lab. Przem. Tyton. 1966(3-4):17-21.

Jardot, R. 1966a. Effets de la lumière sur la sporulation de *Peronospora tabacina* Adam. Parasitica 22:55-63.

Jardot, R. 1966b. Effets de la température sur l'incubation de *Peronospora tabacina* Adam en milieu conditionné. Parasitica 22:208-215.

Jardot, R. 1966c. Essai de transposition en laboratoire de l'étude de l'incidence des variations de l'humidité sur la dissémination de *Peronospora tabacina* Adam. Parasitica 22:223-229.

Jenkins, S. F., and Valli, V. J. 1966. Studies on the effect of relative humidity and temperature on conidia release by *Peronospora tabacina*. Tob. Sci. 10:63-64.

Keene, C. K., and Wagner, G. J. 1985. Direct demonstration of duvatrienediol biosynthesis in glandular heads of tobacco trichomes. Plant Physiol. 79:1026-1032.

Kröber, H. 1965. Über die Lebensdauer der Konidien von *Peronospora tabacina* Adam. Phytopathol. Z. 54:328-334.

Kröber, H. 1967. Der Einfluss der Benetzungsdauer auf die Entstehung der Blauschimmelkrankheit an Tabac. Phytopathol. Z. 58:46–52.

Kröber, H. 1969a. Über das Infektionsverhalten der Oosporen von *Peronospora tabacina* Adam an Tabak. Phytopathol. Z. 64:1–6.

Kröber, H. 1969b. Befall von Kohlrabi durch *Peronospora parasitica* (Pers.) Fr. und von Tabac durch *P. tabacina* Adam in Abhängigkeit von der Konidienkonzentration. Phytopathol. Z. 66:180–187.

Kröber, H., and Massfeller, D. 1962. Erfahrungen mit der Blauschimmelkrankheit des Tabacs (*Peronospora tabacina*) in der Bundesrepublik Deutschland in Jahre 1961. Nachrichtenbl. Dtsch. Pflanzenschutzdienstes (Braunschweig) 14:107–109.

Kröber, H., and Weinmann, W. 1964. Der Nachweis von Blauschimmelinfektionen durch Oosporen von *Peronospora tabacina* Adam. Phytopathol. Z. 51:79–84.

Leppik, R. A., Hollomon, D. W., and Bottomley, W. 1971. Quiesone: An inhibitor of the germination of *Peronospora tabacina* conidia. Phytochemistry 11:2055–2063.

Lucas, G. B. 1975. Diseases of Tobacco. 3rd ed. Biological Consulting Associates, Raleigh, NC. 621 pp.

Markhaseva, V. A. 1963. Metodika vȳyavleniya oospor vozbuditelya peronosporoza v Tabachnom sȳr'e. Tabak (Moscow) 24:44–45.

Moss, M. A., and Main, C. E. 1985. Temperature tolerance of *Peronospora tabacina* in the U.S. (Abstr.) Phytopathology 75:1341.

Pawlik, A. 1961. Zur Frage der Überwinterung von *Peronospora tabacina* Adam Boebachtungen über Oosporenkeimung. Z. Pflanzenkr. 68:193–197.

Peresȳpkin, V. F., and Markhaseva, V. A. 1966. Ekologichni osoblivosti formuvannya spor griba *Peronospora tabacina* Adam. Zakhist Rosl. 1966(3):72–77.

Peresȳpkin, V. F., and Zrazhevskaya, T. G. 1967. Zhiznesposobnost'konidii *Peronospora tabacina* Adam. Mikol. Fitopatol. 1:235–240.

Person, L. H., Lucas, G. B., and Koch, W. G. 1955. A chytrid attacking oospores of *Peronospora tabacina*. Plant Dis. Rep. 39:887–888.

Pinckard, J. A. 1942. The mechanism of spore dispersal in *Peronospora tabacina* and certain other downy mildew fungi. Phytopathology 32:505–511.

Populer, C. 1962. La dissémination du *Peronospora* du tabac *Peronospora tabacina* Adam. Parasitica 28:1–7.

Populer, C. 1966. La dissémination des spores du mildiou du tabac, *Peronospora tabacina* Adam. II. Etude des facteurs réglant la libération des spores. Bull. Rech. Agron. Gembloux 1:111–139.

Rayner, R. W., and Hopkins, J. C. F. 1962. Blue mould of tobacco. A review of current information. Commonw. Mycol. Inst. Misc. Publ. 16. 16 pp.

Rotem, J., and Cohen, Y. 1970. The effect of temperature on the pathogen and on the development of blue mold disease in tobacco inoculated with *Peronospora tabacina*. Phytopathology 60:54–57.

Rotem, J., Wooding, B., and Aylor, D. E. 1985. The role of solar radiation, especially ultraviolet, in the mortality of fungal spores. Phytopathology 75:510–514.

Shepherd, C. J. 1962. Germination of conidia of *Peronospora tabacina* Adam. I. Germination in vitro. Aust. J. Biol. Sci. 15:483–508.

Shepherd, C. J., and Mandryk, M. 1962. Auto-inhibitors of germination and sporulation in *Peronospora tabacina* Adam. Trans. Br. Mycol. Soc. 45:233–234.

Shepherd, C. J., and Mandryk, M. 1963. Germination of conidia of *Peronospora tabacina* Adam. II. Germination in vivo. Aust. J. Biol. Sci. 16:77–87.

Shepherd, C. J., Simpson, P., and Smith, A. 1971. Effects of variation in water potential on the viability and behaviour of conidia of *Peronospora tabacina* Adam. Aust. J. Biol. Sci. 24:219–229.

Smith, A. 1970. Biometric studies on conidia of *Peronospora tabacina*. Trans. Br. Mycol. Soc. 55:59–66.

Smith, W. D., Whitty, E. B., and Kucharek, T. A. 1979. Blue mold incidence in tobacco as affected by nitrogen fertilization. Soil Crop Sci. Soc. Fla. Proc. 39:140–141.

Svircev, A. M. 1983. A study of blue mold of tobacco caused by *Peronospora hyoscyami* f. sp. *tabacina*. Ph.D. Thesis, University of Western Ontario, London, Ontario, Canada. 203 pp.

Uozumi, T., and Kröber, H. 1967. Der Einfluss des Lichtes auf die Konidienbildung von *Peronospora tabacina* Adam an Tabakblättern. Phytopathol. Z. 59:372–384.

Valli, V. J. 1966. Biometeorological factors affecting conidia release by *Peronospora tabacina*. Tobacco 163:30–32.

Waggoner, P. E., and Taylor, G. S. 1955. Tobacco blue mold epiphytotics in the field. Plant Dis. Rep. 39:79–85.

Waggoner, P. E., and Taylor, G. S. 1958. Dissemination by atmospheric turbulence: Spores of *Peronospora tabacina*. Phytopathology 48:46–51.

Wolf, F. A., and McLean, R. A. 1940. Sporangial proliferation in *Peronospora tabacina*. Phytopathology 30:264–268.

Wolf, F. A., Dixon, L. F., McLean, R., and Darkis, F. R. 1934. Downy mildew of tobacco. Phytopathology 24:337–363.

Wolf, F. A., McLean, R. A., and Dixon, L. F. 1936. Further studies on downy mildew of tobacco. Phytopathology 26:760–777.

Yarwood, C. E. 1937. The relation of light to the diurnal cycle of sporulation of certain downy mildews. J. Agric. Res. 54:365–373.

Yarwood, C. E. 1943. Onion downy mildew (*Peronospora destructor*). Hilgardia 14:595–691.

Chapter 10

The Canadian 1979
Blue Mold Epiphytotic

W. E. McKeen
Department of Plant Sciences
The University of Western Ontario
London, Ontario, Canada N6A 5B7

This chapter presents the events, actions, and interactions surrounding a catastrophic epiphytotic of tobacco blue mold in Canada in the summer of 1979. The key characters who influenced the course of events leading to and during the epiphytotic—the Ontario Flue-Cured Tobacco Growers' Marketing Board, farmers, florists, tobacco companies, the media (Plate 10), politicians, insurance companies, crop experts, lawyers, and plant pathologists— interacted in a way that permitted an unnecessary calamity. What follows is an account based on my observations of the events before, during, and after this devastating epiphytotic.

Tobacco in Ontario

Ninety percent of the Canadian tobacco crop is grown in southern Ontario, on a strip of sandy soil north of Lake Erie between the 42nd and 43rd parallels of latitude (Fig. 1). This region is divided into the "old tobacco belt" in the Harrow-Kingsville district and the "new tobacco belt" in the Delhi-Tillsonburg area. Tobacco was the most valuable crop in Ontario until recently, when antismoking pressure reduced tobacco demand and acreage.

Tobacco production in the new tobacco belt started during the 1920s in Haldimand-Norfolk and surrounding counties. In time, this region became the main tobacco-growing area of Ontario. Haldimand-Norfolk County alone produces 50% of the tobacco grown in Ontario. As the demand for cigarettes increased, flue-cured tobacco became the dominant crop in the new tobacco belt. The old belt near Harrow has over the years produced more burley tobacco than flue-cured tobacco.

Tobacco was the first cash crop grown in the infertile soil of the Haldimand-Norfolk Sand Plain. The soils of the region belong to the Plainfield Sands and Fox Sands soil groups (Schaus, 1980). The latter soil type is ideal for tobacco because it is well drained and acidic. Many of the tobacco producers succeeded in producing excellent tobacco on land previously considered useless. Once the "golden leaf" became established in this area, land values rose significantly.

To maintain soil fertility, a two-year crop sequence of tobacco and winter rye is practiced. Sometimes wheat is substituted for rye. To

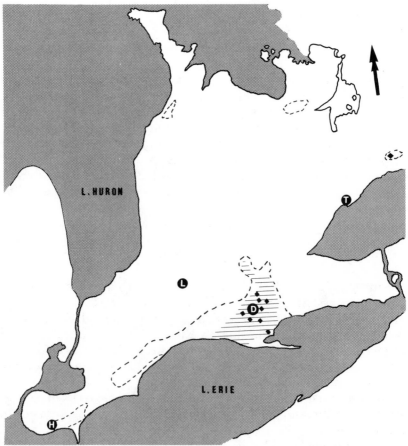

Figure 1.   Southwestern Ontario: cities (D = Delhi, H = Harrow, L = London, T = Toronto), tobacco-growing areas (inside dashed lines), location of the blue mold epiphytotic (shaded area around Delhi), and speedling placement (small diamonds).

protect soil against rain and wind, a green-manure crop is sown between rye harvest and land preparation for tobacco.

The climate of this region is moderated by Lake Erie. In the summer, the prevailing winds from the southwest bring warm, humid conditions. The north winds are generally drier and cooler when present in the summer. The Maritime-Tropical air mass is dominant in the summer and is characterized by warm temperatures and high relative humidity (Schaus, 1980). Since relative humidity is high within the air mass, only slight lifting is necessary to bring about convection, cumulus development, and thunderstorms. These warm temperatures, in combination with the well-drained, heavily fertilized soil, produce a high-quality tobacco crop. Historically, the Ontario tobacco crop has never contained fungicidal residues because foliar pathogens have not been a problem; this freedom from chemical residues has helped to build the good reputation of Ontario tobacco.

Nicotiana tabacum L. 'Virginia 115' produces high yields and became the cultivar of choice when tobacco growing in Ontario was under acreage control limitation (see below). Because the same genome is present in all the Virginia plants, all are equally susceptible to any pathogen. In addition, cultivars Delhi 76 and Coker 319 are planted in some fields.

The Canadian tobacco crop is unique because of the short growing season. The frost-free period in the area ranges from 88 to 175 days and averages 145 days (Brown et al, 1968). Well-timed planting in late May usually allows enough time for the crop to grow and fully develop, but the relatively short frost-free period means that the crop must be planted in the fields within a one- to two-week period. The seedlings are grown and hardened off (Zilkey, 1980) in the greenhouse; once the likelihood of frost has passed, they are transplanted to the fields.

The tobacco crop in Ontario is grown and marketed under the authority of the Ontario Flue-Cured Tobacco Growers' Marketing Board, which regulates production by assigning quotas to growers. Initially, quotas were set in terms of area, but more recently they have been assigned in terms of weight. Growers were assigned production quotas of 10–40 ha, much larger than the average allotment of 1.6 ha in the United States in 1974, and many of the farms became large. The Marketing Board has played a major role in developing a first-rate product and in setting and maintaining the high standard of the Ontario tobacco industry.

Production was initially structured to meet domestic demand. The general acceptability and high quality of the Canadian leaf resulted in expansion beyond the domestic market. The bulk of exports are to the United Kingdom.

The Government of Canada operates research stations in both the old and the new tobacco belts, at Harrow and Delhi, respectively. The Delhi station continues to be used solely for tobacco research, and an advisory committee was formed to maximize the station's efficiency and communication with growers.

Importation of Speedlings

To lessen the shock of transplanting "bare-rooted" seedlings, an entrepreneur began to market individual seedlings in V-shaped Styrofoam containers. When these tobacco plants, called "speedlings," are transplanted into the field, the soil in the container remains around their roots, thus preventing shock and unthriftiness after transplanting. The name speedlings emphasizes the all-important time advantage of this product compared to the commonly used bare-rooted tobacco seedlings.

In 1979 the entrepreneur, instead of propagating the speedlings in a local greenhouse, had them produced in Sun City, Florida. The tobacco blue mold pathogen, *Peronospora hyoscyami* de Bary, has been endemic in Florida since 1931. In contrast, *P. hyoscyami* caused serious trouble in Ontario only in 1945 and 1946, when it infested and destroyed some seedbeds. At that time the infestation of the Ontario crop was attributed to windborne spores carried northward from diseased fields in Ohio and the southern United States (Conners and Savile, 1946; Stover and Koch, 1951) (Fig. 2).

The dangers of planting seedlings grown in another country or locality are well known. For instance, *P. hyoscyami* was transported on tobacco plants from England to The Netherlands and from The Netherlands to Germany in 1959 (Peyrot, 1962).

In Florida the fungus remains in an active vegetative state, first in the seedbeds, then in the fields, later in the suckers, and finally in refuse plants. The resting oospores may assure the ability of *P. hyoscyami* to overwinter in Florida (McGrath and Miller, 1958). Since 1978 it has been postulated that sporangia from nearby Cuba, where a winter crop of tobacco is grown, may blow into Florida (Lucas, 1980) (Fig. 2).

P. hyoscyami was first officially reported in Florida in 1979 on May 16 (Kucharek, 1979). Inspectors from the Florida Department of Agriculture and Consumer Services on April 16 and 24 and May 30 certified the entrepreneur's speedlings healthy (Walsh, 1983).

On June 1, 1979, 98,640 speedlings were packaged in cardboard boxes and loaded into refrigerated trucks at temperatures between 16 and 18° C. The trucks reached the Detroit-Windsor border on June 3 and were allowed to pass without inspection. An officer of Agriculture Canada instructed that the speedlings were to be inspected

Figure 2. The major tobacco-growing areas in eastern North America: Florida (FLA), Kentucky (KY), North Carolina (NC), Ohio (OH), Ontario (ONT), Pennsylvania (PA), South Carolina (SC), Virginia (VA), and West Virginia (WVA).

257

upon reaching their final destination in Delhi.

These instructions were not followed, and the speedlings were planted on nine farms, eight of which were in the heart of the new tobacco belt (Fig. 1). Two days after planting, inspectors visited a single farm, on which 400 speedlings had been planted. The plants were certified healthy. Later in the season, however, two tobacco growers described the speedlings as yellow, small, spindled, and pale in appearance. This was the first indication of a possible problem with the Florida-grown tobacco plants.

Disease Outbreak

During the first week of July, one grower observed spots on the leaves of his unthrifty speedlings, which were still small and pale. On July 8, he observed a few spots on his homegrown plants adjacent to the speedlings. He then took a diseased plant for professional examination. The problem was diagnosed as cold-weather injury from which the plants would recover once the weather became warmer. Spots on this grower's tobacco continued to multiply and appeared on all of his tobacco plants. The malady appeared to be spreading from the speedlings to other nearby plants.

About July 24, five or six days after his neighbor to the east irrigated his tobacco field, numerous spots appeared on the leaves of the neighbor's tobacco plants. The irrigation appeared to have provided suitable conditions for eastward-blown spores of the pathogen to infect the neighbor's plants. On July 11 another grower noticed many large spots on the leaves of plants in her 5-ha speedling plot, which was on the west side of her 21-ha tobacco field. On July 12 the disease was diagnosed as blue mold caused by *P. hyoscyami* (Plate 1).

Only in 1951, 28 years previously, had there been concern over the occurrence of a small amount of blue mold in Ontario tobacco fields (Conners and Savile, 1951). By 1951 American growers were practicing better sanitation, and blue mold was no longer a problem in the northern American states. Canadian growers had not observed blue mold since 1951, and consequently most of the 1979 producers had never seen or heard of the disease. However, a few sporadic cases had occurred between 1951 and 1966 (Gayed, 1980).

In an attempt to control the fungus, the 21-ha tobacco crop was sprayed with captan, the only fungicide registered for use on tobacco. However, spots on the tobacco leaves increased and appeared over the whole field. The plants were then sprayed with maneb. Spots continued to increase in diameter, and a few more spots appeared.

Maneb and ferbam fungicides have controlled blue mold in Europe since 1961 and in Australia (Fig. 3) for many years (Akehurst, 1981; Lucas, 1975; O'Brien, 1978). Because maneb is the least stable from a residue viewpoint, processors prefer it to ferbam (Akehurst, 1981).

On July 27 the affected tobacco was plowed down after officials of the Ontario Crop Insurance Commission agreed to compensate the grower. The grower had also been told that tobacco companies would not purchase fungicide-sprayed tobacco. The Marketing Board did not want Canadian tobacco contaminated with the fungicides that had become prevalent in tobacco products from other countries (Lucas, 1980). Canadian tobacco commanded a premium price because of its purity.

A manager of the Ontario Crop Insurance Commission stated that "if forecasts continue for rain and temperatures below 16, blue mould will spread rapidly. The only way blue mould . . . can be stopped is by hot, dry weather" (The London Free Press, 1979a, Aug. 1). The reference to 16°C was taken from earlier work (Miller, 1959) regarding overwintering and how early the blue mold pathogen appeared in Florida. Miller found that the pathogen appeared late in the spring and caused little damage if the January temperatures in Florida were below 16°C but appeared early if the January temperatures were 16°C or above. The 16°C did not apply to disease development in Ontario.

On August 1, a manager of the Ontario Crop Insurance

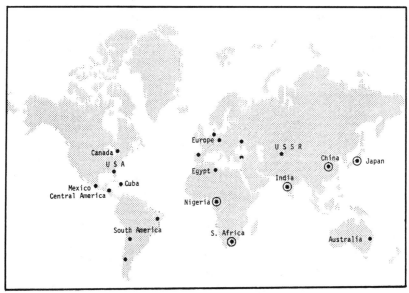

Figure 3.   Areas of blue mold infestation (•) and areas free of blue mold (○).

259

Commission decided that an epidemic would not be declared until the disease had spread to 300 farms (The London Free Press-Evening, 1979a, Aug. 1). At this time it was generally agreed by the Ontario Crop Insurance officials, the Marketing Board, and others, as reported in the *Press,* that the disease had arrived on the speedlings. A director of the Marketing Board warned of repercussions because of infected seedlings slipping through customs: "It all comes down to negligence. When the dust settles on this, there are going to be lawsuits like you wouldn't believe" (The London Free Press, 1979b, Aug. 4). The statement proved prophetic.

Epiphytotic Forecast

Primarily out of scientific curiosity and for teaching purposes, I visited the new tobacco belt on July 30. I found that the mildew was much more serious than had been reported. I also found that the tobacco growers were well aware of the seriousness of the disease and knew there was little use in following normal cultural practices, as they had been recommended to do.

Fields were severely infected only in a band less than 2 km wide and no more than 4 km long, which extended northeastward from the field that had been plowed under. Outside this band tobacco plants were free from blue mold symptoms.

Two days later I found that growers were more apprehensive, and the pathogen spore population was many times greater. The disease had spread to more tobacco fields from all infection foci, mainly northeastward. It was intensifying within the infected fields, and many plants drooping with mildew contained millions of spores. The owners of fields completely covered with downy mildew knew they had no salable "golden leaves."

The tobacco leaves had by this time formed a complete canopy over the fields, and consequently a microclimate had formed underneath with high humidity, long dew periods, and abundant shade. These conditions provided the prerequisites for a downy mildew explosion on a susceptible host. *P. hyoscyami* had not only produced large numbers of windborne spores and spread northeastward to adjoining fields, but also had survived exceptionally hot and dry weather during July. From July 11 to 16, the maximum temperatures fluctuated between 28 and 30°C, and from July 19 to 25, the maximum temperatures were above 29°C. Between July 11 and July 25, only 0.5 mm of rain fell. The total rainfall for July was 32 mm, compared to normal rainfall of 72 mm (Fisheries and Environment Canada, 1979).

I was interviewed on local television on August 2. I said that the blue-tinged fungus did not stop development at temperatures around 16° C but grew exceedingly well and rapidly at temperatures up to 28°C. I warned that the disease was developing rapidly and that the only possibility was a devastating epiphytotic, which would probably destroy the tobacco in the Tillsonburg-Courtland area.

Government Action

On August 3 a special meeting was held at the Delhi Research Station. The Honourable John Wise, the Minister of Agriculture for Canada, participated in the meeting, along with representatives of agencies associated with the tobacco industry. The major concern of the speakers was not the developing epiphytotic in 1979 but the probable severity of blue mold in 1980. The speakers felt that blue mold would be extremely serious since, in their opinion, the spores would overwinter in soil and tobacco stalks and infect the 1980 tobacco crop. However, the asexual spores and mycelium could not survive the cold Ontario winters, although there was some evidence that the sexual spores could overwinter in Ontario (Stover and Koch, 1951). However, the sexual spores historically have never been proved to overwinter and cause infection in Canada. Valleau (1947) stated that the blue mold fungus could not maintain itself in Kentucky or Tennessee unless spores were blown in from the south and that the same was probably true in the Carolinas and Virginia.

Wise reassured the audience of about 350 that "we will make sure you aren't placed out of your homes and put onto the roads" (The London Free Press-Evening, 1979b, Aug. 3) because of the tobacco disease resulting from contaminated speedlings that "weren't scientifically tested before crossing the border at Windsor" (The London Free Press, 1979b, Aug. 4). He stated that the problem was serious but not a disaster. He informed the farmers that he had formed a task force of experts from Ottawa, along with specialists from Delhi.

The first recommendation of the task force, on August 3, was to remove the bottom four leaves on each plant to increase air circulation in tobacco fields and prevent further development of the disease. When this recommendation was announced, an agitated grower strode to the front of the audience with a five-foot-tall diseased tobacco plant. The plant was "mildewed" from top to bottom and probably was carrying millions of spores. He asked the speaker if he really believed removing the bottom four leaves would alleviate the situation when the upper leaves were producing millions of spores.

Later that day the task force also recommended that farmers continue their normal cultural practices such as topping, spraying for suckers, and irrigating during the daytime. However, the recommended irrigation schedule prolonged the infection period into the daylight hours, and the pathogen flourished in wet, humid environments sometimes 24 hr per day. Irrigation would have been better limited to when the tobacco leaves were wet with rain or dew.

The tobacco growers insured by Ontario Crop Insurance removed the bottom four leaves from their plants because Ontario Crop Insurance officials had guaranteed $100/ha for this task to all their clients. The insured farmers considered this a liberal sum, especially since the bottom four leaves are sand leaves, which are of little economic value. However, the growers who were not insured by Ontario Crop Insurance felt that the task was futile and did not follow the recommendation.

The task force did not ask the Minister of Agriculture to obtain the right by Order-in-Council to order, with compensation, the plowing under of completely infected tobacco fields and to order the spraying of fungicides on nearby fields. They did not request the immediate registration of metalaxyl (Ridomil), the new systemically translocated fungicide that had proved effective in Australia in 1977 and 1978 and in Europe since 1975.

Catastrophic Epiphytotic

By July 23 blue mold had been reported on all speedling plots. These plots were the focal points from which *P. hyoscyami* was spreading. Until July 30 the disease remained limited to small areas around the speedling plots. The fungus had spread mainly in a northeasterly direction. The farthest it had spread was about 5 km from one farm that grew 10 times as many speedlings as any other speedling farm. The border between diseased and disease-free fields was very distinct. In the mildewed fields, lesions were numerous and sporulation was prolific.

There was some rain on seven of the nine days between July 25 and August 2, and on August 4 and 5, fog and mist persisted until midday, and the wind was light and mostly from the southwest. The fungus multiplied very rapidly in this ideal environment and exploded into many fields. All the leaves in many tobacco fields were completely covered with lesions by August 12.

On August 7 the task force canceled its August 3 instructions for the removal of the bottom four leaves because the Marketing Board had "learned Tuesday that blue mould is a systemic disease that will relentlessly eat away the stalk of the tobacco plant" (The London Free Press, 1979c, Aug. 8).

In many states of the United States, many blue mold-diseased plants are systemically infected in the seedbeds. For example,

Skoog (1979) reported that in Pennsylvania damage was due to systemic infection that most likely came from plant beds. However, Watson (1979), a tobacco specialist at Delhi, reported that systemic infection was not believed to have been a significant factor in Ontario. I also did not find systemic infection but observed slight wrinkling and elongation of the top two or three leaves. However, Gayed (1985) reported systemic infection during 1979 in mature plants.

Insurance adjusters advised farmers not to plow down their crops until they had been inspected, which sometimes took up to three weeks. As a result, an abundant supply of inoculum was present during the remainder of the season. When plow down was approved, it was typically done during the hottest part of the day, when the wind is strongest, humidity is lowest, and the mildew sporangia are most readily released and blown to distant tobacco fields.

During the epiphytotic the effect of humidity was extremely noticeable. In relatively level fields with a slight depression of a meter or less, an extreme variation in disease incidence was observed. In the slightly lower areas, the plants were covered with sporulating lesions, while the surrounding plants had only a few spots. Tobacco in flood plains was much more likely to be diseased.

On August 1, 2, 3, 13, and 25, blue mold had been reported on 60, 350, 600, 900, and 1,500 farms, respectively. By August 25, the fungus had spread 200 km westward. By September, the entire crop had been cut down on 460 farms and portions had been plowed under on another 200 farms. The crops that were cut down were within 40 km of the speedling plots and frequently were large.

Blue mold was much more severe in Ontario than in the United States, where losses were 1–5% (Todd, 1979). Weather conditions in the two countries could not account for this difference, because unseasonably cool, wet weather in the United States was ideal for extensive destruction (Lucas, 1980; Nesmith, 1983). In southern Ontario, temperatures were normal. However, rainfall was normal in June, 44% of normal in July, and 33% above normal in August. One-third of the rainfall in August occurred August 7, and another third occurred during the last week of August, after much of the tobacco crop had been harvested (Fisheries and Environment Canada, 1979).

About 30% of the Ontario flue-cured crop (gross value $1.1 billion) was destroyed, with consequent effects on the 36,000 jobs created by the tobacco industry. The Ontario Crop Insurance Commission, which insured many growers, was forced to borrow $40 million from the Ontario Treasury to meet commitments. Losses to the provincial and federal treasuries were unquestionably sizable (McKeen, 1981).

Insurance and Compensation

Many tobacco growers had insurance with private companies rather than Ontario Crop Insurance because the former paid for total loss in any field whereas the latter paid for 80% loss of the farmer's total crop. Those insured with private companies soon learned that their insurance covered only common diseases. Since blue mold had not occurred in Ontario for many years, a claim could not be made. Much litigation resulted.

About 60% of the crop was insured with the Ontario Crop Insurance Commission, 25% with private companies, and 15% had no insurance. During the epiphytotic, tobacco farmers considered litigation against the growers of the speedlings and the distributor. They soon realized, however, that this was inadvisable because intent was not involved and there was no possibility the growers and distributor could pay the enormous losses. Financial assistance was requested from the federal government. The Department of Agriculture determined, however, that no compensation could be given to the uninsured farmers.

Tobacco farmers who did have government insurance and were authorized or directed by Ontario Crop Insurance officials to cut down their crops were compensated for 80% of their loss. Some 1,800 insured farmers were so compensated, and the Crop Insurance Commission paid out $45 million in claim settlements, which were shared by the federal and provincial governments.

Trial

In the autumn of 1979, George Fulop, Jr., George Fulop Ltd., and 119 additional persons (mostly farmers who did not have Ontario Crop Insurance in 1979) took legal action against Her Majesty The Queen in the right of Canada as a result of losses and lack of compensation from the federal government. During the next three years, there were extensive preliminary proceedings, motions, production of documents, and examinations for discovery.

PLAINTIFF CHARGE

The plaintiffs attributed the 1979 epiphytotic to the entry into Canada and distribution to nine tobacco farmers of 98,640 tobacco plants originating in Sun City, Florida. They contended that no proper inspection was made and that the inspection made in the field was insufficient. They also contended that the imported plants were infected with blue mold and should have been destroyed or returned to their place of origin. They further contended that blue mold spread from the fields in which the imported, infected plants had been planted to tobacco plants in their fields.

The plaintiffs further contended that the inspectors were not qualified or adequately trained or instructed with regard to the inspection of tobacco plants. They were given no manual or written instructions relating to tobacco diseases and were not made aware of the prevalence of blue mold in Florida. Therefore the Minister of Agriculture and such other servants of the defendant in the Department of Agriculture who were responsible for the training and instruction of inspectors were negligent and in breach of their respective duties under the Act and Regulations.

The plaintiffs further contended that early in July 1979, servants of the defendant or the advisory staff at the Delhi Research Station, which was maintained and operated by the defendant, negligently advised the plaintiffs and others that they should not cut down their diseased plants because the disease would be contained and would die out in the warmer summer weather. It was alleged that this advice was erroneous and that because the plants in infected fields were not cut down, the disease spread to the plaintiffs' fields.

DEFENDANT STATEMENT

The defendant issued its pretrial Statement of Defense on January 4, 1983. It stated that on or about June 1, 1979, upon presentation of a phytosanitary export certificate issued by the State of Florida, a truck containing the tobacco speedlings shipped from Sun City, Florida, to Delhi, Ontario, was admitted to Canada at Windsor without inspection but with instructions for inspection at the greenhouse at the destination of the shipment. An officer of Agriculture Canada issued a document (Notice Arrival of Nursery Stock), which was given to the driver to be delivered to the importer, and which provided, among other things, that shipments forwarded to destination for inspection must not be unpacked before the arrival of the inspector.

Inspectors visited the importer on June 6, where they found that the said tobacco speedlings had been unpacked and had been trucked to a number of tobacco farms, where they had already been planted in the ground. The inspectors went to one of the farms, where 450 speedlings were growing, and conducted an inspection from which it appeared to them that the tobacco speedlings were healthy.

The defendant's statement further noted that it was not until July 12 that a first report was received at the research station operated by the Department of Agriculture at Delhi indicating that some of the tobacco speedlings were suspected to have a disease known as blue mold. On July 13 and for several days thereafter, Dr. Gayed, a plant pathologist at the research station, inspected six of the farms where

265

speedlings had been planted. He found that some of the imported tobacco speedlings as well as some of the other tobacco plants were infected with blue mold.

Before the 1940s, infestations in the Province of Ontario had always been contained by summer heat. No infestation had been encountered in the Delhi area since the late 1940s. No tobacco seedlings had been imported from Florida or elsewhere in the United States for a considerable period of time. Thus the defendant contended that its agents had no reason to suspect that the speedlings were likely to be infested. It further contended that at the time of inspection, it was impossible to determine by the usual methods of inspection that the said tobacco speedlings were infested with blue mold.

The defendant also pleaded that the Act and Regulations do not create any duty by the Minister or the agents of the defendant to the plaintiffs and that they had no power to order the destruction of infested tobacco plants. The owners of the farms whose plants were infected were not prepared to voluntarily destroy them without compensation, if at all, and the Minister has no power or authority to pay any compensation to tobacco farmers who voluntarily destroy any infected tobacco plants.

The defendant pleaded that the inspectors were properly qualified and that there was no statutory or other duty toward the plaintiffs with respect to such qualification or training.

The defendant denied that the advice of which the plaintiffs complained was given by servants of the defendant as alleged and that moreover, the defendant and her servants owe no duty in law to any plaintiff by reason of damages suffered by such plaintiffs as a result of reliance upon any allegedly negligent advice made by some person other than a plaintiff.

PLAINTIFF EXPERT WITNESS

I was the only expert witness for the plaintiff. I was very familiar with the 1979 epiphytotic because of my many visits to the new tobacco belt and my conversations with tobacco farmers and speedling growers. During the trial I mentioned that diseases are often spread on transplants and that the serious black shank disease was spread throughout the Atlantic Seaboard by tobacco seedlings shipped from state to state. In my testimony, I pointed out that blue mold did not appear in American states immediately south of Ontario until some time after it was present in Ontario. For example it was not present in Kentucky until July 26 (Smiley, 1979) or in Ohio until August 3 (Wells, 1979). Stover and Koch (1951) stated that "evidence indicates that wind borne inoculum (conidia) in mass quantities, probably originating in Kentucky and Ohio, were likely

266

responsible for the severe outbreaks of blue mold in Ontario at least in 1945 and 1946." Thus I argued that airborne *P. hyoscyami* spores could not have initiated the epiphytotic in Ontario in 1979 and furthermore that windborne spores could not have dropped selectively onto speedlings and not onto other tobacco plants in Ontario.

I argued that the speedlings, which were obviously yellowed, should not have been allowed into Canada or should at least have been quarantined. Their yellowness was confirmed by Dr. George Todd, president of Speedlings Corporation, and by at least three speedling growers.

I explained that because of the lack of a canopy over the tobacco fields and the cold weather in June, the speedlings did not show specific symptoms, the pathogen developed slowly, and diseased plants showed spots on their leaves only after they had been exposed to warm or hot temperatures. The spots became obvious only after the hot temperatures in early July.

I also reported that the blue mold disease was first observed on Delhi 76 speedlings on July 8 but officials at the Delhi Research Station diagnosed the disease as probably due to cold weather.

DEFENDANT EXPERT WITNESSES

Three defense expert witnesses, Dr. Robert Bruck, Dr. Charles E. Main, and Dr. G. B. Lucas, were from North Carolina. Bruck and Main stated that if the Florida speedlings had been defective, blue mold signs and symptoms should have appeared earlier because the 15 days before July 2 were suitable for blue mold development and sporulation of the pathogen. They also stated that because the Delhi staff on July 12 had observed lesions that were yellow and not brown or necrotic, they were primary lesions, and there was no evidence of earlier infection. Such lesions observed on or about the same dates at widely separated locations were evidence, they stated, that the probable cause of infection was a spore shower rather than a spreading local focus of infection.

In their affidavits, Bruck and Main reported data from a survey of tobacco growers in southern Ontario, stating (Main, 1982):

that by July 18, 1979 ... the tobacco fields in southern Ontario were a) already generating sufficiently huge quantities of blue mold inoculum (conidia) and b) had already infected so many other tobacco fields which were still in an incubation stage that the cutting down of badly infected tobacco fields would have had negligible if any effect on the progress of the epidemic; the sole limiting factors would be the availability of susceptible tobacco plants and favourable climate factors—the inoculum existed in abundance.

That by July 18, 1979 (let alone August 3, 1979) similarly the

267

spraying of sporulating tobacco fields with a protectant fungicide would have been epidemiologically ineffective, the spraying of infected tobacco fields in the incubation stage with a protectant fungicide would also have had negligible effect on the progress and spread of the epidemic and the spraying of uninfected tobacco fields with a protectant fungicide, given the widespread extent of the epidemic and the huge amount of inoculum already generated, and the mode of protectant fungicide, would probably have been ineffective in stopping the regional epidemic.

Lucas argued that the theory that blue mold originated from the imported speedlings was unlikely because symptoms did not occur in Ontario until July 12 in spite of favorable conditions in June and July. In cross-examination he conceded that in the 1980 outbreak, there was a normal progression from Florida in April to Virginia in May, North Carolina in June, Kentucky in July, and not to Ontario until August. He also conceded that never previously had an epidemic come to Canada first.

Dr. Furney Todd, president and general manager of Tobacco Consultants Inc., upon whom the provincial and federal staff at the Delhi Research Station, the Marketing Board, and the task force relied for advice, also testified at the trial. In his affidavit he mentioned that Milt Watson (Ontario Ministry of Agriculture and Food) asked him in late July 1979 what advice could be given. Todd gave Watson the same advice he had given to U.S. growers, namely, to do nothing and wait for hot weather. This advice was accepted and was publicized in *The London Free Press*.

Dr. Lucia Kapica of McGill University, Montreal, testified to the possibility of long-distance transport of spores by wind. In her affidavit she reported the state of knowledge as it relates to fungal spores being carried over the Arctic and oceans. Kapica, however, lacked information regarding the viability of blue mold spores when exposed to drying and sunlight.

Mr. Bhartendu Srivastava of the Atmospheric Environment Service of Environment Canada, Ontario, testified relative to the nature of air mass trajectories arriving in southwestern Ontario in June and July 1979. This information could be used to determine whether or not airborne sporangia of *P. hyoscyami* could have been carried to Ontario from tobacco regions in the United States that were already affected by blue mold. Srivastava concluded that during 1979 conidia from Virginia, traveling near the earth's surface, could have arrived in Brant, Elgin, Haldimand-Norfolk, Oxford, and Middlesex counties on June 29 and 30, when moisture and temperature conditions were favorable for germination.

Dr. Simsek Pala of the Ontario Centre for Remote Sensing, Surveys and Mapping Branch of the Ministry of Natural Resources, produced observations and maps relating to the tobacco-growing regions of southwestern Ontario derived from LANDSAT earth satellite images produced on June 20 and July 7, 1979. Good resolution revealed features as small as 0.4 ha. An analysis from the infrared images permitted differentiation between healthy and diseased crops, according to Pala. Healthy vegetation could be identified by bands that covered the spectral signature of chlorophyll. A color composite map of the satellite-recorded information was printed on acetate and overlaid on a topographic map in squares of 1 km on which the tobacco farms could be located. The affidavit concluded that the areas that appeared yellow on the acetate overlay indicated the reduction of chlorophyll in the vegetation. Hence, according to this witness, the plants were suffering from stress, which, having ruled out other possibilities, indicated the presence of disease.

During cross-examination, the counsel for the plaintiff noted that tobacco farmers plant part of their farms with rye and that by July 7 the rye would be partially ripe, and its chlorophyll would be degenerating and turning brown. For example, on one farm where the topographic map showed a house and a barn, the farmer testified that the area in question, which appeared yellow in the overlay, was planted with rye. Furthermore, along Lake Ontario and north of the fields in question, the satellite indicated chlorophyll loss on farms that never had blue mold disease (Walsh, 1983).

VERDICT

After considering the mass of evidence, Justice Walsh concluded (Walsh, 1983) that it was not possible to decide whether the disease originated from windborne spores or infected speedlings. However, there was at least sufficient indication to conclude that it may have started with the imported speedlings. This reasoning did not deny the plaintiffs' claim but also did not conclude in their favor. They still had to establish fault by one or more representatives of the Department of Agriculture.

Although there was evidence that the importation of tobacco plants was banned in 1980 as a result of the 1979 epiphytotic, the fact that the importation was not banned in 1979 did not in itself create a cause of litigation. The liability, if any, of the defendant had to be based on the state of knowledge in 1979 and not on hindsight. Drs. Lucas and Todd, in their testimony, stated that there was danger in transplanting from one area to another. Dr. Bruck disagreed. Justice Walsh stated, "I do not think that the weight of evidence justifies a conclusion that there should have been a ban in 1979 as was subsequently imposed in 1980" (Walsh, 1983).

According to the law the inspectors were qualified to inspect tobacco because they had a degree from an agricultural college. However, this did not mean that they could recognize blue mold or the symptoms it produces on tobacco. They had no special printed information regarding tobacco diseases, but they claimed to have some knowledge of downy mildews.

In the Reasons for Judgment, Justice Walsh stated (Walsh, 1983) that:

if they could not find any evidence of blue mould when they inspected the plants on June 6th on the Clarysse farm where they had been planted it is evident that they would not have found any symptoms a few days earlier if the inspection had been carried out in the . . . greenhouse as it should have been.

. . . The evidence is rather vague as to who did give advice. . . . Quite aside from who gave advice and when, it appears very doubtful whether any wrong advice was given in the light of the situation prevailing in 1979. . . . While some insecticides [sic] were tried on some fields the consensus of expert opinion is that once infection has developed they are of little use. Ridomil might have helped and might even have been obtained at relatively short notice but it had not been approved for field use in 1979 although it was subsequently approved on a one year basis in 1980, and in the absence of such approval it would not have been proper for Defendant's representatives to have recommended its use. There is some suggestion that the tobacco companies would have refused to purchase tobacco sprayed with it as little was known at the time of the effect of residue on the leaves.

. . . Plaintiffs' own witnesses could not point out what, if any, bad advice they complained of. Plaintiff Fulop alleged that on July 31st, Doctor Gayed told him that he did not think that blue mould was active. There is no corroboration from Doctor Gayed that he ever made this statement or in fact that he ever spoke to Mr. Fulop and in fact his notes indicate that it is highly unlikely that he would have made such a statement on or about July 31st, as he was very concerned with the spreading of the disease.

In conclusion, Justice Walsh pointed out that the Department of Agriculture is under no obligation and owes no duty to farmers to protect them from all conceivable plant diseases.

The defendant succeeded in its defense of the action on legal grounds due to lack of proof of fault. Costs were not given to either side.

Conclusion

Since 1979 blue mold has been unimportant in Canada and has always appeared in the states adjacent to the Canadian border before its appearance in Canada.

Everyone involved in the controversy that developed after the epiphytotic agreed that the primary inoculum in 1979 came from south of the Canadian border; only its means of transportation was debated. If *P. hyoscyami* entered Canada in early June on the speedlings, then the blue mold organism required numerous generations to build an inoculum level to the critical point where the pathogen exploded throughout the tobacco fields around Delhi and Tillsonburg. For it was not until the first week of August that the epiphytotic mushroomed from 50 to 100 to 250 to 600 farms in the area. The pathogen probably completed up to four generations before it was first observed in the field July 8 and another four to five generations before the disease reached epiphytotic proportions the first week of August. However, if *P. hyoscyami* sporangia entered Canada on air currents on June 29 or 30 or early July and were deposited in localized spots, the pathogen built its inoculum level to a critical point in four or five generations during some hot, dry weather.

Blue mold may have appeared first in the speedling fields because the speedlings were more susceptible than adjacent tobacco plants or in some instances because of restricted air circulation and higher humidity resulting from their placement next to a woodlot. However, the observations by Nesmith (1988) that in Kentucky since 1980, the pathogen, probably from Texas, has appeared first in one part of the state and that in every instance infection occurred in all fields in that locale, support the theory that the Canadian epiphytotic was not caused by airborne spores.

Although Ridomil was registered in 20 countries for use on 11 crops including grapes, potatoes, and tobacco (Morton, 1979) and was registered for control of blue mold of tobacco in Australia, Bulgaria, Cyprus, Greece, Romania, and Spain, it was not registered in Canada in 1979.

The 1979 blue mold epiphytotic in Ontario brought to light many lessons that should concern all students of plant pathology.

LITERATURE CITED

Akehurst, B. C. 1981. Tobacco. 2nd ed. Longman, New York. 764 pp.

Brown, D. M., McKay, G. A., and Chapman, I. J. 1968. The climate of southern Ontario. Publ. No. 5. Department of Transport, Meteorological Studies, Toronto. 67 pp.

Conners, I. L., and Savile, D. B. O. 1946. Twenty-sixth annual report. Can.

Plant Dis. Surv. 26:58.

Conners, I. L., and Savile, D. B. O. 1951. Thirty-first annual report. Can. Plant Dis. Surv. 31:77.

Fisheries and Environment Canada. 1979. Monthly meteorological summary. Simcoe, Ontario. Pages 1 and 2. Fisheries and Environment Canada, Ottawa.

Gayed, S. K. 1980. Blue mold of tobacco—Past and present. Lighter 50(1):5–10.

Gayed, S. K. 1985. The 1979 blue mold epidemic of flue-cured tobacco in Ontario and disease occurrence in subsequent years. Can. Plant Dis. Surv. 65:23–28.

Kucharek, T. 1979. The epidemic of 1979; first occurrence, loss, special problems. Page 13 in: Report: Blue Mold Symposium 1, North Carolina State University, Raleigh. F. A. Todd, compiler. 85 pp.

Lucas, G. B. 1975. Diseases of Tobacco. Biological Consulting Associates, Raleigh, NC. 621 pp.

Lucas, G. B. 1980. The war against blue mold. Science 210:147–153.

Main, C. E. 1982. Affidavit of expert witness. Federal Court of Canada, Trial Division. Between George Fulop Jr. and George Fulop Ltd. and the other persons listed in Schedule A appended hereto, Plaintiffs and Her Majesty The Queen in the right of Canada, Defendant. Court No. T-5795-79. Ottawa. 87 pp.

McGrath, H., and Miller, P. R. 1958. Blue mold of tobacco. Plant Dis. Rep. Suppl. 250:1–35.

McKeen, W. E. 1981. The 1979 tobacco blue mold disaster in Ontario, Canada. (Letter to the editor) Plant Dis. 65:8–9.

Miller, P. R. 1959. Plant disease forecasting. Pages 562–563 in: Plant Pathology Problems and Progress 1908–1958. University of Wisconsin Press, Madison. 588 pp.

Morton, H. V. 1979. The use of Ridomil in other countries. Pages 55–56 in: Report: Blue Mold Symposium 1, North Carolina State University, Raleigh. F. A. Todd, compiler. 85 pp.

Nesmith, W. C. 1983. The blue mold situation in the U.S. Pages 20–27 in: Blue Mold Symposium III, 30th Tobacco Workers Conference. J. J. Reilly, compiler. Virginia Polytechnic Institute and State University, Williamsburg. 61 pp.

Nesmith, W. C. 1988. The North American blue mold warning system. In: International Symposium on Blue Mold Disease, Raleigh, NC. (In press)

O'Brien, R. G. 1978. Systemic chemicals for tobacco blue mold control. Plant Dis. Rep. 62:277–279.

Peyrot, J. 1962. Tobacco blue mold in Europe. FAO Plant Prot. Bull. 10:73–80.

Schaus, B. L. 1980. The blue mold epidemic: Its pattern and causes. Senior Rep. Department of Geography, University of Western Ontario, London, Canada. 69 pp.

Skoog, H. A. 1979. The epidemic of 1979; first occurrence, loss, special problems. Page 20 in: Report: Blue Mold Symposium 1, North Carolina State University, Raleigh. F. A. Todd, compiler. 85 pp.

Smiley, J. H. 1979. The epidemic of 1979; first occurrence, loss, special problems. Pages 18 and 19 in: Report: Blue Mold Symposium 1, North Carolina State University, Raleigh. F. A. Todd, compiler. 85 pp.

Stover, R. H., and Koch, L. W. 1951. The epidemiology of blue mold of tobacco and relations to the incidence of disease in Ontario. Sci. Agric. 31:225–252.

The London Free Press. 1979a. Mold menacing tobacco crop. Aug. 1, page A1. London Free Press Printing Co. Ltd., London, Ontario, Canada.

The London Free Press. 1979b. U.S. tobacco seedlings facing ban. Aug. 4, pp. A1 and A4. London Free Press Printing Co. Ltd., London, Ontario, Canada.

The London Free Press. 1979c. Growers to abandon tobacco salvage. Aug. 8, page A15. London Free Press Printing Co. Ltd., London, Ontario, Canada.

The London Free Press-Evening. 1979a. Tobacco belt helpless to combat blue mould. Aug. 1, pp. A1 and A4. London Free Press Printing Co. Ltd., London, Ontario, Canada.

The London Free Press-Evening. 1979b. Last hope for tobacco crop; Anti-mould chemical sought. Aug. 3, page A4. London Free Press Printing Co. Ltd., London, Ontario, Canada.

Todd, F. A. 1979. The epidemic of 1979; first occurrence, loss, special problems. Page 11 in: Report: Blue Mold Symposium 1, North Carolina State University, Raleigh. F. A. Todd, compiler. 85 pp.

Valleau, W. D. 1947. Can tobacco plant beds in Kentucky and Tennessee be infected by *Peronospora tabacina* blown in from Texas? Plant Dis. Rep. 31:480–482.

Walsh, A. A. M. 1983. Reasons for judgment. Federal Court of Canada, Trial Division. Between George Fulop Jr. and George Fulop Ltd. and the other persons listed in Schedule A appended hereto, Plaintiffs and Her Majesty The Queen in the right of Canada, Defendant. Court No. T-5795-79. Ottawa. 54 pp.

Watson, M. 1979. The epidemic of 1979; first occurrence, loss, special problems. Pages 22 and 23 in: Report: Blue Mold Symposium 1, North Carolina State University, Raleigh. F. A. Todd, compiler. 85 pp.

Wells, J. 1979. The epidemic of 1979; first occurrence, loss, special problems. Page 21 in: Report: Blue Mold Symposium 1, North Carolina State University, Raleigh. F. A. Todd, compiler. 85 pp.

Zilkey, B. F. 1980. Evaluation of certain seedling hardening-off techniques on flue-cured tobacco production. Lighter 50(1):22–24.

Index

275

Clarke, D. D., 114
Clarke, J. F., 208
Clayton, E. E., 3, 5, 11, 44, 94, 144, 145,
  146, 147, 149, 151, 152, 153, 156, 157,
  158, 159, 160, 219, 222, 240, 241, 244
Clergeau, M., 36
Cline, K., 119
Cobb, N. A., 1, 4
Coevolution, of host and pathogen, 144,
  166, 177
Coffey, M. D., 66
Cohen, Y., 52, 74, 111, 119, 124, 182, 183,
  184, 187, 204, 205, 225, 226, 228, 229,
  237, 240, 244, 245, 248
Cold weather injury, 258, 267
Collins, B. G., 220
Colonization, 61–66
Communication, between host and
  pathogen, 85, 99, 166, 171, 172
Compatibility, host-pathogen, 127–130
Conidia. See also Sporangia
  cryogenic storage of, 239–240
  dissemination of, and environment,
    231–235
  effect of environment on, 217–248
  formation of, and environment,
    219–229
  germination of, 247–248
    and infectivity of, 240–244
  longevity and viability of, 235–239
  metabolism of, 124–125
  release of, 229–231, 247
  winter survival of, 240
Connecticut, 206, 207, 209
Conners, I. L., 256, 258
Control of blue mold, 30–39
  chemical, 33–38
Cooke, M. C., 4, 5, 19
Cooperative Center for Scientific
  Research Relative to Tobacco. See
  CORESTA
Copper
  oxychloride, 36
  residues, 33
Corbaz, R., 3, 20, 22, 25, 31, 32, 33, 146,
  148, 150, 154
CORESTA, 19, 24, 34
  Phytopathology Group, 27, 34, 37
  trap collection, 27–30
  warning system, 20, 22, 38, 39
Cotyledon test, 26–27, 37, 38, 154, 158
Court, W. A., 188
Courtland (Canada), 261
Coussirat, J. C., 25, 26, 31, 109, 112, 113,
  114, 122, 123
Cowan, S. T., 7

"Critical relative humidity," 220
Cruickshank, I. A. M., 44, 49, 52, 74, 79,
  109, 111, 159, 170, 182, 187, 204, 205,
  217, 219, 220, 221, 222, 223, 224, 225,
  226, 227, 229, 231, 234, 240, 241, 243
Crute, I. R., 165
Cryogenic storage of conidia, 239–240
C-74 (cultivar), 146, 149
Cuba, 3, 9, 14, 19, 34, 203, 256
Cucumber, 184
Cucumber mosaic virus, 120
Cucurbits, 184
Cullis, C. A., 192
Cultivar, and infectivity of conidia, 243.
  See also Resistant cultivars
Cultural practices, 31, 260, 261
Cuticular wax, 52, 107, 159, 187, 243
Cymoxanil, 34, 38
Cyprus, 271
Czechoslovakia, 24, 36

Daly, J. M., 127
Dark-induction, 74, 229, 248
Darkness
  and conidial dissemination, 233
  and sporulation, 205, 224, 225–227,
    229
Darnell-Smith, G. P., 243
Dashkeeva, K. N., 115
Davenport, J. C., 124
Davenport, R., 124
Davis, J. M., 3, 9, 201, 204, 206, 207, 208,
  210, 212
Day, A. W., 85, 87
Day, P. R., 178
De Baets, A., 33
de Bary, A., 1
de Kuijper, E., 35
De Mey, J., 85
Dean, C. E., 150, 156
Dean, R. A., 178, 184
Dedham, J. R., 167
Dehydrogenases, 112, 113, 115, 124, 128
Delhi (Canada), 253, 258, 265, 266, 271
Delhi Research Station, 256, 261, 263,
  265, 267, 268
Delhi 76 (cultivar), 255, 267
Delon, R., 19, 29, 30, 35, 37, 109, 112,
  113, 114, 128, 146
Dennis, R. W. G., 7
Department of Agriculture (Canada),
  264, 265, 269, 270
Deverall, B. J., 178
Dew, 243, 260
Dichlorophenyl-dimethylurea (DCMU),
  226

277

residues, 255, 259, 270
systemic, 34–38, 211, 212
Furalaxyl, 34
Fusarium, 119, 121

GA 955 (cultivar), 10, 143
Gaines, J. G., 44, 219, 222, 240, 241, 244
α-Galactosidase, 119, 124
β-Galactosidase, 119, 124
Galben, 34
Gardiner, R. B., 87
Gaspar, T., 106, 111
Gat-Edelbaum, O., 180
Gäumann, E., 5
Gayed, S. K., 141, 201, 240, 258, 263, 265, 270
Gene expression, 109, 123
Gene pyramiding, 143
Gene-for-gene theory, 85
George Fulop Ltd., 264
Georgia, 141, 207, 208, 211, 212
Georgieva, J. D., 111, 112, 116, 117, 119, 120, 124, 171
Geotrichum candidum, 49
Geotropism, 61
Gera, A., 180
Gerlach, W., 19
Germ tubes, 45–49, 50, 52, 53, 54, 58, 60, 94–95, 96, 99, 125, 126, 168, 169, 170, 187, 241, 242
Germany, 3, 24, 36, 256
Federal Republic of, 19, 25
German Democratic Republic, 19, 25
Germination
inhibitors, 44, 49–52, 107, 114, 169, 187–188, 229, 240, 243, 248. *See also* Autoinhibition of germination
and metabolites, 125–126
plant-pathogen interactions during, 169–170
of sporangia, 44–49
in vitro, 235–236, 237, 240–243, 248
in vivo, 243, 248
Gianinazzi, S., 122, 179, 180
Gicherman, G., 179
Gillham, F. E. M., 11, 143, 148, 159
Glazener, J. A., 117
Glucosamine, 170
Glucose-6-phosphate dehydrogenase, 113, 114, 124, 128
α-Glucosidase, 119, 124, 171
β-Glucosidase, 119, 120, 121, 124, 171
Glucosidases, 171
Glutamate dehydrogenase, 128
Glutamate oxalacetate transaminase, 128, 129

Glycine max, 66
Glycosidases, 117, 119, 120, 126, 130
Godfrey, G. H., 3
Gold. *See* Protein A-gold
Goodman, R. N., 181
Govi, G., 9
Gradouteaud, J., 126, 127
Grafting, 186, 189
Graham, T. L., 181
Grechushnikov, A. J., 106
Greece, 22, 23, 271
Green, S., 8, 74, 244
Grijseels, A. J., 178
Grosso, J. J., 145
Growth regulators, 109
Guedes, M., 184
Gulf of Mexico, 209

Hadjiska, E. J., 122
Haldimand-Norfolk County (Canada), 253, 254, 268
Halverson, L. J., 166, 171
Hansen, V. J., 8, 10, 11
Harding, H., 93
Hare, R., 116
Harkness, H. W., 3, 5
Harrow (Canada), 253
Harrow Research Station, 256
Haustoria of *P. hyoscyami*, 66–73, 98
Heath, M. C., 115
Hecht, E. I., 181
Heffter, J. L., 207
Hemmes, D. E., 49
Henderson, R. G., 168, 169, 170, 243
Heritability
estimates, 11
values for resistance, 155, 156
Herr, L. J., 116
Heterosis values, 150
Hickey, E. L., 66
Hicks (cultivar), 146, 147, 148, 151, 153
Hill, A. V., 1, 5, 6, 7, 8, 11, 13, 25, 44, 49, 52, 74, 107, 141, 142, 143, 145, 156, 157, 172, 205, 217, 218, 230, 231, 233, 234, 235, 236, 237, 238, 240, 243, 244, 245
Hill, L. M., 181
Hill reaction, 226
History of blue mold, 1, 3
Hitier, H., 33
Hoch, H. C., 170
Hogenboom, N. G., 166, 168
Hohl, K. R., 49
Holland. *See* Netherlands
Holliday, P., 3, 6
Hollomon, D. W., 45, 126, 169

279

Honduras, 9, 14
Hopkins, J. C. F., 156, 217
Host range of *P. hyoscyami,* 11–13
Host-parasite relations
  biochemistry, 105–130
  morphology and ultrastructure, 43–99
Hughes, I. K., 13
Hungary, 25, 36
Hydrolases, 117, 124, 126
Hydrolytic enzymes, 117–120
Hyoscyamus, 11
  albus, 5
  bohemicus, 5
  muticus, 5, 7, 12
  niger, 1, 5, 7, 8, 11, 13
Hyperparasites, 81
Hypersensitive reaction, 98, 115, 130,
  159
Hyphae, metabolism of, 124
Hyphal knots, 74–76, 81, 99

Immunity, 93–98
Immunization, 178–179
  against bacteria, 181
  against blue mold, 182–193
  against fungi, 181–182
  against viruses, 179–181
  persistence of, 189–193
Immunocytochemistry, 44, 84–87
In vitro fertilization, 148
Inagaki, H., 182
Incubation period, 204, 206, 222, 244,
  245, 246, 247
  length of, and sporulation intensity,
  222
Induced resistance. *See* Resistance,
  induced
Infection, 52–61, 204
Infectivity, 236–237
  and germination in vivo, 243
Ingram, D. S., 43, 165, 166
Inhibitor of viral replication, 180
Inhibitors of germination. *See*
  Germination inhibitors
Inman, R. E., 93
Inoculum
  concentration, 236, 244
    and disease reactions, 157, 245–246
    and infectivity of conidia, 243
    and penetration, 94–96
    and resistance, 190
  movement, 204, 211. *See also* Long-
  distance transport of inoculum
Institute of Genetics (Sofia, Bulgaria),
  110
Interferon, 179–180

International Code of Botanical
  Nomenclature, 6
Interspecific hybridization, 146
Ioannidis, N. M., 148, 150
β-Ionone, 127, 184, 185, 186–187, 193
Iran, 25
γ-Irradiation, 120
Irrigation, 205–206, 258, 262
Iskender, G., 106
Isocitrate dehydrogenase, 112
Israel, 36
Israel, H. W., 179
Italy, 20, 22, 23, 35, 36
Ivancheva-Gabrovska, T., 9
Izard, C., 26, 31, 94, 115, 126, 127, 154,
  158

Jamet, E., 122
Jankowski, F., 8, 25, 237
Jardot, R., 224, 225, 230, 233, 244
Jenkins, S. F., 230
Jensen, A. W., 91
Johnson, G. I., 1, 6, 7, 8, 9, 35
Jones, D. H., 114
Jurina, E. V., 128

KA 596 (cultivar), 10, 143
Kajiwara, T., 70
Kaminskyj, S. G., 85
Kampmeijer, P., 201
Kampuchea, 3, 20
Kapica, L., 268
Karjieva, R., 109, 113
Kartashova, E. R., 128
Kassanis, B., 179
Kato, S., 111
Keen, N. T., 127
Keene, C. K., 243
Keitt, G., 178
Kentucky, 141, 206, 207, 211, 261, 266,
  268, 271
Kentucky 14 (cultivar), 185, 188, 192
Kentucky 17 (cultivar), 149
Kinetin, 109, 159
Kingsville (Canada), 253
Kiraly, Z., 114, 115
Klinkowski, M., 3
Knots (hyphal), 74–76, 81, 99
Koch, L. W., 141, 256, 261, 266
Koelle, G., 106, 159
Komar, J., 113
Kosuge, T., 113
Krebs cycle, 52, 112
Kritzman, G., 119
Kröber, H., 5, 7, 13, 81, 115, 125, 168,
  171, 205, 224, 225, 236, 238, 243, 245,
  246, 247

Kuć, J., 94, 127, 159, 177, 178, 179, 181, 182, 183, 184, 185, 186, 187, 188, 189, 190, 240
Kucharek, T. A., 205, 206, 256
Kutova, I., 130

Lake Erie, 253, 255
Lake Ontario, 269
Lamb, S., 1
LANDSAT, 269
Lar'kina, N. L., 148
Latin America, 203, 211
Lea, H. W., 10, 147, 148, 153
Leach, C. M., 79
Leaf boundary layer, 219, 220, 247
Leaf disk technique, 229–230
Leaf movement
  and conidial dissemination, 234
  and conidial release, 247
Leaf position, and susceptibility, 52
Leaf water potential, 205
Leaf wetness period, effect on disease, 245–246
Lectin, 167, 172, 181
Ledez, P., 24
Legenkaya, E. I., 13
Legrand, M., 114
Leppik, R. A., 49, 126, 127, 184, 187, 240
Lerch, B., 180
Lewis, D. M., 93
Libbert, E., 127
Life cycle of *P. hyoscyami*, 218
  asexual, 217, 247
  sexual, 217, 247
Light, 248
  action spectrum, 227–228
  and conidial dissemination, 233–234
  and enzyme regulation, 93
  infrared, 80
  and germination, 242
  and resistance, 109
  and sporulation, 74, 224–229, 247
  ultraviolet, 209, 235, 238–239, 242
  and vegetative development, 61
Light-temperature interactions, 225
Lignin, 106, 107, 113
Lipoxygenase, 111, 188
Lippincott, B. B., 166
Lippincott, J. A., 166
Littlefield, L. J., 169, 171
Loebenstein, G., 178, 179, 180
London Free Press, The, 259, 260, 261, 262, 268
London Free Press-Evening, The, 260, 261
Long-distance transport of inoculum,

39, 202, 203, 206–209, 210, 211, 212, 234–235, 268
Lovrekovich, L., 181
Lucas, G. B., 6, 22, 35, 105, 142, 165, 207, 246, 256, 259, 263, 267, 268, 269
Lucas, J. A., 44, 94, 190
Lycopersicon
  esculentum, 13, 93
  pimpinellifolium, 13

Magnesium
  cations, 125
  ions, 109–110, 123, 130. *See also*
    Mg^{2+}-grown seedlings
  salt, 27
  sulfate, 242
Main, C. E., 44, 146, 160, 201, 203, 204, 206, 207, 223, 224, 267
Malate dehydrogenase, 112, 128
Mancozeb, 33, 35, 36, 37, 38
Mandryk, M., 8, 49, 52, 107, 114, 115, 125, 126, 145, 156, 157, 159, 165, 168, 172, 182, 184, 187, 240, 243
Maneb, 33, 35, 36, 37, 38, 258, 259
Manganese toxicity, 120, 122
α-Mannosidase, 119, 124
β-Mannosidase, 119, 124
Manolovi, A., 148
Marani, A., 11, 141, 146, 148, 154, 155, 156, 157
Marcelli, E., 13, 31
Markhaseva, V. A., 246
Marks, C. F., 10
Marks, J. L., 192
Marshall, D. R., 128
Martin, C., 115
Martin-Tanguy, J., 115
Maryland, 141
Masefield, G. B., 202
Masiak, D., 123
Massfeller, D., 5, 7, 13, 246
Mastigomycota, 49
Mastigomycotina, 3
Matsuoka, M., 122, 123
Matthews, P., 144, 147, 157
Maximo, Y., 3, 20
Mayama, S., 170
Mayr, H. H., 114
McAlpine, D., 1
McGill University, 268
McGrath, H., 5, 256
McIntyre, J. L., 182, 184
McKeen, W. E., 9, 43, 54, 61, 66, 76, 85, 94, 142, 157, 168, 169, 170, 171, 253, 263
McKenny, R. E. B., 3